DESIGN FOR AIR COMBAT

Ray Whitford

JANE'S

Copyright © Ray Whitford

Second impression 1989

First published in the United Kingdom in 1987 by
Jane's Information Group Limited
Sentinel House, 163 Brighton Road
Coulsdon, Surrey, CR3 2NX

Distributed in the Philippines and the USA
and its dependencies by
Jane's Information Group Inc
1340 Braddock Place, Suite 300
PO Box 1436, Alexandria
Virginia 22313-2036

ISBN 0 7106 0426 2

Printed in the United Kingdom by
Butler & Tanner Ltd
Frome and London

PREFACE

This book is concerned with the design of the
modern combat aircraft, dealing with the shapes of
such aircraft and their aerodynamic rationale.
Embraced for the first time in a single volume is the
complete range of aerodynamic design features
found on the exciting breed of aircraft that
appeared in the 1970s, as well as those likely to
enter service in the 1990s.

Design for Air Combat is aimed at a wide
audience, including aviation enthusiasts, students
of science and engineering, recent entrants to the
aerospace industry, and professional engineers
and others in industry and the armed services who
are involved with aircraft and need a basic
briefing on design practices.

I have set out, making use of specific and topical
examples, to answer some of the questions put by
students of aeronautical engineering over many
years. The result is not intended as a textbook, but
rather as an adjunct to the many excellent texts
which deal with aerodynamic theory. Only the very
basic formulae needed to grasp the essentials are
given, the emphasis being on a physical understanding of concepts. This of course presents a
dilemma: making the explanations too straight-
forward and brief creates a risk of oversimplifying
the subject matter. This book should therefore be
seen as an introductory one covering a broad
spectrum of complex issues.

Design for Air Combat begins with basic aerodynamics and a discussion of the nature of combat
aircraft. The major airframe components are then
examined in turn. It is however a mistake to regard
these components as self-contained, such is the
degree of integration now practised in aircraft
design. Indeed, the interactions between major airframe assemblies are so carefully considered that
the whole is far greater than the sum of the individual parts. The text also traces a little of the
history of the major innovations, including supercritical aerofoils, area ruling, combat flaps,
variable-sweep wings and the control-configured
vehicle concept. Developments likely to appear on
future generations of aircraft — such as the
revamped canard layout, rectangular exhaust
nozzles, more widespread use of stealth technology, and forward-swept wings — are also discussed. But a volume of this size cannot be
all-inclusive, and some omissions have been
necessary. Chief amongst these are VTOL aerodynamics, boundary-layer control, airbrake design
and weapon carriage. One major regret is that so
little factual information on Soviet design philosophy can be included, but it is hoped that the
reader will be able to make the connection between
the shapes of Western combat aircraft and those of
their Warsaw Pact counterparts.

My gratitude is extended to the numerous
individuals, aerospace companies and professional organisations who provided material for
this venture. Thanks also to J.L., whose typing skill
and stoicism helped me through some anxious
times. Finally, a debt of gratitude is owed to my
wife and family, whose forebearance and patience
have permitted this project to come to fruition.

RAY WHITFORD

CONTENTS

ABBREVIATIONS

A, AR	aspect ratio, b^2/S
A	nozzle area
AB	afterburner, reheat
AC	aerodynamic centre
ACT	active control technology
AFCS	automatic flight control system
AGARD	Advisory Group for Aeronautical Research and Development
AIAA	American Institute of Aeronautics and Astronautics
AOA	angle of attack
ARI	aileron/rudder interconnect
ASW	aft-swept wing
a	lift curve slope, $dC_L/d\alpha$
a	speed of sound
BAe	British Aerospace
BLC	boundary-layer control
BPR	bypass ratio
b	wing span, tip to tip
CASJ	*Canadian Aeronautics and Space Journal*
CCV	control-configured vehicle
C_D	drag coefficient, $\dfrac{D}{1/2\rho V^2 S}$
C_{D_v}	vortex drag coefficient
$C_{D_{min}}$	minimum drag coefficient
C_{D_0}	zero-lift drag coefficient
C_{D_w}	wave drag coefficient
CG	centre of gravity
C_L	lift coefficient, $\dfrac{L}{1/2\rho V^2 S}$
$C_{L_{max}}$	maximum lift coefficient
C_{L_T}	tailplane lift coefficient, $\dfrac{L_T}{1/2\rho V^2 S_T}$
$C_{L_{trim}}$	trimmed lift coefficient (i.e. at $C_{m_{CG}} = 0$)
C_l	rolling moment coefficient: $\dfrac{L}{\rho V^2 Ss}$
C_{l_β}	non-dimensional rolling moment derivative due to sideslip: $dC_l/d\beta$

C_m — pitching moment coefficient: $\dfrac{M}{1/2\rho V^2 S \bar{\bar{c}}}$

C_{m_o} — pitching moment coefficient about the aerodynamic centre for the aircraft less tail

C_n — yawing moment coefficient: $\dfrac{N}{\rho V^2 Ss}$

C_{n_β} — non-dimensional yawing moment derivative due to sideslip: $dC_n/d\beta$

$C_{n_{\beta_{dyn}}}$ — dynamic directional stability parameter:
$$C_{n_\beta} - \frac{I_z}{I_x} C_{l_\beta} \sin\alpha$$

CP — centre of pressure

C_p — pressure coefficient, $\dfrac{p_{local} - p_\infty}{1/2\rho\, V_\infty^2}$

c_t — tip chord length

c_r — root chord length

c — wing chord length

$\bar{c}$ — mean geometric chord

$\bar{\bar{c}}$ — mean aerodynamic chord

D — drag

D_0 — zero-lift drag

DLC — direct lift control

$\dfrac{dC_L}{d\alpha}$ — lift-curve slope

$\dfrac{dC_m}{dC_L}$ — slope of $C_m \sim C_L$ curve, static margin

$\dfrac{du}{dy}$ — velocity gradient in boundary layer

EAP — Experimental Aircraft Programme (BAe)

ECM — electronic countermeasures

FBW — fly-by-wire

FSW — forward-swept wing

g — gravitational acceleration

H_0 — stagnation pressure

h — altitude

ICAS — International Council for Aeronautical Sciences

IR — infra-red

I_x — moment of inertia about rolling axis

I_z — moment of inertia about yawing axis

KIAS — knots indicated airspeed

L — rolling moment

L — total lift on aircraft

L_F — foreplane lift

L_W — wing lift

L_T — tail lift

L/D — lift-to-drag ratio

LE — leading edge

LEX — leading-edge extension

LERX — leading-edge root extension

l_F — vertical tail moment arm length

l_T — horizontal tail moment arm length

M — pitching moment

M — Mach number

M_{crit} — critical Mach number

M_D — drag-rise Mach number

ΔM — increment in Mach number

MAC — mean aerodynamic chord

MBB — Messerschmitt–Bolkow–Blohm GMBH

$\dot{m}$ — mass flow rate

N — yawing moment

NACA — National Advisory Committee for Aeronautics

NASA — National Aeronautics and Space Administration

NP — neutral point

n — Normal acceleration (in units of g) = normal load factor − 1

Δn — increment in normal load factor

PACT — Precision Aircraft Control Technology

p — rate of roll

p — static pressure

p_b — static back pressure

p_e — static exit pressure

p_r — total pressure recovery

p_t — throat pressure

p_0 — stagnation, total pressure

q	dynamic pressure, $1/2\rho V^2$	W	weight of aircraft
q_v	dynamic pressure at vertical tail	W/b	span loading
		W/S	wing loading
R_e	Reynolds number, $\dfrac{\rho V c}{\mu}$	x	distance from leading edge measured along chord line
RAE	Royal Aircraft Establishment	x/c	fraction of chord length
RAeS	Royal Aeronautical Society		
RoC	rate of climb	Y	sideforce
R&D	research and development	y	distance measured normal from surface in boundary layer
RMS	root mean square		
RSS	relaxed static stability		
S, S_w	wing area	α	angle of attack
SAFE	Safety and Flight Equipment Manufacturers Association	α_0	angle of attack for zero lift
		α_{stall}	stalling angle of attack
S_F	vertical tail area	β	sideslip angle
S_T	tailplane area	Γ	circulation
SEP	specific excess power: $\dfrac{(T-D)V}{W}$	Γ	dihedral angle
		δ_{nose}, δ_n, δ_{LE}	nose flap deflection
SF	shear force	δ_{flap}, δ_{TE}	trailing-edge flap deflection
SFC	specific fuel consumption	θ	shock-cone angle
SM	static margin	Λ	angle of sweep
s	stagnation point	$\Lambda_{c/4}$	quarter-chord sweep angle
s	wing semi-span, $\dfrac{b}{2}$	λ	taper ratio, c_t/c_r
		μ	dynamic viscosity
		μ	Mach wave angle
T	propulsive thrust	ρ	air density
T	torque	σ	sidewash angle
TE	trailing edge		
TFX	Tactical Fighter Experimental		
TOD	take-off distance		
T/W	thrust/weight ratio		
t	thickness		
t/c	thickness/chord ratio		
u	velocity parallel to surface in boundary layer		
V	velocity		
VFE	variable-flap ejector nozzle		
VIFF	vectoring in forward flight		
V_{s_1}	stall velocity in 1g flight		
VTOL	vertical take-off and landing		
v	increment in velocity		

INTRODUCTION

This book is about the shape of combat aircraft and deals primarily with the design of such aircraft from an aerodynamic viewpoint. The first part of this introduction is intended to acquaint the reader with enough basic aerodynamics to permit an understanding of how the fundamental physical laws of fluid mechanics govern the behaviour of flow around an aircraft. Subsequent sections show how aircraft designers work within the limits of these laws to achieve their ends, and examine some of the basic requirements that combat aircraft must meet. It is the task of the designer to balance physical constraints and requirement, cost and timescale, in order to produce the most combat-effective machine possible.

BASIC AERODYNAMICS

This section is sufficient to give the reader a grasp of the essentials of aerodynamics. For a deeper understanding, the texts listed in *Further Reading* should be consulted.

When visualising the flow around an aircraft, it is usually easier to imagine the aircraft as stationary with the flow passing over it. This has been shown conclusively to be a satisfactory approach and is the basis of wind-tunnel testing. The following description of airflow makes this assumption.

Aircraft reference axes

The standard reference axes shown in Fig 1 originate at the aircraft's centre of gravity and are fixed relative to the aircraft. All directions shown are positive, so that positive pitching moment is nose-up, positive rolliing moment is right-wing-down, and positive yawing moment is nose-right. Aerodynamic forces cannot normally be shown on such an axis system; this is because they are referred to the direction of flight, which does not necessarily coincide with the direction in which the aircraft is pointing. The three forces of lift, drag and sideforce are shown mutually perpendicular, with drag measured in a direction opposite to the direction of motion.

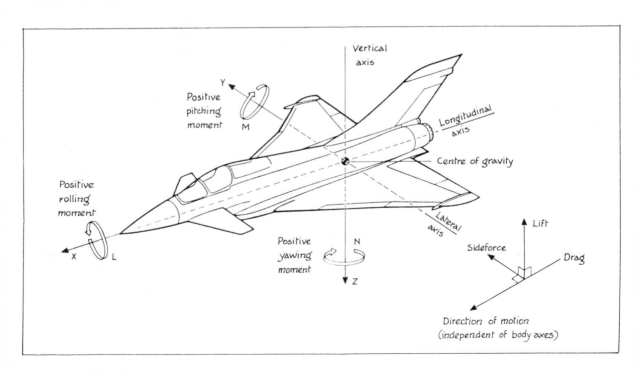

Fig 1 Aircraft body axes.

The source of aerodynamic loads

The aerodynamic loads imposed on the skin of an aircraft in flight are due to the distribution of pressure which arises from the wide range of local flow velocities of the air as it passes over the aircraft. The link between pressure and velocity is derived by means of Newton's Second Law of Motion, which relates force to rate of change of momentum. In essence,

total pressure = static pressure + dynamic pressure

where total presure is the pressure measured at a point in the flow where the velocity has been reduced to zero without any losses; static pressure is the pressure measured at a point moving with the flow; dynamic pressure is the difference between the total pressure and static pressure and contains the velocity term.

Although air is compressible, it is helpful to assume for the moment that it is incompressible because of the great simplification that this offers. Given this assumption, the above relationship between the various pressures is usually written as:

$$p_0 = p_s + \tfrac{1}{2}\rho V^2$$

where p_0 = total pressure, p_s = static pressure, ρ = air density, V = air velocity, and the term $\tfrac{1}{2}\rho V^2$ represents the dynamic pressure

This is known as the Bernoulli Equation. In the form given it has certain restrictions, the main one being that the air is assumed incompressible. This is approximately true provided that the air velocity is low: up to about 100m/sec the error in assuming constant density is around five per cent.

The Bernoulli Equation shows the direct link between static pressure and velocity. This relationship must be grasped if many of the points made in the following chapters are to be understood. The following example should help. Consider the wind tunnel shown in Fig 2, which comprises a very large pressurised container A, a converging section B, a throat section C, a diverging section D and a valve E. With the valve E closed the whole system is at pressure p_0 (the total pressure), with the subscript "0" indicating zero velocity. Opening the valve E causes a flow to start and, providing that tank A is sufficiently large, the flow through sections B, C and D has negligible effect on pressure p_0 in tank A (i.e. p_0 is assumed to remain constant).

At this point it is necessary to introduce the principle of the conservation of mass, which states that matter can be neither created nor destroyed. Applied to Fig 2, the Continuity

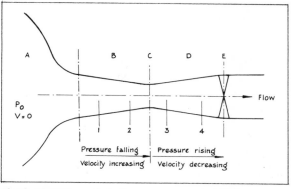

Fig 2 Variation of static pressure and velocity.

Equation affirms that the mass flow per unit time ($\dot{m}$) through the device remains constant, i.e.

$\dot{m}$ = density × area × velocity = ρAV

and $\rho_1 A_1 V_1 = \rho_2 A_2 V_2 = \rho_3 A_3 V_3 = \rho_4 A_4 V_4$

(subscripts indicate stations 1, 2, 3 and 4)

This can be simplified, by neglecting changes in density, to give:

$$A_1 V_1 = A_2 V_2 = A_3 V_3 = A_4 V_4.$$

If we now turn our attention to the flow in the converging section B, it is apparent that as the flow passes along the convergence, with its reduction in cross-sectional area, a speeding-up occurs (this is known as the "nozzle effect"). We can now use the Bernoulli Equation to examine what is happening to the pressure in B as the flow accelerates. This states that

$$p_0 = p_{s_1} + \tfrac{1}{2}\rho V_1^2 = p_{s_2} + \tfrac{1}{2}\rho V_2^2$$

The total pressure p_0 will remain constant throughout the duct providing there are no dissipative processes (e.g. friction, turbulence) occurring in the flow. If we look at a streamline coincident with the duct centreline this is essentially true.

The cross-sectional area at Station 2 is smaller than at Station 1 and the velocity is higher. Thus, according to the Bernoulli Equation, the static pressure at Station 2 is lower than that at Station 1. In other words, as the velocity increases so the static pressure decreases. In fact a velocity increase always causes a reduction in static pressure.

At Station 3, beyond the throat, the cross-sectional area is starting to increase, so that Station 4 has a larger cross-sectional area than Station 3. This implies that the velocity at Station 4 is lower than that at Station 3. Again the Bernoulli Equation links the static pressure with flow velocity:

$$p_0 = p_{s_3} + \tfrac{1}{2}\rho V_3^2 = p_{s_4} + \tfrac{1}{2}\rho V_4^2$$

This indicates that the static pressure at Station 4 is higher than that at Station 3. The implication of this is that a velocity decrease results in an increase in static pressure.

The flow in the diverging section D is passing into a region where the pressure is rising. This is known as an adverse pressure gradient, as opposed to a favourable pressure gradient, in which the pressure falls in the direction of flow. An adverse pressure gradient like that existing in section D can have dire consequences for the airflow, as will be demonstrated later.

Lift production

Having established that an increase in flow velocity is accompanied by a reduction in static pressure and vice versa, we can now turn our attention to flow over a wing section to examine how lift is produced. At a point near the leading edge of the wing shown in Fig 3 one particular streamline comes to rest after gradually slowing down as it approaches the wing. This is the stagnation streamline, so called because its velocity stagnates to zero at the stagnation point. As the air particles come to rest, their kinetic energy, represented by dynamic pressure, is converted into an

Fig 3 Flow around wing section.

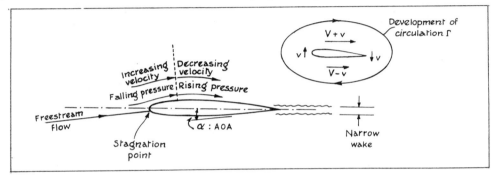

Fig 4 Wing-section pressure distribution

$$\left(C_p = \frac{p_{local} - p_\infty}{\tfrac{1}{2}\rho V_\infty^2}\right)$$

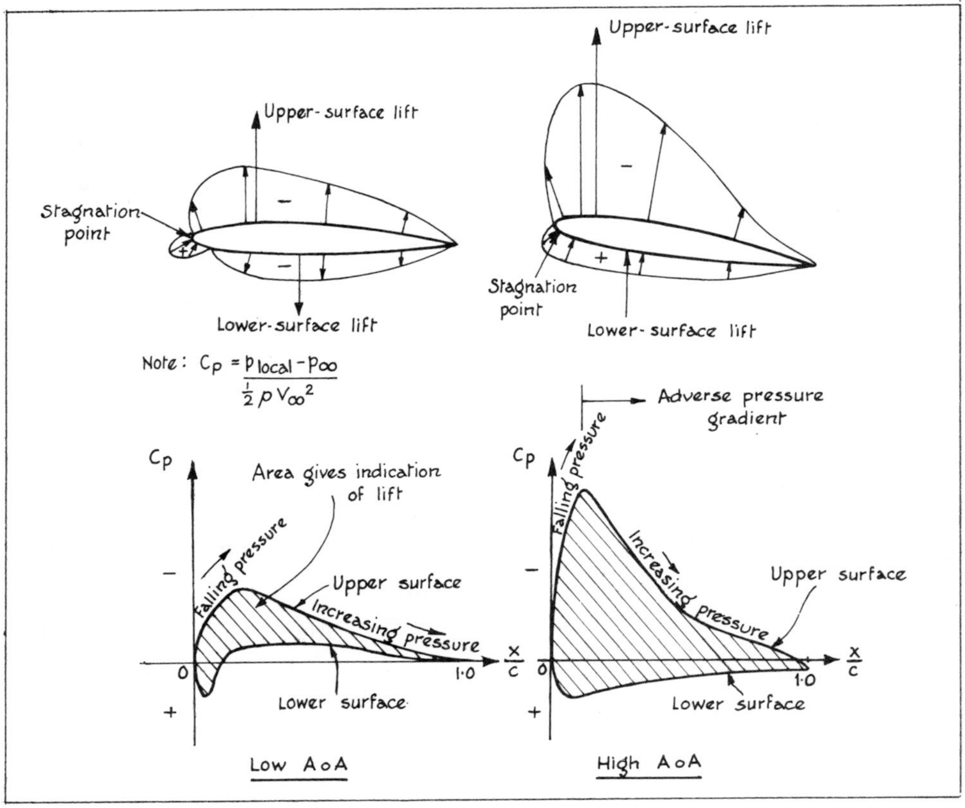

Note: $C_p = \dfrac{p_{local} - p_\infty}{\tfrac{1}{2}\rho V_\infty^2}$

Low AoA

High AoA

increase in static pressure so that at the stagnation point the static pressure equals the total pressure of the flow.

In an ideal flow the stagnation streamline then divides and flows around both upper and lower surfaces of the wing, accelerating as it does so. This velocity increase results in a reduction in static pressure, as shown by the Bernoulli Equation. The velocity to which the dividing streamline accelerates depends upon the shape of the wing section and the angle at which it is inclined to the oncoming flow. This angle is known as the angle of attack (AOA) and is given the symbol α (Fig 3). The aerofoil shape and AOA govern the static pressures existing on the upper and lower surfaces of the wing and, as discussed further in Chapter 1, give rise to the lift force generates by the wing.

Circulation

Because of the different accelerations to which the air flowing over the upper and lower surfaces of the wing is subjected, the lift can be related mathematically to what is termed "circulation". For the case of a wing with higher velocities on the upper surface than on the lower, the flow field can be regarded as a circulatory flow superimposed upon a uniform flow of freestream velocity V_∞. The concept is shown in Fig 3, in which the net clockwise motion is the circulation. In essence, it is the generation of circulation around the wing section that produces lift. An everyday example of circulation is the Magnus Effect, used in many ball games (e.g. tennis): spin is put on the ball to generate a force perpendicular to the line of flight, causing the ball to swerve.

The distribution of the static pressures on a typical wing section at low AOA is shown in Fig 4. A region of high pressure can be seen near the stagnation point, followed by, on the upper surface, a significant low-pressure region with its peak suction about one-third of the section length, known as the chord (c), back from the leading edge. Another, less intense, suction region exists on the lower surface. It is the difference between the high suction on the upper surface and the smaller suction on the lower surface which contributes most to the lift produced by the section at this low AOA.

Fig 4 shows the conventional way of representing pressure distributions. This plots the pressure coefficient (C_p) versus chordwise position (x/c). The sign of the pressure coefficient, which is the ratio of pressures $\frac{p_{local}-p_\infty}{\frac{1}{2}\rho V_\infty^2}$, indicates whether the local static pressures on the wing section are above (+) or below (−) the static

pressure of the flow far upstream and therefore unaffected by the wing. Negative C_p values exist over much of the upper and lower surfaces of the wing section at low AOA, and the lift generated is a function of the area enclosed by the pressure loop.

In contrast, at higher AOA the previously low pressures on the lower surface are replaced by high pressures, though the maximum pressure still occurs at the stagnation point, which has moved aft, further under the leading edge. The lift generated, again approximately indicated by the area contained in the pressure loop, continues to result from the suction pressures on the upper surface, but is now added to by the increased pressures on the lower surface. As a rule of thumb, about two-thirds of the total lift is generated over the forward one-third of the wing section length. The importance of the correct shaping of the wing leading edge is given further consideration in Chapter 1.

Factors determining the lift produced by a wing

The variation of the forces and moments acting on a wing depends upon:

Freestream velocity : V_∞
Freestream density : ρ_∞ (altitude-dependent)
Wing size : S (wing area)
Angle of attack (AOA) : α
Wing section shape
Air viscosity : μ_∞ (temperature-dependent)
Compressibility : M_∞

$$\left(\text{Mach number} = \frac{\text{Flow velocity}}{\text{Sound velocity}} = \frac{V_\infty}{a_\infty}\right)$$

The subscript "∞" refers to freestream conditions (i.e. conditions far upstream of the wing.)

The lift force L can be shown to be a function of all the above parameters, i.e. $L = f(V_\infty, \rho_\infty, S, \alpha, \mu_\infty, a_\infty,$ section shape). From this can be derived a non-dimensional term called the lift coefficient (C_L):

$$C_L = \frac{\text{Lift force}}{\text{Dynamic pressure} \times \text{area}} = \frac{L}{\frac{1}{2}\rho_\infty V_\infty^2 S}$$

where C_L is a function of section shape, AOA, compressibility and viscosity.

Variation of lift coefficient with angle of attack

At low AOAs the variation of lift coefficient with AOA is similar for all wing sections, as shown by the lift curves in Fig 5. It is when the higher AOAs are approached that the characteristics of the four fundamentally different wing sections become apparent. The principal features of any lift curve are the lift curve slope ($dC_L/d\alpha$), angle of attack for zero lift (α_0), maximum lift coefficient ($C_{L_{max}}$),

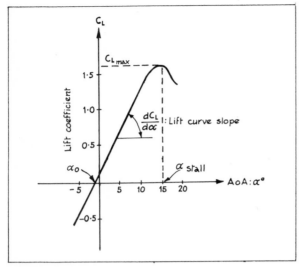

Fig 5 Basic lift curve.

stalling angle (α_{stall}) and the shape of the curve around the $C_{L_{max}}$ value.

Aerodynamic drag

Aerodynamic drag is the force which retards the movement of an aircraft through the air, acting in a direction opposite to the direction of motion. There are many contributions to the total drag of an aircraft, the chief ones being trailing-vortex drag, profile drag (comprising surface friction drag and form drag) and wave drag (including separation).

Trailing-vortex drag

A major source of drag is the process of lift production itself. Formerly known as lift-induced or lift-dependent drag, this is now usually referred to as trailing-vortex drag.

In discussing the generation of lift, reference was made to the pressure differences between the upper and lower surfaces of the wing due to the different local airflow velocities. Generally speaking, pressures are lower on the upper surface. Although there is a natural tendency for the air to flow from a higher pressure to a lower pressure, the surface of the wing acts as a solid impediment to this — except, that is, at the wing tips, where no pressure difference can be sustained and there is an equalisation of pressure. This process does not occur abruptly, however, there being a gradual reduction in the pressure difference from the root of the wing to the tip; this is most noticeable near the tips, as shown in Fig 6a. From this it can be inferred that there is also a

reduction in lift across the span, so that no lift is generated by the extreme tips of the wing.

The spanwise variation in pressure causes a spanwise flow of air. On the lower surface of the wing, for example, the pressure at the tips is lower than it is near the wing root, resulting in a tendency for air to flow from root to tip (Fig 6a). The reverse is true of the upper surface, where the pressure is lower at the root than at the tip and an inward flow from tip to root results.

The opposite motion of the upper and lower-surface spanwise flows affects flow conditions at the wing trailing edge. As the two flows stream off the trailing edge, they form spiral flows known as vortices. The strength of the vortices depends upon the spanwise rate of change of pressure, which is greatest near to the wing tips. As the vortices are shed from the wing trailing edge they coalesce, somewhat inboard of the wing tips, to form single large trailing vortices, one from each wing. Viewed from behind, the left wing produces a trailing vortex rotating in a clockwise direction while the right wing generates one rotating counter-clockwise, as shown in Fig 6b.

The rotational speed of the flow in the core of these vortices can be very high, while the pressure is low. Given sufficient atmospheric humidity, water vapour condenses under the low pressure in the cores of the vortices to form visible streamers. What is seen under these conditions is only a very small proportion of the total vortex motion. The full extent of the flow is better demonstrated by high-flying transport aircraft, the engine condensation trails of which are picked up by the trailing vortices and start to wrap around each a few fuselage lengths behind the aircraft.

The formation of trailing vortices is important for two reasons:

1 The energy needed to give the air this rotational motion can only be supplied by the engines. This energy requirement shows up as trailing-vortex drag.

2 The spanwise region between the two trailing vortices is subject to a downward flow (Fig 6b) called downwash. This, as will be seen later, has very important consequences for the tailplane, located somewhere aft of the wing. The influence of the vortex system is also felt at the wing itself in that the effective AOA is reduced by an amount equal to the downwash velocity at the wing divided by the aircraft's forward speed. In addition, upwash occurs ahead of the wing.

Since it is the existence of the wing tips which allows the spanwise loss of lift, it could be argued that increasing the wing span could limit the proportional loss of lift. This is indeed true and it is

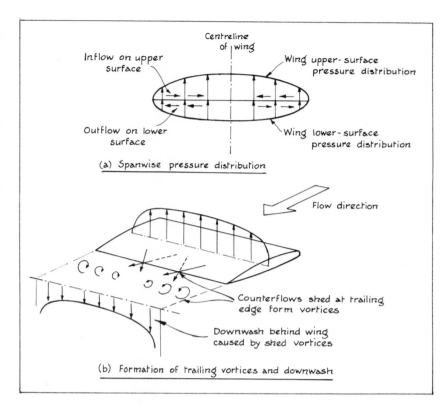

Fig 6 Tip effects.

Centreline of wing

Inflow on upper surface

Wing upper-surface pressure distribution

Outflow on lower surface

Wing lower-surface pressure distribution

(a) Spanwise pressure distribution

Flow direction

Counterflows shed at trailing edge form vortices

Downwash behind wing caused by shed vortices

(b) Formation of trailing vortices and downwash

Fig 7 Effect of aspect ratio on lift and vortex drag coefficients.

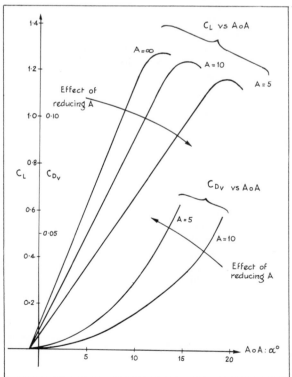

the practice for aircraft designed for maximum range or endurance to have long, narrow wings; such wings have a high aspect ratio (A), which is the ratio of wing area to span squared. But this is an impractical solution for combat aircraft, except for those with variable-sweep wings. With a fixed wing a very careful balance has to be struck between the conflicting requirements of aspect ratio, as shown in Chapter 1, and most combat aircraft have low aspect ratios of less than 3.5.

The effect of aspect ratio on trailing-vortex drag and lift is shown in Fig 7 to have adverse effects. The trailing-vortex drag coefficient (C_{D_v}) does in fact increase with the square of the lift coefficient (i.e. $C_{D_v} = kC_L^2$ where k depends primarily on the inverse of the aspect ratio). A reduction in aspect ratio reduces the slope of the lift curve, so that for a given AOA the lift coefficient is reduced. This is due to the reduced effective AOA caused by the influence of downwash at the wing, referred to earlier.

Trailing-vortex drag typically represents 75% of the total drag in maximum sustained manoeuvring flight (air-to-air combat), roughly 50% in the economic cruise condition, and only 5–10% in low-altitude high-speed flight. In supersonic flight, shock-wave drag (see page 17 *et seq*) assumes greater importance.

Profile drag

This comprises two components: surface friction drag and normal pressure drag (form drag).

Surface friction drag

This arises from the tangential stresses due to the viscosity or "stickiness" of the air. When air flows over any part of an aircraft there exists, immediately adjacent to the surface, a thin layer of air called the boundary layer, within which the air slows from its high velocity at the edge of the layer to a standstill at the surface itself. Surface friction drag depends upon the rate of change of velocity through the boundary layer, i.e. the velocity gradient. There are two types of boundary layer, laminar and turbulent, the essential features of which are shown in Fig 8. Although all combat aircraft surfaces develop a laminar boundary layer to start with, this rapidly becomes turbulent within a few per cent of the length of the surface. This leaves most of the aircraft immersed in a turbulent boundary layer, the thickness of which increases with length along the surface. The velocity and hence pressure variations along the length of any surface can have adverse effects on the behaviour of the boundary layer, as will be discussed later.

Surface friction drag can amount to more than 30% of the total drag under cruise conditions.

Fig 8 Boundary-layer velocity profiles.

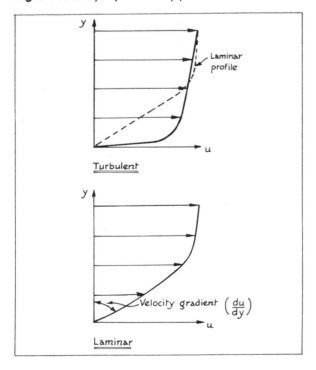

Normal pressure drag (form drag)

This also depends upon the viscosity of the air and is related to flow separation. It is best explained by considering a typical pressure distribution over a wing section, as shown in Fig 4, first at low AOA and then at high AOA.

At low AOA the high pressures near the leading edge produce a component of force in the rearward (i.e. drag) direction, while the low pressures ahead of the maximum thickness point tend to suck the wing section forward, giving a thrust effect. The low pressures aft of the maximum thickness point tend to suck the wing rearwards, since they act on rearward-facing surfaces. Without the influence of the boundary layer, the normal pressure forces due to the above drag and thrust components would exactly cancel.

As shown in Fig 4, there is a favourable pressure gradient up to the minimum pressure point, with the pressure falling in the direction of flow. This helps to stabilise the boundary layer. Downstream of the minimum pressure point, however, the thickening boundary layer has to flow against an adverse pressure gradient. Viscous effects reduce momentum within the boundary layer, and the thickness of the layer further increases so that the external flow "sees" a body which does not appear to close to a point at the trailing edge. A narrow wake is formed as the boundary layer streams off the section. This prevents the pressures on the aft-facing surface of the wing section from recovering to the high value obtaining near the stagnation point on the leading edge, as they would have done if a boundary layer had not formed. There is thus a lower than expected pressure acting on the aft-facing surface, giving rise to normal pressure drag. In the low-AOA case this component is small, most of the profile drag being made up of surface friction drag.

As the AOA of the wing section is increased, the point of minimum pressure moves towards the leading edge, with increasingly high suction being achieved. This means that the pressure then has to rise by a greater extent downstream of the minimum pressure point and that the length of wing surface exposed to the rising pressure is increased. The resulting adverse pressure gradient becomes more severe as AOA is increased. This has serious implications for the boundary layer, which is always likely to separate from the wing surface under such conditions.

Flow separation

This is a very wide topic and only an introduction to it can be given here, though references to its effects will appear throughout later chapters. Flow will always separate from a surface if a severe enough adverse pressure gradient exists in the flow. The mechanisms giving rise to adverse pressure gradients are numerous; in some cases they will cause temporary flow separation with subsequent reattachment, in others they will cause total separation with no reattachment. In almost all cases flow separation is undesirable (though Chapter 1 contains examples of wings designed for applications which actually require the flow to separate).

Why does a flow separate? To answer this question we need to examine how the pressure gradient acts on the velocity profile in the boundary layer. With an adverse pressure gradient, fluid elements in the boundary layer have to work their way "uphill" against the rising pressure. Retarded by fluid friction, fluid elements deep inside the boundary layer have low velocity and hence low momentum. Their momentum falls to a point at which they can no longer make headway against the increasing pressure; they then come to a halt and reverse direction (i.e. start to flow upstream). Reversal causes the flow field to separate from the surface. If reattachment does not take place, the flow separation will form a deep wake which leaves the surface in a roughly streamwise direction. On the relatively thick wings typical of the early jet fighters, the point of separation was found to occur initially near the trailing edge, and then to move forwards along the wing upper surface as AOA was increased. The pressure on the wing downstream of separation is roughly that at the point where separation occurs. This is inevitably less than the freestream pressure, so that nothing like full pressure recovery is possible. Thus an increasingly large normal pressure drag results as AOA steepens (Fig 9).

Fig 9 Breakdown of profile drag.

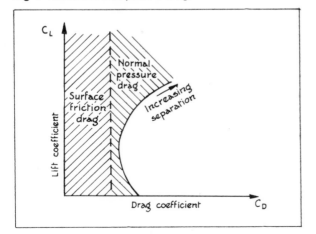

Flow-separation characteristics depend very much on the shape of the wing section. Generally speaking, as wing section thickness decreases, the forward motion of the separation point becomes more rapid as AOA is increased. This has important consequences for the type of stall, or sharp loss of lift, which results, as shown below.

Wing-section low-speed stalling   Since the stalling of wings is a separated-flow phenomenon it is appropriate to mention the subject here. The following discussion is restricted to wing-section stall; the effects of taper and sweep, which markedly complicate wing flow behaviour at high AOA, will be examined in Chapter 1.

There are three types of wing-section stall: trailing-edge, leading-edge, and thin-aerofoil. Trailing-edge stall occurs on relatively thick wing sections and is characterised by rounded suction peaks and moderate pressure gradients, with the turbulent boundary layer initially separating close to the trailing edge. The separation point moves forward slowly with increasing AOA. This behaviour produces a rounded lift curve, giving a gradual loss of lift (Fig 10a). The extent of the flow separation at maximum lift may be up to 50% of the chord length. The normal pressure drag increases with forward movement of the separation point, and there is a nose-down pitching moment (see page 19). These effects are due primarily to the increased suctions under the separated regions over the aft part of the surface.

Leading-edge stall occurs on moderately thick sections (thickness/chord ratio of approximately 9%). The laminar boundary layer abruptly separates as a result of the adverse pressure gradient just aft of the suction peak. Transition to turbulence then occurs, followed by subsequent reattachment as a turbulent boundary layer. The abrupt separation near the leading edge may occur in one of two ways, both of which are associated with a small region of separation known as a "short separation bubble" and extending over perhaps only 1% of the chord length. This significantly affects the pressure distribution only in its immediate vicinity. In the first case, increasing AOA decreases the length of the bubble to a critical point at which it suddenly bursts into a large separated region occupying the entire chord length. This is due to an incompatibility between the boundary layer and external flow, which causes the reattachment process to fail. In the second case, the turbulent boundary layer, a short distance downstream of the bubble, separates because of its weakened state, again resulting in a large separated region. This type of stall is charac-

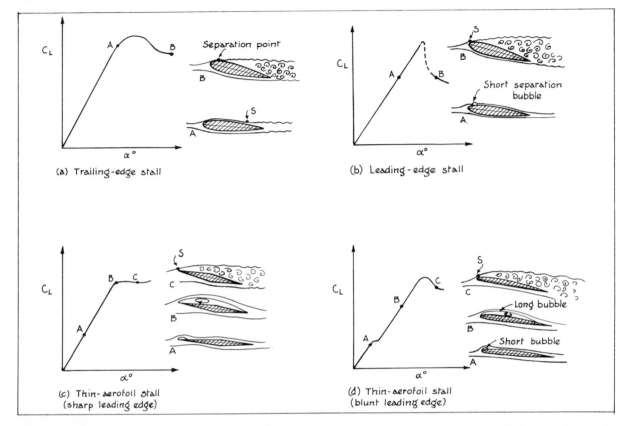

Fig 10 Aerofoil stalling.

teristic of many combat aircraft. As can be seen in Fig 10b, leading-edge stall can produce an abrupt lift loss.

Thin-aerofoil stall occurs on all sharp-edged wing sections and on thin sections with rounded leading edges. For sharp leading edges the lift varies linearly with AOA up to approximately 5°, whereupon there is a laminar boundary-layer separation at the leading edge, with transition to turbulence; reattachment is not however as rapid as in the second case above. The region between separation and reattachment is called a "long bubble" and differs primarily from its shorter counterpart in that it grows in length with AOA, with the point of reattachment moving aft until at maximum lift the bubble reaches the trailing edge. As shown in Fig 10c, this type of stall is not as abrupt as leading-edge stall. There is a large increase in drag due to the loss of leading-edge suction, together with an initially nose-up pitching moment followed by a large nose-down pitching moment.

On thin, rounded wing sections, a short bubble usually forms at low AOA. This then bursts into a

long bubble at an AOA well below the stall, resulting in the characteristic kink shown in Fig 10d. The bubble is much shorter than the chord length but grows until the AOA for maximum lift is reached.

The distinction between leading-edge and thin-aerofoil stalls is not clear-cut, and different stalling behaviour may occur over the aircraft's speed range. In addition, "combined" stalls may occur, with separations arising at both leading and trailing edges. Finally, the use of high-lift devices radically alters stalling behaviour. For example, leading-edge camber can suppress leading-edge stall, while trailing-edge camber will increase leading-edge suctions, creating a tendency towards leading-edge stall.

Summary of flow-separation effects There are three basic consequences of flow separation:

1 Drastic loss of lift, or stalling. It is however important to note that not all of the lift is lost, and when account is taken of the taper and sweep of the wing and the lift generated by the aircraft's fuselage, the stall condition revealed by a lift curve for an entire aircraft is far less obvious than it is in

Fig 10. Nevertheless, aircraft stalling is an extremely important phenomenon and so requires definition. The stall can be defined as the condition in which flow breakdown, primarily over the main wing, causes significant non-linear effects in the pitching and/or rolling planes. The stall speed, usually assuming 1g flight, has been defined as the speed at which a large-amplitude pitching or rolling motion, not immediately controllable, is encountered. However, for our purposes stall speed can be defined as:

$$V_{stall} = \sqrt{\frac{\text{aircraft weight}}{\frac{1}{2} \times \text{density} \times \text{wing area} \times C_{L_{max}}}}$$

2 A major increase in pressure drag. This is due to the appearance of a severe adverse pressure gradient, often caused by a steep slope on a rearward-facing surface, which prevents the flow negotiating the contour of the surface.

3 Wake effects. Although this discussion of flow separation has been limited to wing sections, such a condition can exist over many parts of an aircraft. Often a deep, turbulent wake having low kinetic energy and little aerodynamic potential may be shed. Such flows can have serious implications for parts of the aircraft downstream of the surface on which the separation is taking place. The numerous examples given in subsequent chapters indicate the importance of preventing flow separation where possible and adopting measures to overcome the resulting problems when separation is unavoidable.

Wave drag

The varying accelerations applied to the air particles passing over and under the wing result in velocities higher than the flight velocity on the upper surface and lower velocities on the under surface. As the speed of the aircraft approaches the speed of sound, the higher velocities on the wing's upper surface will reach and eventually exceed the local acoustic velocity, producing regions of supersonic flow. The usual way for such a flow to decelerate back to the flight speed is via a shock wave. This is a very thin pressure wave pulled through the air by the wing and across which extremely abrupt changes of flow properties occur. Static pressure, temperature and density of the air all increase through a shock wave, while the velocity and Mach number drop. There is also a reduction in total pressure. This is the term which is equated to the static and dynamic pressure in the Bernoulli Equation. As a result, the equation cannot be applied across a shock wave, since one of the assumptions is that the flow is continuous (i.e. flow properties change gradually). Across a shock

wave the flow is anything but continuous. The loss of total pressure and the abrupt increase in static pressure add up to a loss of momentum which gives rise to wave drag.

When localised supersonic flow terminated by a weak shock wave first appears on a wing, the loss of total pressure is not particularly significant. The dominating parameter is the adverse pressure gradient resulting from the abrupt rise in static pressure. This will cause at least a thickening of the boundary layer, if not separation. Just above the flight speed at which sonic flow first occurs, known as the critical Mach number, the shock wave is not strong enough to cause flow separation and the effects on drag are barely perceptible. However, further increase in the flight Mach number causes the supersonic region to enlarge and the strength of the terminating shock wave to grow. The interaction between the shock wave and boundary layer will eventually cause boundary-layer separation (Fig 11). This prevents the static pressure at the wing's trailing edge from recovering to the freestream value, leaving the aftmost, rearward-facing surface of the wing at a lower than expected pressure. This increases the pressure drag and is one of the main contributors to wave drag. With further speed increase the shock wave moves aft, gathering strength but reducing the surface exposed to flow separation. The influence of wing section design on this undesirable behaviour, together with other adverse effects, is discussed in later chapters.

Fig 11 Shock-induced boundary-layer separation.

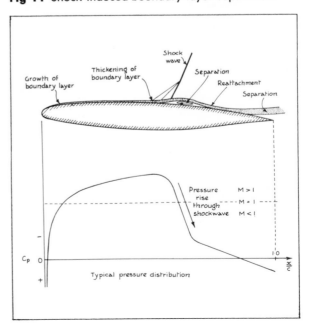

Supersonic flight

At a higher but still subsonic flight speed, a shock wave forms on the wing's lower surface. At a speed very close to that of sound, both waves finally reach the trailing edge of the wing, whose surface is now almost totally immersed in supersonic flow. Further increase in speed causes another shock wave, the bow wave, to move in from upstream of the wing and settle close to or at the wing leading edge.

The formation of the bow wave is caused by weak pressure waves propagating forward from the wing's leading edge at the local speed of sound. When the aircraft's speed is very close to that of sound, these waves meet a flow moving at the same speed and so are unable to travel out ahead of the wing. The air thus has prior warning of the approach of the wing and can adjust itself to flow around it in an orderly fashion. At sonic and super-sonic speeds, the air can have no such warning and has to adjust itself instantaneously to the shape of the wing. This is achieved by the bow wave, the prime function of which is to change the direction of flow. Provided the change of direction is not too large and the leading edge is sharp, the bow wave will move in and become attached to the leading edge as the speed increases. Further increase in speed serves to incline the wave increasingly so that it becomes oblique (Fig 12a).

If the required angular deflection is too large, whether because the leading edge is blunt or because the wing is inclined at an excessive angle, the bow wave stands off from the leading edge. The foremost portion of the wave is then at right angles to the flow, forming what is called a normal shock,

with downstream portions bending back to form an oblique shock wave (Fig 12b). Normal shock waves produce much higher losses in total pressure than do oblique waves. This phenomenon is discussed at length in Chapter 2, dealing with air intakes.

Thus to minimise wave drag wing profiles optimised for supersonic flight have sharp leading edges, as in the case of aircraft such as the Lockheed F-104 and missiles featuring wings with low leading-edge sweep. But most combat aircraft also have to operate efficiently at low speed, and such sharp-edged wings are prone to thin-aerofoil stalling. A combination of sweep with blunt leading edges helps to resolve this conflict between the requirements for high and low-speed performance, as discussed in Chapter 1.

Fig 13, illustrating the variation of wing drag coefficient with Mach number, reveals a rapid increase in drag well below the speed of sound. This is due primarily to the shock-induced boundary-layer separation. For a wing alone the aft movement of the shock waves towards the trailing edge greatly reduces the drag due to separation; the drag coefficient then falls away beyond Mach 1.

The wave pattern in fully supersonic flight around a simple, thin, sharp-leading-edge wing section is shown in Fig 12. The flow is quite different from that at subsonic speeds, as demonstrated by the resulting pressure distribution. This shows that the forward-facing wing surfaces now have pressures exceeding the freestream static pressure. This is caused by the abrupt rise in pressure as the air crosses the leading-edge shock waves. These higher pressures produce forces with rearward components (i.e. they produce drag), the opposite of the case in subsonic flow. On

Fig 12 Supersonic flow.

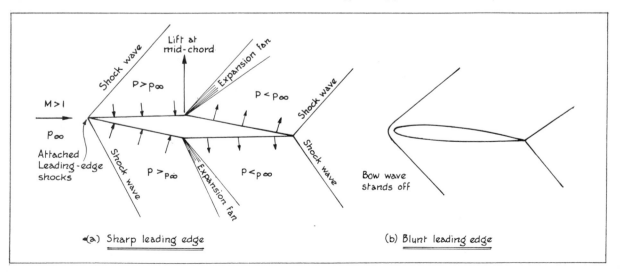

(a) Sharp leading edge   (b) Blunt leading edge

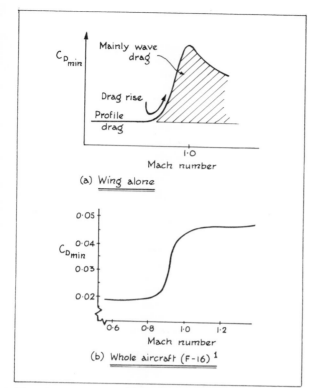

Fig 13 Variation in drag coefficient with Mach number.

reaching mid-chord, the flow expands to lower pressure in a series of Mach waves forming an expansion fan. At the trailing edge the flow has its pressure increased as it passes through the shock waves located there. The drag produced by this flow pattern is critically dependent on the flow deflections encountered. In the simplest analysis the drag is found to vary with the square of both the thickness/chord ratio of the section and AOA. Since lift depends on the pressure distribution, which is a function of AOA, the drag can be split into two terms, one called wave drag due to thickness, the other being wave drag due to lift.

Drag considerations aside, it should be noted when examining Fig 12 that whereas the centre of lift of a simple wedge-shaped aerofoil is well forward at subsonic speeds, it shifts to mid-chord at supersonic speed. This aft movement of the centre of lift as the transonic speed range is traversed has very important implications for aircraft stability and control, as will be discussed in later chapters.

It must be emphasised that the variation in drag coefficient with Mach number shown in Fig 13a relates to the drag of a wing alone, and that the supersonic drag reduction is due to the decline in

flow separation from the wing. Other parts of the aircraft also suffer shock wave formation, however, and this, together with interference effects (see Chapter 3), produces additional drag. The apparent reduction in drag is thus either smaller than expected or even totally absent. An example of how total aircraft drag varies with Mach number is shown in Fig 13b: the F-16's drag coefficient increases by a factor of 2.5 through the transonic regime before reaching a plateau at supersonic speed.

Summary of aerodynamic drag

The relative importance to a typical supersonic fighter of the various forms of drag is shown in Fig 14. Surface friction drag and trailing-vortex drag are the two most important contributors at subsonic speed, while at supersonic speed wave drag becomes predominant.

The variation of drag with lift for both subsonic and supersonic flight is shown in Fig 15. Most noticeable here are the rapid increase in vortex drag as lift is increased, and the increase in zero-lift drag which occurs at supersonic speed.

Aerodynamic pitching moments

The distribution of pressure over a surface is a source of aerodynamic moments as well as forces. Illustrating this fact is the pressure distribution and resulting lift forces acting on the cambered wing section shown in Fig 4. The net lift in the low-

Fig 14 Drag breakdown for a typical supersonic fighter.[2]

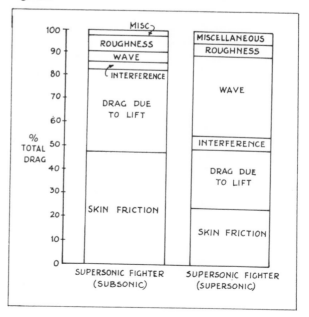

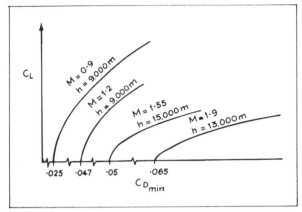

Fig 15 Drag polar variation with Mach number (F-16).[3]

AOA case is the difference between the upper and lower-surface lift forces. The point along the chord at which the distributed lift can be considered to act and at which there is no nose-up or nose-down tendency (i.e. zero pitching moment) is termed the centre of pressure. The position of this point moves as the AOA and lift coefficient are varied.

To give zero lift the upper and lower-surface lift forces must be equal, and for a cambered wing section this will occur at a negative AOA. As shown in Fig 4, these lift forces do not act through the same point, resulting in a nose-down pitching moment. As AOA is increased, the upper-surface lift is increased, lower-surface "lift" decreases and the centre of pressure moves forward. While there has been a change in lift, there is a point within the wing profile about which no change in moment occurs. This is known as the aerodynamic centre. Alternatively, this can be seen as the point at which all changes in lift effectively take place. For a typical wing section the aerodynamic centre is located at approximately 25% of the chord length from the leading edge. It does not move with angles of attack well below that of the stall. Addition of a fuselage to the wing relocates the combined aerodynamic centre somewhat ahead of the quarter-chord position, the displacement depending on the forward length of the body, while adding a horizontal tail moves it rearwards. The aerodynamic centre of the complete aircraft is known as the neutral point (see Chapters 1 and 4).

Although the position of the aerodynamic centre is fixed for a given configuration and does not by definition move with AOA, at least for attached flow, it is influenced by speed. The radical change in pressure distribution which occurs when an aircraft traverses the transonic regime causes an aft movement of the aerodynamic centre. At supersonic speed the aerodynamic centre of a simple wing section shifts from 25% chord to 50% chord. This has the effect of increasing the nose-down pitching moment on the wing, which causes significant problems. Not least of these is the trim drag caused by the tailplane deflection required to trim out the unwanted pitching moment.

The flight envelope

The operational environment of an aircraft lies within a boundary drawn against the axes of speed and height called the flight envelope (Fig 16). The left-hand side of the diagram indicates the speed at any height below which there is insufficient lift for straight-and-level flight. Flight to the left of this line can only be transient. Some aircraft exhibit a dip in the curve around Mach 1 due to increased wave drag and decreased aerodynamic and propulsive efficiency. The right-hand side of the curve represents the propulsive and structural limits imposed by the higher speeds. Beyond them the resulting kinetic heating (due to skin friction) and high dynamic pressures would require a stronger and heavier structure. The diagram shows flight envelopes for two aircraft, the Northrop F-5E and F-20, at two load factors, 1g and 4g. Several points stand out:

1 The F-20 is a Mach 2 aircraft and displays a significantly extended high-speed envelope whereas the F-5E is limited to Mach 1·64 at typical combat weight, albeit at the same 11,000m altitude.

2 Sustained manoeuvring (the 4g load factor case is shown) greatly curtails the flight envelope for both aircraft as a result of the large increase in lift-dependent drag.

3 The primary air battle zone, shown shaded, is limited to subsonic speeds. This is because pilots

Fig 16 Flight envelope.[4]

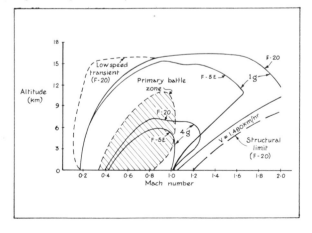

tend to fly their aircraft to maximise turn rate — so as to gain an angular position on their opponents — and this can currently be achieved only at subsonic speed. In Vietnam and subsequent conflicts in which adversaries had Mach 2 + aircraft at their command, the combat speed range was predominantly Mach 0·5–0·9, with very little time being spent above Mach 1·1.

DESIGN AND REQUIREMENTS OF COMBAT AIRCRAFT

Preliminary design

The preliminary design of a new combat aircraft is not normally based on a completely defined specification. The processes of fixing the major design parameters in order to arrive at the optimum configuration and developing a workable specification for the weapon system are mutually influential. Furthermore, this period of definition now takes so long that there are sometimes profound changes of opinion about how the aircraft should best be used. Other and just as radical changes of view take place following a type's entry into service.

The operational lifetime of a modern combat aircraft type can be 20 years or more. For example, the F-4 Phantom first entered service in 1960 and is unlikely to be totally withdrawn before the year 2000. Clearly, aircraft now entering service will be operating well into the 21st century. Combined with a lengthy project gestation, such extended operational lives can mean that a requirement has to be defined some 10 or 20 years before it is put to the test of combat. The odds against accurately foreseeing what will be needed are thus very great, and are lengthened still further by the current rapid development of the weapon and sensor technology which might be deployed by and also against any new aircraft.

At present there is more technology available than can be included in any single aircraft if cost is to remain within bounds. This has meant that the 1950s philosophy of "doing what can be done" has been replaced by "doing what should be done" or "doing what can be afforded". Even "doing what should be done" is difficult when the nature and strength of an anticipated threat can only be guessed at. This problem has given rise to the maxim "You never fight the war you design for".

The only certain thing about the next generation of aircraft is the fact that they will have to do everything that the current generation is capable of, but better and at a comparable price. The designer's task is not necessarily to invent some completely new concept, but rather to determine in what respects existing combat aircraft are inadequate and to judge which of the emerging ideas is worth pursuing.

The requirements of combat aircraft

The basic attributes of combat aircraft are lethality, manoeuvrability, handling qualities, range, persistence, visibility, stealth, and resilience.

Lethality

This is a function of the destructive power of the aircraft's weapons, which must be easy to use, reliable, non-counterable and effective. The lightest, cheapest, easiest to use, hardest to counter and most effective air-to-air weapon is the cannon. The 20mm cannon is adequate for dogfighting with other aircraft, though ideally it should be complemented by the short-range infra-red (IR) guided missile, which prevents disengagement. Interceptors operating against less manoeuvrable, radar-equipped aircraft are armed with medium to long-range missiles which can home in on radar emissions. Larger-calibre guns are required for operations against surface targets. There is also a wide variety of other ground attack weapons, ranging from iron bombs to TV and laser-guided missiles. A single aircraft can carry a wide mix of types on a single mission, creating the need for an effective fire-control system tailored to the aircraft's anticipated roles.

Manoeuvrability

Also known as agility, this is the ability of an aircraft to change position and velocity rapidly in order to gain an advantage in air-to-air combat or to evade anti-aircraft defences.

In air-to-air combat, in which high manoeuvrability is essential, there are four basic objectives:

1 To gain an energy advantage over the opponent at the beginning of the engagement.

2 To convert energy advantage into an angular position advantage.

3 To achieve an advantageous angular position in sustained combat.

4 To force an overshoot if the opponent has an energy or heading advantage.

The parameter known as specific excess power (SEP) is used to assess acceleration along the flight path or rate of climb at a given load factor (g). Expressed in metres/sec, it is derived from excess thrust × velocity ÷ weight. The parameters used to assess an aircraft's turning performance are load factor, turn rate and turn radius, with turn rate regarded as the most important. Combat superiority is seen as depending on the product of SEP, sustained turn rate (maximum turn rate without loss of speed) and instantaneous or attained turn rate (maximum achievable turn rate with transient loss of speed). Forthcoming aircraft will require quicker engine acceleration, faster-operating airbrakes and very high rates of roll and pitch, with commensurately higher g tolerances for airframe and crew.

Handling qualities

The aircraft should have handling qualities which permit the pilot to use the full extent of the manoeuvring performance envelope with ease and safety. Up to the late 1950s most high-performance aircraft were limited to subsonic speeds and were designed primarily for air-to-air combat. Their basic design characteristics meant that the wing stalled before a loss of directional stability occurred. They were thus difficult to spin inadvertently.

In the late 1950s and early 1960s design emphasis was placed on high manoeuvrability and large speed envelopes. The resulting aircraft had relatively sharp wing leading edges; high wing sweep; large, flat fuselages that continued to lift after the wing had stalled; and large horizontal tails, needed to obtain the desired supersonic manoeuvrability. This type of configuration could be manoeuvred to increasingly high AOA at subsonic speed, leading to a new flight condition in which the aircraft continued to produce lift beyond the AOA at which directional stability was lost. A divergence in yaw and loss of control often followed, sometimes taking the pilot completely by surprise.

These aircraft clearly had less than desirable stall/spin characteristics, and an enormous effort was made to give the subsequent generation of fighters much better high-AOA handling qualities. Air combat is already stressful enough for the pilot, without the aircraft adding further difficulties. Indeed, superior handling qualities are essential if the full performance potential of the aircraft is to be achieved, and "carefree manoeuvring" is now a prime objective.

Range

Much of the ability of an aircraft to reach and attack its target and return depends on its range. This in turn is influenced by the nature of the combat in which the aircraft is engaged. For the air-superiority fighter the main arena may be close at hand, with combat consisting primarily of linear

and turning accelerations. For the ground attack aircraft the target may be distant and only one weapon-firing pass may be possible. The best aircraft is the one that can perform most combat-relevant manoeuvres at a given radius of action, or achieve the longest radius of action for a given combat requirement.

The fuel fraction (i.e. fuel load/take-off weight) is critical to range and is dictated by the radius of action, loiter time and combat requirements. Sometimes the mission can require attributes that are difficult to combine in one airframe: long-range combat air patrol, for instance, calls for both high fuel capacity and agility. Such conflicts have generally been resolved by the use of external fuel tanks. Though this is an inefficient method in terms of fuel usage (typically half of the external fuel carried is used to overcome the additional drag of the tanks), it does avoid having an excessively big, heavy and costly aircraft for other missions.

Multi-role aircraft have to meet very disparate requirements. This is generally made possible by the use of variable sweep, which allows wing geometry to be optimised for each phase of every mission. The major proviso is that the range required is sufficient to ensure that the fuel saved offsets the weight and volume penalties of this solution.

Persistence

This is the ability of an aircraft to stay in combat while continuing to achieve superior manoeuvring performance. It is expressed in units of time, assuming a specified radius of action and fuel load for given flight-to-combat profiles. The ability to do without afterburning greatly improves an aircraft's capacity to stay and fight. Even at maximum dry (i.e. unreheated) thrust, the fuel consumption may be twice that of economic cruise. Full afterburning consumes fuel at an alarming rate, increasing the flow rate by a further factor of five to six. At the resulting overall factor of around 12, an aircraft that could cruise for an hour at low altitude would exhaust its fuel supply in five minutes with full reheat. An adequate dry thrust/weight ratio (T/W) is made all the more important by the fact that any attempt to break off close combat is extremely dangerous if the opponent has an unused missile.

To demonstrate the value of persistence the USAF ran a test with two F-4Es and one YF-16. One of the F-4Es (low dry T/W) and the YF-16 (high dry T/W) engaged in combat until one aircraft achieved a gun kill. The first F-4E was at minimum fuel after three such engagements. The second F-4E then took off and the process was repeated. The YF-16 won

Not Northrop's Advanced Technology Bomber (ATB) but its YB-49 flying wing of the late 1940s. With its rounded surfaces and submerged intakes, the YB-49 had some of the features needed for stealth. Similar qualities allowed RAF Vulcans on exercise to penetrate US airspace undetected. (Northrop)

all the engagements and outlasted both F-4Es with enough fuel remaining to fly over 300km.

Visibility

This is the ability to detect the target first and keep it in view. High-speed ground attack aircraft are likely to use sensor-directed weapons more and more, so that a very high degree of visibility is not crucial. This is also true of interceptors which operate against targets well beyond the visual range. For air superiority fighters, however, unobscured forward and aft vision is vital for target detection and warning of rear-hemisphere attack. Though this principle was forgotten between the late 1950s and mid-1960s, high-visibility teardrop canopies were back in fashion by the early 1970s, even at the expense of additional supersonic drag.

Stealth

This is the ability of an aircraft to attack its target with the maximum amount of surprise. It can be achieved by reducing the aircraft's visual, radar and infra-red signal strengths. All three are minimised by keeping the aircraft small and may be further reduced as follows:

Visual

Elimination of the smoke trail with and without afterburner. Camouflaging the aircraft by painting it in the colours predominating its mission environment, and reducing the size, number and visibility of identification markings.

Radar

Reduction of radar cross-section by avoiding surfaces at right angles to each other (to limit the number of corner reflections) and the use of radar-absorbent materials. Minimising energy emissions from the aircraft's own sensors. Provision of electronic countermeasures (ECM) and chaff.

Infra-red

Less use of afterburner, with its enormous IR

The location of the Fairchild A-10's turbofan engines was chosen to reduce their infra-red signature—improving survivability against heat-seeking missiles — and to lessen the risk of foreign object damage. The large nose-down pitching moment resulting from their high thrust line has a major influence on the tailplane power needed to raise the nosewheel on take-off.

signal. Shielding of engine exhaust, since the very short afterburners now employed have increased the angular detection range. Use of decoy systems such as flares.

As defences have become increasingly impenetrable the importance of stealth has grown. This trend is typified by the B-1B, which is claimed to have only 1% of the radar cross-section (RCS) of the B-52, and Northrop's Advanced Technology Bomber, with a still smaller RCS.

Resilience

This is the ability of a force of aircraft to return repeatedly to the battle arena after the first engagement. The availability of large numbers of aircraft can provide this, though maintainability, survivability and repairability are also important. Though the use of simple aircraft against comparatively soft targets avoids the squandering of "brittle" forces (i.e. sophisticated and costly weapon systems), it is no guarantee of high resilience.

The ability of an aircraft to survive battle damage depends on how well its four most vulnerable components — the crew, powerplant, fuel and flight control systems — are protected. Threat awareness on the part of the crew is the first line of defence, and this can be assisted by rearwards-looking radar and the maximum use of head-up displays in the battle zone.

Vulnerable components can be protected in the following ways:

Crew
Armour and flak curtains (though the former is heavy). Location of equipment ahead of and to the rear of the cockpit to help stop splinters.

Powerplant
Twin engines should be sufficiently far apart to prevent damage to one from leading to loss of the other. Tail and rear-fuselage surfaces should provide whatever screening is possible to the tail-pipe, but be remote enough to limit fragment damage to the tailpipe and adjacent secondary structure. Engines and intakes should be remote from fuel tanks; this is however usually impracticable, the sole contemporary example being the A-10.

Fuel system
Fuel tanks should be integral, with minimum exposure of tank surfaces, though with wet wings this is not usually feasible. Tanks should be foam-filled and unpressurised during combat, and the most threatened tanks should be emptied first. Active fire-suppression should be incorporated.

Flight-control system
Multiplex, independent and redundant power sources and associate systems should be provided.

Classification of combat aircraft

While there appears to be broad agreement on what is required of a combat aircraft, there is no unanimity on the relative value of the various factors. One thing is sure, however: isolated emphasis on any single factor such as manoeuvrability, range or persistence, would be dangerous.

The classification below identifies four categories of combat aircraft, and lists their distinguishing characteristics. But some major types are hard to pigeonhole: despite being concerned as an air combat fighter with "not a pound for air-to-ground," the McDonnell Douglas F-15 can now also be found acquitting itself very ably as a ground-attack fighter.

Interceptor fighter
Usually directed towards a non-manoeuvring target by ground or airborne control radar. It requires high speed and longitudinal acceleration, together with good high-altitude performance and long range. Its weapon load is characterised by long-range all-altitude missiles and associated radar. Since neither turning performance nor capability in low-speed combat are important, the primary aerodynamic design is largely governed by low profile and wave drag, and high cruise lift/drag. Low fuel consumption is also significant.

Air-combat fighter
This type approaches its target either under ground or airborne direction, using its own radar, or by chance, at low to medium altitudes, and armed with a gun and highly manoeuvrable short/medium-range missiles. While the highest supersonic speeds are not necessary, the best possible instantaneous turning performance is essential. Airfield performance is important, since the fighter will be operating from first-line-of-defence bases. Its aerodynamic design will be governed by the need for good lift/drag at high g, high usable lift, low drag at all speeds, and high control power. It will require high thrust/weight with and without afterburning, and low combat fuel consumption.

Ground-attack fighter
Operates primarily at high speed and low altitude and has enough manoeuvrability to attack targets acquired at low search altitudes. The requisite low wing loading may however have a detrimental effect, giving poor ride quality in rough air at low altitude. Aerodynamic design is governed mainly by a requirement for low subsonic drag with external stores and efficient high-lift devices for adequate airfield performance. A high thrust/weight ratio without afterburner is also needed.

Long-range strike aircraft
Such types initially approach the target at high altitude, descending for a nap-of-the-earth, high-speed penetration in the terminal phase. There is less emphasis on manoeuvrability, so that high wing loadings are permissible; indeed they are desirable, giving acceptable ride quality in sustained flight in rough air. Aerodynamic requirements are high cruise lift/drag ratio and low weapon drag. Low fuel consumption and a high unreheated thrust/weight ratio are also required.

CHAPTER 1

WING DESIGN

INTRODUCTION

This chapter is concerned with that most important component, the wing, the shape of which, more than any other design feature, influences the performance and handling characteristics of aircraft. The modern combat aircraft has to meet a broad spectrum of requirements across an extensive flight envelope. Inevitably, this can only be achieved by a series of compromises.

The chapter starts by focusing on lift production, with reference to aerofoil section shape in general. A description of the development of modern aerofoils in response to thickness effects on high-speed behaviour is followed by a discussion of supercritical aerofoils and their current and future applications. Lift augmentation by means of leading and trailing-edge devices is discussed in depth, and the various types of device compared. Boundary-layer control (BLC) in the form of leading-edge and trailing-edge flap blowing is not covered, however. Used in the past to further enhance lift, it has become unfashionable since the 1960s.

The subject of wing planform is introduced by way of a look at aspect and taper ratios. The influence of wing size on various performance requirements is examined, leading to an analysis of the kind of conflicts that can only be settled with a variable-sweep design. Wing sweep is treated as a subject in its own right since it has many manifestations, including aft, forward and variable sweep. The emergence and use of the delta wing is dealt with, and the developments which have created renewed interest in this type of planform for combat aircraft are described.

The high-AOA handling problems of the first and second-generation swept-wing fighters are illuminated by discussion of the nature of the flow over swept wings, including the occurrence of buffeting and lateral/directional instabilities. Recent wing design innovations aimed at improving matters include manoeuvre flaps, variable-camber wings, and the harnessing of vortex flows with leading-edge root extensions.

The lateral (i.e. roll) stability and control of aircraft is examined, and the use of ailerons, spoilers and differential tailplanes to meet control requirements in the face of compressibility and aeroelastic

effects is described. The vertical position of the wing and the wing's dihedral angle are shown to be important influences on lateral/directional stability.

Finally, there is a description of the various palliatives used to prevent, delay or suppress flow separation. Referred to as "aerodynamic crutches," they include wing fences, sawteeth, notches and vortex generators.

AEROFOIL SECTIONS

Terminology

As shown earlier, the shape of the wing section and its inclination to the airstream are the two fundamental determinants of the pressure distribution which gives rise to the aerodynamic forces acting on the section. Fig 17 shows the basic features of the aerofoils typically used on combat aircraft. Represented are both the more conventional section shape and those features of the supercritical sections developed in recent years. The main points to note are the maximum thickness of the wing and where it occurs, the distribution of thickness, the camber (i.e. the displacement of the mean line from the chord line), and the leading-edge radius. These properties are given as fractions or percentages of the chord length.

Aerofoil thickness

This is commonly expressed as a thickness/chord ratio or thickness ratio (t/c).

Early jet fighters had thickness ratios of 12–14%, typical of their piston-engined predecessors. With its 13% root and 7% tip the Spitfire was atypical and was capable of very high Mach numbers in dives, the highest recorded value being Mach 0·92. German research during the 1940s showed a clear appreciation of the value of reduced thickness for high-speed flight. The thinner sections shown in Fig 18 not only have lower drag coefficients but also delay the onset of drag rise due to shock wave formation. The latter was the main argument in favour of thin sections, which, together with sweepback, have been

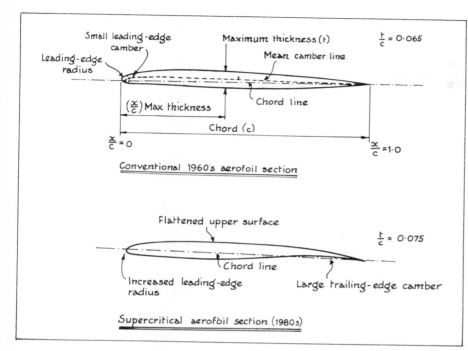

Fig 17 The evolution of high-speed aerofoils.

Fig 18 Effects of wing thickness/chord ratio on critical Mach number.

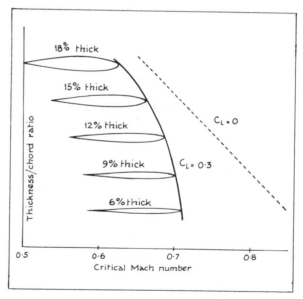

successfully employed on all subsequent high-speed aircraft.

Following the introduction of sweepback on aircraft such as the F-86 Sabre, with its 35° of leading-edge sweep, the thickness ratio was held at 12% because it was felt that the delay in the drag rise did not warrant the structural weight penalty of a thinner wing. In addition, a wing of conventional thickness, permitted by the use of sweepback, maintained reasonably high maximum lift and provided room for both leading and trailing-edge lift devices, together with useful fuel volume and stowage for the undercarriage.

At higher speeds, thick sections are impracticable because the excessive airflow acceleration over the surface produces velocities which exceed the local sonic velocity and lead to premature shock wave formation. This can be delayed by more sweepback, as explained later, since 30° sweep plus 10% thickness is roughly equivalent at subsonic speeds to 40° sweep plus 12% thickness.

Increased sweep had its drawbacks, however. Major problems were a tendency to pitch up uncontrollably, the result of combining sweep with fairly high aspect ratio, and a relatively large reduction in the lift effectiveness of trailing-edge flaps when the hinge lines were also swept. In addition, cross-wind landing problems arose as a result of rolling induced by sideslip. The solution was bigger ailerons, which led to smaller flaps and sometimes a bigger wing to restore airfield performance. (These and other drawbacks of sweep are dealt with later). Thus a demand arose for thinner sections to counter adverse compressibility effects, which included stability and control problems, shock-wave drag and shock-induced boundary-layer separation, which is itself a major contributor to the transonic drag rise.

Spanwise thickness variation

Because the wing-root section suffers the greatest bending moment it needs a large structural depth.

The North American Sabre was the classic early swept-wing fighter, introducing a pitot intake in the nose, powered controls and all-moving tailplanes while retaining the excellent visibility of the company's earlier P-51 Mustang. The F-86H shown has a short wing fence and two 120gal drop tanks braced to the wing.

Wings therefore taper in both thickness and thickness ratio towards the tip to maintain an adequate strength/weight ratio while minimising weight. Such a variation is typified by the Grumman F-14 wing, which tapers in a distinctly non-linear manner from 10·5% thickness ratio at the root to 7% at the tip.

Shock stall

This was the name given to the behaviour exhibited by early high-speed aircraft when they encountered compressibility effects. Fig 19 shows how the pressure distribution and lift on a contemporary 10%-thick aerofoil varied in a dramatic way with change in Mach number.

At a flight Mach number of 0·75 there is a region

Fig 19 Flow changes over an aerofoil through the transonic range (angle of attack constant).[5]

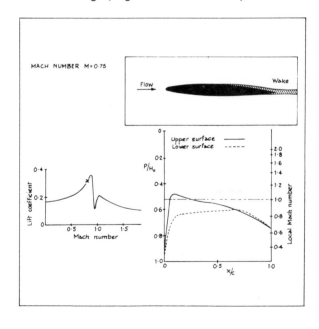

of slightly supersonic flow on the upper surface just aft of the leading edge. Suctions exist over virtually all the upper and lower surfaces apart from near the leading edge. As the speed is increased to Mach 0·8 a shock wave appears on the upper surface, preceded by a more extensive region of supersonic flow. The abrupt pressure rise through the shock wave has caused the boundary layer to thicken, giving a deeper wake aft of the aerofoil. The shock wave in itself has no appreciable effect on the lift coefficient versus Mach number curve, which continues its steady climb. The slight rise in lift coefficient is represented by the larger area bounded by the pressure distri-

bution. On the lower surface the flow velocity has just reached the sonic condition.

Following a further increase in Mach number a shock wave appears on the lower surface. With a now intensified shock wave on the upper surface, the boundary layer there is likely to separate, causing a thicker wake and a reduction in pressure at the trailing edge. Under the influence of this reduced pressure the lower-surface shock moves rapidly aft as Mach number increases, while the upper-surface shock remains almost stationary. The resulting pressure distribution produces a steep drop in lift coefficient. The large extent of supersonic expansion ahead of the lower-surface

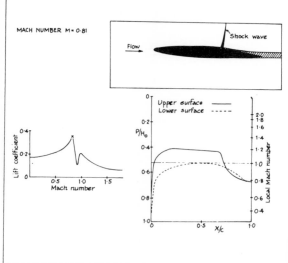

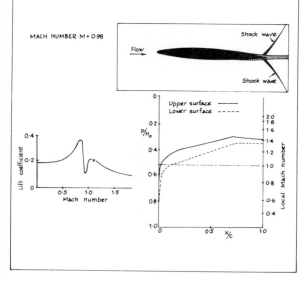

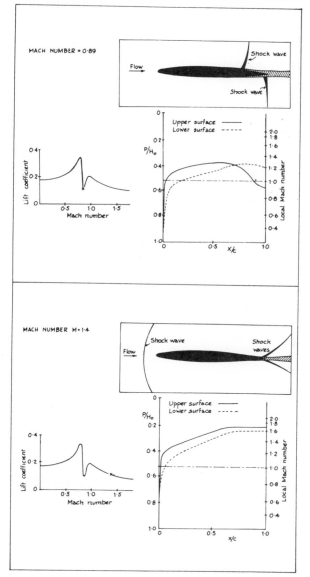

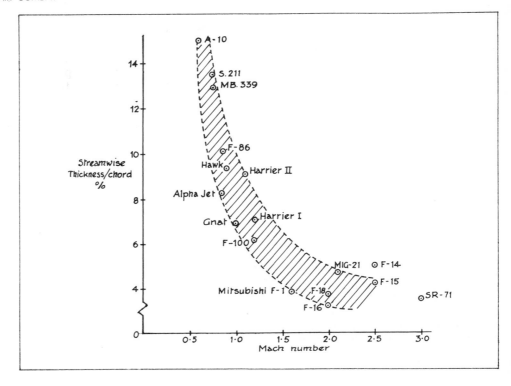

Fig 20 Speed
increase demands
thinner wings.

shock produces an area of suction towards the rear
of the aerofoil's under surface which cuts deeply
into the net upward suction further forward.

With a further increase in speed the lower
surface shock reaches the trailing edge and the
upper shock moves back likewise so that the lift
tends to recover somewhat. The boundary-layer
separation and wake thickness diminish, causing a
fall in the drag coefficient.

This sequence of events is what is loosely called
the shock stall. Its characteristic out-of-step movements of the shock waves and their influence on the
wing's pitching moment caused many of the stability and control difficulties afflicting the early transonic fighters.

Thicker aerofoils were found to aggravate the
above behaviour and cause it to occur at lower
speeds. It was conclusively established in the late
1940s that thinner sections could greatly alleviate
these effects and postpone the drag rise to higher
Mach numbers. The trend towards reduced thickness ratio for higher speed for a range of aircraft is
shown in Fig 20. Since the wave drag due to thick-
nes is proportional to thickness ratio squared, the
demand for aircraft capable of penetrating the
fully supersonic flight regime caused thickness
ratio to tumble even further, being stopped short of
structural limits only by increases in sweepback.

Successor to the F-86 was the F-100, the 45°
sweep and 6% thickness of which allowed it to
become the world's first operational supersonic
aircraft. The Mach 2 XF-104 Starfighter had
stubby unswept wings, a thickness ratio of 3·36%
(giving a maximum thickness at the root of barely
10cm) and a leading-edge radius so small as to be
positively sharp. Other contemporary aircraft of
similar top speed, like the Mirage III and Lightning,
had 60° sweep and 5% thickness ratios and so
could embody more rounded leading edges, thereby
deferring flow separation to higher AOA without
leading-edge devices. Later delta-wing designs
took advantage of their planform's inherent structural benefits to reduce thickness ratio further;
both the Avro CF-105 and BAC TSR.2 had wings of
about 3·7% thickness.

The reduction in thickness demanded by supersonic flight produced sections whose leading-edge
radius was also reduced (Fig 21) so that the
trailing-edge boundary-layer separation typical of
the older, thicker sections gave way to leading-edge
separation during subsonic manoeuvres. This
caused wing buffet at relatively low AOA, so that
at higher lift buffeting became so severe as to
render the aircraft ineffective as a gun or missile
platform. The large regions of separated flow also
led to poor handling, leading to restrictions on

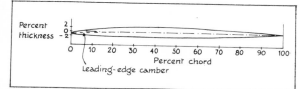

Fig 21 Aerofoil section for Northrop F-5 (4.8% thick, 24° quarter-chord sweep).[6]

allowable AOA and prompting the development and use of manoeuvre flaps (see *Manoeuvrability*).

Advanced and supercritical sections
Early British sections
Several Mach 2 fighters were operational by the beginning of the 1960s, with others under development, and it was beginning to be appreciated that the headlong thrust for yet higher speeds had produced aircraft with less than desirable transonic characteristics. Furthermore, demands were being made to increase the efficiency of subsonic commercial aircraft by postponing the drag-rise Mach number (M_D). Thus attention began to refocus on transonic characteristics, specifically on improved aerofoil sections.

Much of the early work on aerofoils to improve M_D and buffet limits at high subsonic speed was done by Pearcey at the National Physical Laboratory. The basic approach was to contour the leading edge in order to expand the flow rapidly from the stagnation point and to generate supersonic flow over the nose region. The expansion Mach waves so created would then reflect as a series of compression waves from the sonic line (Fig 22). These compression waves would then gradually reduce the local Mach number so that the final shock wave was thereby weakened, causing less severe flow separation aft of the shock

Fig 22 Weakening of shock wave by a single expansion wave generated at leading edge.[7]

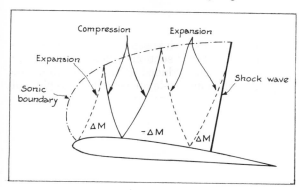

and so reducing aerofoil drag. It was believed that the flow could be decelerated with minimal loss from maximum local Mach numbers as high as 1·4 without the intense shock which would normally terminate such a supersonic flow. Such an ideal situation would admittedly occur for a given aerofoil at only one isolated design point (i.e. combination of M and AOA), but it was found that the rate of growth of shock waves off the design condition was usually slow, making a practical design possible.

Fig 23 Comparison of pressure distributions of early and current high-speed wing sections.[8]

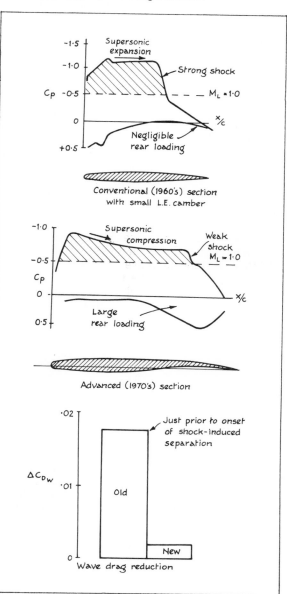

The resulting pressure distribution has a marked suction peak near the leading edge, with the result that this type of aerofoil was described as "peaky". It also featured increased rear loading, achieved by means of a reflex, cusped trailing edge generating large positive pressures on the lower surface. The extra lift provided by this compensated for the reduced lift from the much flatter upper surface (Fig 23), itself designed to reduced disturbances to the more sensitive boundary layer on the upper surface. The use of a blunt trailing edge was intended to reduce upper-surface slope, lessening the likelihood of boundary-layer separation. It also helps isolate the upper and lower-surface trailing-edge pressures. The improvement in performance of the peaky section compared with the earlier ones can be seen in Fig 23.

Peaky sections which deliberately generate high suctions at the leading edge can suffer during air-combat manoeuvring at high AOA as a result of excessive shock strength, causing a sudden loss of lift well below the design Mach number. When this type of section, with uniform isobar sweep, was applied to the Kestrel, precursor to the Harrier, simultaneous stall over a large portion of the wing occurred above Mach 0·8. This led to severe wing rocking at AOAs at which only light buffet might have been expected, a phenomenon caused by sudden stalling switching from one wing to the other. An increased aerofoil nose radius, together with other modifications, was an effective cure and has characterised subsequent sections.

American supercritical sections

Further development of Pearcey's pioneering work has continued, with much interest being created by the research by Whitcomb of NASA Langley, where the description "supercritical" was coined. This is in fact a misnomer, since all high-speed aerofoils have regions of supercritical (i.e. super-sonic) flow. The Whitcomb sections and subsequent developments have a camber distribution designed to reduce further the adverse pressure gradients by means of an even flatter upper surface. A larger leading-edge radius is used to reduce velocities over both upper and lower surfaces but especially to attenuate the leading-edge suction peak. More lower-surface camber at the rear was introduced to increase aft loading without reducing M_D. A reduction in lower-surface velocity is needed to avoid the formation of a shock wave, the pressure rise of which, superimposed on the pronounced pressure increase of the rear camber, would produce the tendency towards flow separation.

Using advanced aerofoils

The benefits offered by the advanced sections may be used:

1 To increase the drag-rise Mach number (M_D) for a given thickness ratio and sweep.

2 To allow the use of a thicker wing for a given M_D and sweep, in order to improve available wing volume and either reduce the wing structure weight or increase the aspect ratio.

3 To reduce wing sweep for a given M_D and thickness ratio, so improving lift and lift/drag ratio for take-off and landing and increasing the design cruise lift coefficient. The choice of benefits from these improvements includes a decrease in wing area leading to a reduction in wing drag, particularly if applied as a reduction in wing chord at constant span; an increase in cruise altitude to save fuel on long-range flight by reducing equivalent airspeed at a constant Mach number; or simply a reduction in Mach number to save fuel on a short-range flight.

A combination of any of these attributes could be used, depending on the aircraft's intended role.

The BAe/McDonnell Douglas AV-8B Harrier II is an excellent example of the benefits of the newer sections, offering a comparison of the old and the new, as shown in Fig 24. The Harrier I/AV-8A has a relatively peaky section. In redesigning for the AV-8B the main requirement was to improve payload/range capability. Choice of a supercritical

Fig 24 Harrier wing comparison.[9] Besides its greater span and area, the AV-8B wing has 4° less leading-edge sweep (36°), 2% greater thickness/chord (10.5%), and 980kg more fuel capacity (2,250kg).

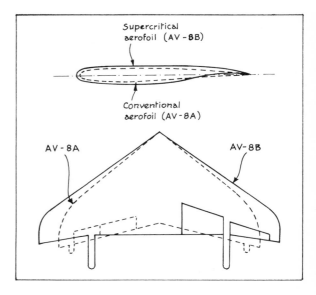

Above: BAe Sea Harrier trailing tip vortices from its snagged, fenced and vortex generator-equipped wing. In navalising the Harrier the RAF version's front end was redesigned to house Blue Fox radar and additional avionics and improve visibility by raising the seat. The forward, cold, nozzle of the Pegasus turbofan is scarfed, or cut off at an oblique angle. (BAe)

Below: An early development BAe/McDonnell Douglas Harrier II displays its vertical lift-enhancing dam, just behind the nosewheel leg, and strakes. The leading-edge root extension (LERX), massive circulation-controlled trailing-edge flap, narrow-track outrigger wheels and zero-scarf front nozzles are clearly shown. The second row of intake suck-in doors was later deleted and wing hardpoints were increased to four per side on RAF aircraft. (BAe)

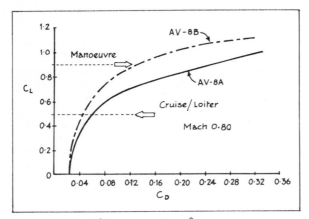

Fig 25 Harrier drag comparison.[9]

section designed to maintain the AV-8A's drag-rise Mach number permitted a thicker wing, reducing both sweep and weight per unit area, increasing the internal fuel volume and improving the buffet boundary. As shown in Fig 24, the AV-8B's wing is thicker and has a larger area, span and aspect ratio, all designed to maintain the M_D and cruise speed. The drag improvements were found to be substantial, as revealed by the AV-8A/AV-8B drag polar comparison at Mach 0·8 (Fig 25). The cruise and loiter lift/drag ratios are increased by about 20%.

The use of extensive aft camber, a characteristic of supercritical wings, can lead to very high nose-down pitching moments on the wing which have to be reduced if excessive trim drag is to be avoided. This was achieved on the AV-8B wing by a careful distribution of twist and camber across the span (Fig 26). In fact the benefits of the AV-8B wing were achieved with no increase in pitching moment at

Fig 26 Harrier II geometric twist distribution.[9]

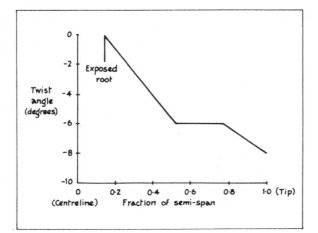

low Mach numbers compared with the AV-8A, and an actual decrease at the cruise condition.

While the application of a supercritical wing to the AV-8B was intended basically to improve the payload/radius of a subsonic attack aircraft, NASA has also researched the use, both subsonically and supersonically, of supercritical wing sections for manoeuvring fighter aircraft. In one series of tests on the F-111, used for its ability to vary wing sweep readily, the basic wing, with a NACA 64A series aerofoil, was replaced by a supercritical wing of identical thickness and planform. As shown in Fig 27, the supercritical wing gives substantial reductions in drag at moderate and high lift and an increase in drag-rise Mach number at cruise and manoeuvring angles of attack.

Fig 27 Benefits of supercritical section (as tested on F-111 at 26° sweepback).[10]

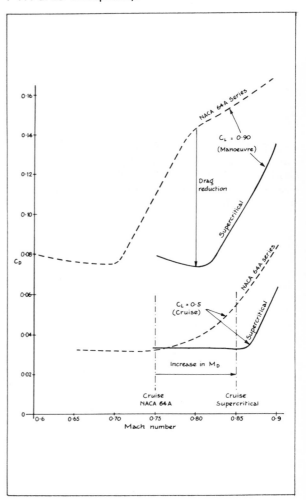

The limits imposed by the buffet boundary can severely restrict the combat effectiveness of a fighter. The great benefit of the supercritical wing was the fact that the lift coefficients for the onset of buffet were increased substantially, especially at the higher Mach numbers. Testing at supersonic speed indicated no adverse effects of the super-critical wing at Mach 1·2, whereas at higher Mach numbers it produced higher drag; in practice, however, both leading and trailing-edge profiles can be varied to optimise section shape.

NASA pursued these studies further with the Transonic Aircraft Technology (TACT) demonstrator. This was a modified F-111 featuring a thinner (7·4%) supercritical aerofoil and reduced aspect ratio to improve the transonic manoeuvrability and cruise Mach number without degrading cruise efficiency, sea-level dash capability, supersonic performance or low-speed characteristics. The programme as a great success, demonstrating a 16% increase in drag-rise Mach number, 6% increase in cruise efficiency parameter $\frac{(ML)}{D}$, 50% increase in manoeuvre lift coefficient (alternatively, a 46% reduction in manoeuvre drag coefficient), and a 100% increase in buffet-onset lift coefficient.

Development of advanced sections can be said to have begun with Pearcey's work in the 1960s. So why have they not been applied to more combat aircraft? The answer lies in the extended gestation period of modern aircraft. Current types such as the F-14, F-15, F-16, F-18 and Tornado were being designed in the late 1960s, when supercritical technology was in its infancy. Advanced profiles were however considered for all the above aircraft. Wind-tunnel tests with the F-16, for example, showed that while a supercritical section offered a 5% gain in mission radius and a 13% gain in subsonic turn rate, the supersonic turn rate fell by 3% and the acceleration by 70%. These drawbacks were considered unacceptable when combined with the development risks associated with an emerging technology. However, the next generation of combat aircraft will have the benefit of further research and development, and will also feature optimised variable-camber devices.

Camber

It was known before the Wright brothers that a cambered aerofoil produced lift more efficiently than a symmetric one. This is particularly true at moderate to high AOA, since the effect of camber is to spread the upper-surface suction more evenly over the chord, reducing the local velocities and so cutting drag. However, all the available evidence showed that camber was detrimental to attempts to increase the maximum speed of the early jet fighters, since it reduced the critical Mach number and hastened the onset of drag rise. Use of a symmetric section on the English Electric Canberra avoided many of the stability and control problems created by cambered sections at high subsonic speeds.

Symmetric sections were used on many of the early supersonic aircraft (e.g. the F-104), since camber is analogous to thickness at supersonic speed; few concessions to off-design performance were made, apart from conical camber (discussed later). One early application of camber was the Northrop T-38, which had a modified basic symmetric 4·8%-thick wing giving very useful improvements (Fig 21). While supersonic performance was still emphasised in the second-generation supersonic fighters (e.g. F-4), more attention was paid to manoeuvrability at lower speeds (though the F-4 did not get leading-edge manoeuvre slats until the middle of its development life). Nevertheless, camber is a disadvantage at low lift and high speed, so a very thin, almost symmetrical section was used on the SR-71 Blackbird Mach 3 high-altitude reconnaissance aircraft.

Excessive camber is also detrimental to aircraft designed for the low-altitude, high-speed penetration role, since in combination with a thin aerofoil it can provoke an early onset of sonic flow under the leading edge. In extreme cases, with large nose camber operating at high speed and zero wing lift, when the fuselage itself can develop sufficient lift, the flow may actually separate from the under surface, thereby placing a limit on the degree of camber. At the same time camber will increase the nose-down pitching moment, requiring tail downloads to balance the aircraft.

As a result of actual combat experience during the 1960s, more emphasis was placed on increased manoeuvrability and improved handling in the aircraft then being designed. The air-superiority fighter was making a comeback, and a demand arose for higher sustained lift to give improved turn rate. This had been limited by the rapid increase of induced drag which occurs on thin, sharp-leading-edge sections at moderate lift. The cause is the breakdown of leading-edge suction, which could be delayed by increased nose radius and camber. This had already been adopted on later versions of the Lightning to improve subsonic cruise and in the form of conical camber on the F-15 for enhanced manoeuvrability.

Conical camber

This type of camber distribution was introduced in

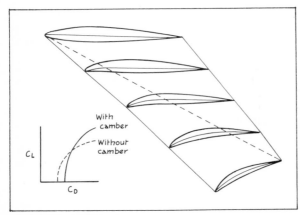

Fig 28 Conical camber.

the 1950s to improve the off-design performance of wings designed primarily for supersonic flight. The wing is cambered progressively from root to tip ahead of an imaginary line joining the wing-root leading edge to the tip trailing edge (Fig 28) so that this surface forms part of a cone. The concept was originally used on the Convair (now General Dynamics) F-102, F-106 and B-58 to postpone the drag break (a rapid rise in drag which occurs at moderate AOA) by suppressing leading-edge separation, and to enlarge the buffet boundary. It was also applied to other delta-winged designs: on the CF-105 Arrow, conical camber combined with other leading-edge modifications almost doubled the lift coefficient before buffet onset at Mach 0·9. Mild conical camber on the outer wing sections of the SR-71 is aimed at moving the centre of lift inboard to relieve the structural loading on the engine nacelle carry-through structure. It also gives a useful reduction in the otherwise very high rolling moment due to sideslip inherent in the highly swept delta wing.

When designing the F-15 wing for high-AOA flight McDonnell Douglas investigated over a hundred different wings. The choice was eventually reduced to two designs, one with an aspect ratio of 2·5 and variable camber provided by leading and trailing-edge flaps, the other with an aspect ratio of 3 and fixed conical camber. The latter was found to have greater supersonic drag and slightly inferior subsonic manoeuvrability. On the other hand, it was lighter, cheaper and simpler to maintain and had lower induced drag, yielding a better lift/drag ratio to give more air miles per litre. In fact the F-15 wing is remarkably simple, having only a plain trailing-edge flap and pronounced conical camber, and no leading-edge devices, fences, dogteeth, or sweep variations.

Wing twist

Wing twist from the root to tip, with angle of incidence reducing towards the tip, is called "washout". It is used for two basic reasons:

1 To prevent tip stalling. Since the onset of separation is largely a function of AOA, a beneficial effect can be obtained by giving the wing built-in downward twist. In this way the effective AOA can be progressively reduced towards the tip to offset the local peak loading which occurs there on a swept and tapered wing and to delay separation in the tip region to higher angles. With upward bending, an aft-swept wing tends to wash itself out naturally so that in high-g combat manoeuvres the aeroelastic twist may reach 10° at the tip. Thus the twist at 1g, largely built-in during manufacture, has to be carefully matched to the high-g deformation. On the F-16, for example, 3° of washout is used in combination with a leading-edge flap to resist the separation from the relatively sharp leading edge of its 4%-thick wing.

2 To adjust the spanwise loading in order to achieve minimum drag at a particular lift level. The aim is to achieve a near-constant isobar sweep by spreading the lift more evenly across the span. The inevitable shock waves should then appear over the whole span at the same flight Mach number, which is higher than that for the unwarped wing. A large degree of non-linear twist combined with camber was applied to the AV-8B wing, culminating in −8° of twist at the tip. This was done partly for the above reason but also to reduce the very large nose-down pitching moment inherent in

Fig 29 How spanwise variation of sweep, twist and camber reduces nose-down pitching moment (Harrier II at Mach 0.80).[9]

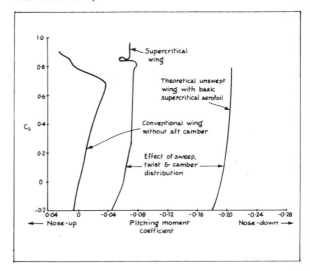

the AV-8B's type of supercritical wing, with its high aft loading (Fig 29).

The ideal condition of constant isobar sweep referred to above can only be achieved at one lift condition, usually designed to be that of cruise in order to maximise the lift/drag ratio. At higher lift the spanwise loading distorts outboard, once again raising the problem of the premature appearance of outboard shocks. This can only be overcome by the use of variable camber.

WING PLANFORM

Aspect ratio

Aspect ratio (A) is defined as the span squared divided by the wing area. Its value has a major influence on trailing-vortex drag and on the lifting ability of a wing at a given angle of attack.

At subsonic speeds the profile drag of a wing is proportional to its area, whereas the drag due to lift is proportional to the span loading squared, i.e. $\left(\dfrac{W}{b}\right)^2$. Thus if the ratio of span squared to wing area (i.e. aspect ratio) can be increased, then lift-dependent drag can be reduced for no increase in profile drag. This has long been recognised as an important means of increasing or at least maintaining the lift/drag ratio of aircraft.

Three aspects of performance benefit especially from low lift-dependent drag and hence a moderate to high aspect ratio. The cruise range of an aircraft is a function of the product M × (L/D), whereas loiter time or endurance is proportional to L/D. In both cruise and loiter the lift-dependent drag may be 50% of the total, so a reduction is very worthwhile. If the long-range requirement is an occasional one — for a ferry flight, say — then bolt-on tip extensions as designed for the Harrier are an option. The F-111B Navy version had extended wing tips to improve loiter performance, and when the Buccaneer S.2 was derived from the S.1 version the wing span was increased by 0·6m.

Sustained manoeuvring is limited by the excess of thrust over drag, and at subsonic speed the dominant drag term is the lift-dependent component, which may be 75% of the total. A low span loading will minimise such drag up to moderate AOA, whereupon, for thin wings at least, the leading-edge thrust is lost as a result of flow separation there. This causes a sharp increase in drag, which having previously depended on span loading, now comes under the influence of lift-curve slope, so that a high aspect ratio is still beneficial. At Mach 0·8, for example, the YF-16 was found in early trade-off studies to increase its turn rate by over 10% when aspect ratio was increased from 3·0 to 4·0. However, the highest aspect ratio for a longitudinally stable wing (i.e. one with a nose-down pitching moment at the stall) is found to increase with increasing taper (i.e. reduced taper ratio) and to decrease with increasing sweepback. An adverse combination can lead to tip stalling and pitch-up (discussed later).

The high lift-curve slope conferred by high aspect ratio is useful on take-off and landing, when the usable angle of attack is restricted by the demands of ground clearance and pilot vision.

High aspect ratio also has its drawbacks. For a given wing area there is a weight penalty, since the higher bending moments arising from the increased span have to be reacted by thinner but more massive root sections matched to the shorter root chord. Wing weight can be very sensitive to aspect ratio beyond a certain value. On the F-16, for example, the start-of-combat weight increased only slightly as aspect ratio increased from 3·0 to 3·5, whereas from 3·5 to 4·0 the weight increase was trebled. In addition there are three areas of performance in which high aspect ratio is actually detrimental, so that an aspect ratio of 3·5 appears to be the upper limit for combat aircraft.

Whereas sustained manoeuvring at both subsonic and supersonic speeds is limited by the excess power, i.e. (T-D)V, the dominant drag term at supersonic speed is wave drag. This is minimised by spreading the lift over a broad chord provided by combining high sweep with low aspect ratio, which gives the smooth lengthwise variaton of cross-sectional area demanded by the various area rules. This is true also for maximum Mach number.

Low aspect ratio also benefits transonic wing flow, alleviating some of the undesirable compressibility effects. Very low aspect ratio at subsonic speed gives high lift-dependent drag, but this is relatively unimportant in the high-speed low-altitude strike role. In this regime the dominant component is profile drag, which can be minimised by a small wing area. This allows the low lift-curve slope characteristic of low-aspect-ratio wings to be exploited in the form of reduced sensitivity to the atmosphere turbulence encountered at low altitude. The result, a smoother ride for aircraft and crew, was the reason behind the use of a highly loaded, very-low-aspect-ratio wing (A = 2) on the TSR.2 low-level strike aircraft.

Choice of aspect ratio can thus require the designer to emphasise certain characteristics very much at the expense of others, a conflict which will become even more evident when variable-sweep wings are discussed (page 63 et seq).

Wing size

Wing area and loading

Choice of wing area — namely the gross wing area including the planform area immersed within the fuselage — produces some of the most intractable conflicts in combat aircraft design. It is the aim of the designer to minimise the wing area, not only because of its impact on drag and performance but also because it plays such a crucial role in sizing the aircraft, which itself determines weight and, to some extent, unit cost. The way in which wing size, expressed in terms of wing loading (i.e. aircraft weight ÷ wing area : W/S) influences take-off weight can be gauged from the following: a 10% increase in wing area to make up a shortfall in usable lift, in order to restore manoeuvrability or improve airfield performance, produces a 5% increase in profile drag and a 1% increase in structural weight. Other aspects of performance must be protected from these adverse effects: for example, extra fuel must be carried to restore range, engine size must increase to restore the thrust/weight ratio for take-off and combat, and a stronger, heavier undercarriage is necessary. The cumulative weight increase which arises then demands an increase in wing area, resulting in a vicious upward spiral, with lift and thrust chasing weight and drag.

Performance requirements

Combat aircraft, unlike airliners, have no specific design point but have to operate effectively over a wide spectrum, performing very well in some areas and not so well in others. The choice of wing loading cannot therefore be pointed so directly at one goal that other, almost equally desirable, goals become unattainable. On the other hand, it is not realistic to expect an aircraft with a given wing loading to excel both as an air-superiority fighter and as a low-level strike aircraft since, as will be shown, the required wing loadings are diametrically opposed.

Airfield performance

High lift coefficients are needed, particularly to reduce landing distance. Though the lifting ability of thin, swept wings is greatly improved by high-lift devices, a low wing loading is desirable.

Subsonic cruise and loiter

This requires a high lift/drag ratio. Needed for this is a high aspect ratio, which generally translates into a medium wing loading.

Subsonic sustained turn rate

Sustained turn rate (deg/sec) or manoeuvre (g) is

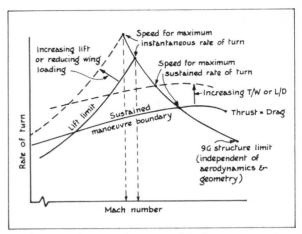

Fig 30 Lift, thrust and structural limits on turn rate (constant altitude).

limited by the equality of thrust and drag at high g, where induced drag is the dominant drag term. This is minimised by a low span loading, yielded by high aspect ratio and thus a low wing loading.

Instantaneous turn rate

This is limited by the maximum lift attainable. A low wing loading is therefore necessary, as shown in Fig 30, which reveals that a reduction in wing loading has a decisive effect on the outcome of combat between two aircraft having the same thrust/weight ratio. Note that the structural limit on g loading means that any attempt to increase lift inevitably lowers the best speed for air combat. This also applies to sustained manoeuvrability.

Supersonic manoeuvring

A long wing chord is required to minimise wave drag due to lift. A relatively large wing area of low aspect ratio is desirable, though its advantages are limited to speeds at which high lift is attainable.

Maximum supersonic Mach number

As maximum speeds were increased in 1950s and 1960s, the trend for the wing loadings of swept-wing interceptors was upwards, reflecting the need for small, thin wings. But the advent of contemporary air-superiority fighters like the F-15 and F-16 has reversed this tendency.

Subsonic specific excess power (SEP)

A measure of an aircraft's ability to increase energy (e.g. rate of climb) rapidly, this is thrust minus drag multiplied by speed and divided by weight, i.e. $(T - D)V/W$. Being proportional to the product of excess thrust and speed in this expression, the wing area has little influence other than on drag.

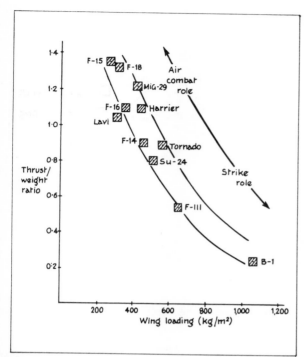

Fig 31 Trade-off between thrust/weight ratio and wing loading in the air combat and strike roles. Full afterburning and internal load are assumed in each case.[11]

Low-altitude high-speed penetration and gust response

This calls for flight at very low lift coefficients. Under these conditions profile drag is perhaps 90% of the total, making a small wing very important. Further, sensitivity to atmospheric gusts is inversely proportional to wing loading, though modern active controls can suppress a larger wing's gust response.

Resolving wing-size conflicts

The demands made on wing size by the airfield, cruise and loiter, and manoeuvrability requirements are in opposition to those for maximum speed and low-altitude strike. This conflict is even more apparent in Fig 31, which shows how wing loading and thrust/weight ratio have been tailored to the roles of various aircraft. For the air-superiority role, in which high manoeuvrability is crucial, the wing loadings are low and thrust/weights high. For the interdiction/strike role the wing loadings are higher and thrust/weight lower. An aircraft such as the Tornado, which has to both intercept and strike, demands a difficult compromise.

The confict can be resolved only by studying a wide variety of wing shapes, the best wing being that which gives the smallest and lightest aircraft capable of meeting the requirement. The alternative is to avoid the most painful compromises and opt for variable sweep, the last resort of designers confronted by demands which are otherwise irreconcilable.

Wing tip shape

Little information on this difficult area has been published, though the curved tip received a good deal of British attention in the 1960s. The aim is constant isobar sweep across the span to reduce transonic wave drag. As noted in Chapter 3, an indented fuselage can be used to reduce the loss of isobar sweep at the wing/body junction. A similar tendency of the isobars to reduce their sweep is encountered at the wingtips. This can be suppressed by locally increasing the wing's leading-edge sweep at the tip, a solution to be found on the BAe Harrier, Hawk and EAP.

Another notable wingtip shape is the raked tip, featured on the F-15. Flight tests on early versions with streamwise tips showed higher-than-predicted wing-root bending moments, caused by the outer wing panels producing more lift than expected. This reduced the safety strength margins and threatened a reduction in fatigue life. Heavy buffet and excessive Dutch roll were also encountered. The problem was solved by removing 0.46m² of wingtip on each side, giving an increased flutter margin. One benefit of straight tips is their ability to carry launcher rails for light air-to-air guided weapons, as on the Mirage F.1, F-16, F-18 and Rafale. This helps satisfy the demand for increased ordnance loads. Furthermore, careful design of the wing/launcher region has yielded worthwhile improvements in wing L/D.

Taper ratio

Taper ratio (λ) is defined as the ratio tip chord/root chord. A small taper ratio allows high leading-edge sweep to be used to minimise supersonic drag, while at the same time providing a low trailing-edge sweep to improve the effectiveness of flaps and ailerons. This allows lower take-off and landing speeds and improved controllability in crosswinds. Many early swept-wing aircraft with taper ratios of 0.5 or thereabouts suffered from crosswind handling problems. This was due to their high rolling moments due to sideslip and low effectiveness of swept trailing-edge controls at high AOA in the landing approach. The "notched delta" planform of the Lightning overcame this drawback by

allowing the ailerons to be mounted on transverse tips, though the flaps were still highly swept. Later aircraft like the F-4 and A-5 used much lower taper ratios ($\lambda = 0.2$), while the Jaguar and F-15 also have kinked trailing edges, resulting in almost zero sweep to the flap hinge line. Even newer aircraft, such as the F-16 ($\lambda = 0.23$) and F-18, have zero sweep across the entire trailing edge.

Tapering of the wing reduces the wing-root bending moments, since the inboard portion of the wing carries more of the wing's lift than the tip. Furthermore, the longer wing-root chord makes it possible to increase the actual thickness of the wing while maintaining the low thickness ratio necessary for supersonic flight. Wing-root thickness has a strong influence on resistance to both bending moment and torsion, and the deeper wing leads to a lighter structure.

While taper reduces the actual loads carried outboard, the effective angle of attack of any outboard section is increased as a result of the

Above: Dassault Mirage F.1 equipped with Durandal runway-denial weapons, fuel tanks and Magic air-to-air missiles. The missile launcher rails were extended forward of the wing leading edge to allow them to act as flutter suppressors.

Opposite
Top: BAe Lightning F6 displays some of the measures used to cure the aircraft's chronic lack of fuel volume. The belly tank and fin size were progressively enlarged during development, and overwing ferry tanks and a flight refuelling probe were offered on the F6. Still in service in small numbers, the Lightning remains a sparkling performer. (MoD)

Right: The turbojet/rocket-powered Republic XF-91 of the 1950s incorporated inverse taper to counter tip stalling and pitch-up. Another bizarre feature of this supersonic aircraft was the tandem-mainwheel undercarriage, which retracted outboard of the fuel tanks into the deep wingtip section.

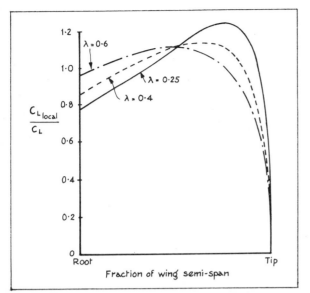

Fig 32 Effect of taper ratio on local lift distribution. An aspect ratio of 3 and quarter-chord sweepback of 39° are assumed.

upwash caused by the vortex-shedding of the inboard sections. As shown in Fig 32, the wingtip tends to work at much higher lift coefficients than the root and to stall first. This can be resisted by twisting down the tip (washout) to reduce the local loading. The tendency towards tip stall is not unlike that of the swept wing. When both sweep and taper are combined, as is usual, tip stall is likely, leading to wing-dropping and, when combined with moderate aspect ratio, to pitch-up. One unusual and unsuccessful application in this context was the inverse taper (i.e. tip chord longer than root chord) of the Republic XF-91 of the 1950s. The classic F-4 Phantom features a highly swept (50° leading edge) tapered (0·2) wing of low thickness ratios (6% at root, 3% at tip), giving a very thin tip prone to early flow separation.

SWEPT WINGS

The birth of sweepback

The ever upward trend in aircraft speeds was given further impetus in the 1940s by the introduction of jet propulsion. Efficient exploitation of this new powerplant in turn demanded advances in aerodynamics. The higher speeds meant compressibility effects due to shock-wave formation,

which appeared in the form of stability and control problems and the rapid drag rise. To some extent these difficulties were countered by using thinner wings, but this solution could not to be taken too far for reasons of wing strength/weight and fuel volume. The great advance came from sweepback, first postulated in Germany in the 1930s and used very successfully since 1945 to improve both transonic and supersonic characteristics.

The use of sweepback to reduce drag at supersonic speeds was proposed by Busemann in 1935, though its application to aircraft was not then regarded as a practical proposition. Indeed, at that time Britain was still fielding biplanes in its frontline fighter force. But by 1939 Betz had shown that sweepback could be used to delay the onset of compressibility problems arising from local regions of supersonic flow terminating in shock waves, and practical applications were not long in following.

Some German aircraft appeared with sweepback in the early 1940s, notably the Me163 Komet tailless rocket fighter. In this design sweepback was however needed principally to locate the mass and aerodynamic centres of the aircraft correctly and to increase the moment arm of the control surfaces on the wing's trailing edge, and its high-speed benefits were seen as largely incidental. The more conventional twin-turbojet Me262 was originally designed with straight wings. But, because it was one of the first high-speed aircraft not to have the forward weight concentration of piston engines, it turned out to be tail-heavy. In order to restore the balance between the lift and mass centres the wing outboard of the engine nacelles was swept back, as it had been earlier on the DC-3 airliner for similar reasons. Eventually the Me262 was given a leading-edge sweepback of $18\frac{1}{2}°$ across the full span, a modest level of sweep which had little effect on drag.

Germany's appreciation of the value of sweepback at high speed advanced quickly, however, so that by the end of the war in Europe its design teams led the world in this respect, incorporating sweepback into many of their future designs. Following in the wake of the Allied occupation forces, research teams found vast quantities of evidence which showed just how advanced German thinking was. The significance of sweep was immediately clear, and it was quickly put to use in both the United States and the Soviet Union. A comparison of the projected Focke-Wulf Ta183 and the MiG-15, which appeared in 1947, clearly shows how much the Russians learned from the Germans. The United States produced the F-86 and B-47, two very successful swept-wing aircraft.

The benefits of sweepback

A wing is said to be unswept if it has zero sweep on any spanwise line between 25% and 70% of the wing chord (e.g. Lockheed F-104 Starfighter).

Delay and reduction of subsonic drag rise

Betz saw that the most immediate benefit of sweep was its ability to delay to a higher speed the subsonic drag rise by postponing the occurrence of local regions of supersonic flow which terminate in shock waves, as shown in Fig 33. Sweep also reduces the subsonic and peak drag coefficients. Benefits are also apparent at supersonic speed, though these were not immediately applicable to the first generation of swept-wing aircraft.

The effects of sweep are most apparent when two wings — one swept, the other straight, but otherwise similar — are compared. Let us assume that the straight wing has a critical Mach number of 0·7. This is the flight Mach number at which sonic flow first appears on the wing. Slightly above this speed shock waves start to form, leading to a rapid rise in drag. If the same wing is now swept back through an angle of, say, 40° two things can be observed. First, the flow component $V\sin\Lambda$ along the wing contributes little to the pressure distribution. This outflow does however become significant at high AOA and large sweep angles. Second, it is the flow component normal to the leading edge, $V\cos\Lambda$, that most influences the aerodynamic characteristics of any given section of the wing. Strictly it is the velocity component normal to the wing isobars (i.e. lines of constant pressure) that matters, but for the time being these can be assumed to be parallel to the leading edge. Sweeping the wing thus allows an increase in the flight speed to $M = 0\cdot7/\cos 40° = 0\cdot91$ before sonic flow appears at some point on the wing. Further increase in sweep can postpone the drag rise to even higher Mach numbers.

The above reasoning is in fact a simplification, since the flow over a typical swept wing of relatively low aspect ratio is a very complex three-dimensional one. The simple $\cos\Lambda$ relationship described above in fact applies only to a yawed wing of infinite span, and the delay in reaching M_{crit} is much less than predicted because of the effects of the wing root and tip. Of course it could be argued that increasing aspect ratio would increase the wing area free from root and tip effects. But the phenomenon of pitch-up (see page 49) places an upper limit on the aspect ratio that can be used with a given sweep angle. Sweep angles of less than 30° on the leading edge are practically useless in postponing the drag rise, but even this degree of sweep is sufficient to produce

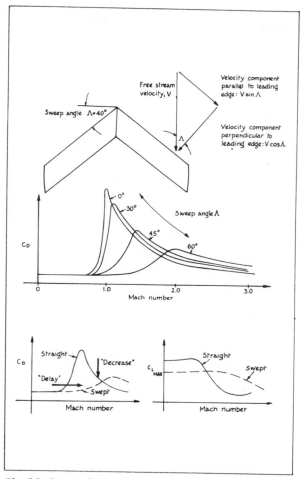

Fig 33 General effects of sweepback.

some of the bad secondary characteristics of sweepback, such as tip stalling and/or loss of aileron control.

Despite the fact that in practice sweepback increases M_{crit} by only half the expected amount, the benefits remain well worth having. So much so that the designers of the early jet fighters were eager to combine then with the higher thrust levels of the evolving turbojets. The use of sweep enabled contemporary wing thickness ratios to be retained while allowing an increase in M_{crit}. Thus it was that the F-86 Sabre had a wing with the moderate thickness ratio of 12%, which allowed room for fuel and relatively uncomplicated flaps. In Britain sweep was used to allow an increase in wing thickness ratio for a given M_{crit}. This was particularly useful for wing structural and storage purposes. On the Handley Page Victor bomber the engines were buried in the 16%-thick wing roots. Quarter-chord

*Handley Page Victor K2 tanker refuelling two
Lightnings. The Victor's crescent wing has
"Kuchemann carrots," trailing-edge fairings designed
to reduce drag at high speed. Also apparent is the
Lightning F6's cropped-delta wing with kinked
leading edge. (MoD)*

sweep was 53°, progressively reducing along with
thickness to 35° and then to 22° at the tip, where
the thickness ratio was 4%. The reduced thickness
suited the lower bending moments outboard and,
by careful design, gave a constant M_{crit} across the
span. Additional and very important benefits of the
low tip sweep obtained with this planform, known
as the "crescent" wing, were better aileron control
and a reduced tendency to tip stall and pitch-up.

In spite of such successful combinations of
sweep with moderate thickness, the subsequent
trend, continuing to the present, was towards
lower thickness ratios in pursuit of reductions in
supersonic drag.

Reduction of transonic trim changes
When the straight-wing piston-engined fighters of
the Second World War first encountered compressibility on their wings, the most obvious effect
was often nose-heaviness or "Mach tuck". This
was due primarily to the development of local
regions of supersonic flow over the wings and the
erratic behaviour of the shock waves which
formed. The net result of traversing the transonic
region is a rearward shift of the aircraft's aerodynamic centre, giving a nose-down trim change.
This is particularly acute for straight-winged aircraft, and contrasts with the smaller and much
more gradual shift of lift centre with Mach number
observable on a swept wing.

More gradual variation in lift coefficient across the transonic region
When sweep is applied to thicker aerofoil sections
the variation of lift coefficient across the transonic
region is more gradual than it would be on a comparable straight wing. However, at higher sweep
angles the lift coefficient for a given AOA is lower.

Extension of buffet boundaries
The phenomenon of buffet is discussed in depth
under *Manoeuvrability*, where an extension of the

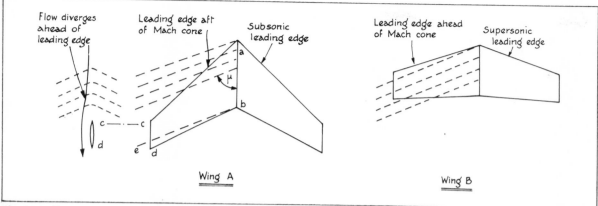

Fig 34 Subsonic and supersonic leading edges.

buffet-free flight envelope (e.g. lift coefficient versus Mach number) is shown to be of great value to combat effectiveness. Sweepback allows such an extension.

Drag reductions in supersonic flight

As predicted by Busemann, use of sweepback allowed the maximum speed of aircraft to be extended deep into the supersonic regime so that by the end of the 1950s several aircraft capable of Mach 2 — including the F-105, F-106, B-58, A-5 and Lightning — were either in or being prepared for operational use.

The physical principles behind the use of sweep-back for supersonic flight can be explained with the aid of Fig 34, which shows two plane wings of different sweepback operating at the same Mach number. At supersonic flight speeds the Mach waves generate a "Mach cone" with a semi-vertex angle μ, called the Mach angle. The fundamental difference between the two wings is not that the sweep is different but that Wing A has its leading edge swept within the Mach cone whereas the less swept Wing B does not. As a result, the central portion a-b of Wing A behaves as though it were unswept in the supersonic flow. As the flow passes over this central section, Mach waves are propa-gated at the local speed of sound to produce further Mach cones. These waves stand out ahead of section c-d far outboard so that the upstream flow ahead of the wing has to pass through them before reaching an outboard section of the wing. The outer flow then starts to deviate around the wing to allow passage of the wing *before* the wing arrives at the point in question. This effect is shown more clearly in the side view of Wing A.

Thus it is the central portion of the wing for which the supersonic drag penalty has to be paid,

since it prepares the air for the passage of the outer wing sections, tending to divide it as in subsonic flow. Indeed, a leading edge swept within the Mach cone is referred to as a subsonic leading edge, the flow it experiences approximating to subsonic flow even though the flight speed is supersonic. This allows sufficiently swept wings to have rounded leading edges similar to those used for subsonic speeds. For example, both the F-111 and F-14 variable-sweep wings have relatively standard NACA 6-series aerofoil sections, while similar sections were used on early versions of the Lightning, with its 60° leading-edge sweep. The delta wing of the SR-71 Blackbird lies within the Mach cone of the long nose and has a very low thickness ratio to minimise wave drag at Mach 3 cruise.

A further sweep-related complication arises at supersonic speed. Although the wing root's leading-edge shock wave lies in front of the rest of the wing, as shown in Fig 34, the wing's trailing-edge shock wave, b-e, falls diagonally across the wing. The effect of this shock is similar to but less intense than that of the shock wave which causes flow separation on a straight wing in high-subsonic flight.

On Wing B, which has insufficient sweep to put the leading edge behind the Mach cone, the whole of the leading edge encounters supersonic flow. Such a wing is described as having a supersonic leading edge, and must be thin, with a sharp leading edge, if excessive wave drag is to be avoided. The prime example of this approach is the F-104 Starfighter.

Arguments over the competing merits of swept and straight wings for supersonic flight raged during the early 1950s. As can be seen in Fig 33, the drag advantage of 45° sweep is confined to speeds below Mach 1.2. The curve for 60° shows this degree of sweep to have an advantage up to Mach 1.3. Beyond these speeds the straight wing shows up to significant advantage. Designers of early supersonic aircraft were undaunted by the high landing speeds associated with high sweep, and speeds of over 300km/hr were not uncommon.

The components of the profile drag for both swept and straight-wing aircraft are shown in Figs 35 and 36. Wave drag predominates in both cases. The wave drag due to thickness is proportional to $(t/c)^2$, and since the geometric effect of sweep is to reduce the effective thickness ratio of the wing without encountering the excessive structural weight and fuel volume limitations of very thin wings, the swept wing can have thicker sections. At Mach 2, however, very thin wings are essential.

Wave drag due to lift is independent of span loading and is minimised by spreading the lift over as broad a chord as possible. This also improves the cross-sectional area distribution. High sweep is thus very beneficial in improving supersonic acceleration and manoeuvrability. This may be obtained by using a large wing area of low aspect ratio.

Very high sweep reduces gust response and is thus of value to aircraft tasked with high-speed penetration. This effect is considered in *Variable-sweep wings* (page 66).

The penalties of sweepback

For all its many useful attributes, sweep does have some disadvantages. Most notable are: reduction of lift-curve slope; increased drag due to lift; increased rolling due to sideslip; tip stalling; reduced effectiveness of high-lift devices; and structural problems.

Reduction of lift-curve slope

Increasing sweep always reduces the lift-curve slope of the wing and increases the AOA for maximum lift, as shown in Fig 37. Typically the lift slope is reduced by 50% by sweeping the wing back by 45°, while a 60°-swept wing may not reach its maximum lift until 30° AOA. Both of these effects influence the operation of combat aircraft.

Reduced lift for a given AOA means nose-high attitudes, especially on landing, which restrict pilot view. Early delta-winged aircraft lacking trailing-edge flaps and designed to operate from aircraft carriers were especially prone to this problem, which called for cockpits that were raised and located well forward (e.g. A-4 Skyhawk and F4D Skyray). Such cockpits could produce excessive drag at high speed. One way of over-

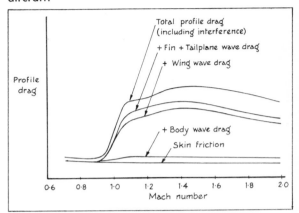

Fig 35 Profile drag components of swept-wing aircraft.

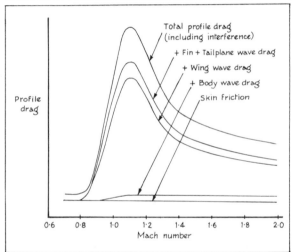

Fig 36 Profile drag components of straight-wing aircraft.

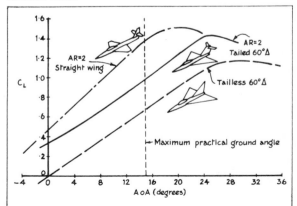

Fig 37 Effect of sweep on lift curve. Aspect ratio is 2 in each case.

Evident as this LTV F-8B Crusader rotates on take-off (note the angle of the slab tailplane) are its two-position wing and small ground clearance angle. Later models had ventral fins. Trailing-edge devices consist of a small inboard flap and outboard flaperon, there being no control surfaces beyond the wing-fold line at 63% of semi-span. (LTV)

coming this was used by Vought on its F-8 Crusader. This naval aircraft operated very successfully with a variable-incidence wing which could be pivoted 11° leading-edge-up about its rear spar for the approach, leaving the fuselage only slightly nose-up and giving the pilot excellent visibility.

The reduced lift slope also limits usable lift for take-off and landing. AOA for maximum lift cannot be attained because the aft end will strike the ground if the aircraft is rotated more than 15° about the mainwheels. This could be overcome by increasing the length of the undercarriage legs, but that would in turn lead to problems of stowage, structural efficiency of the wing, and weight. One way of improving the take-off performance of high-speed wings has been to use extendable nosewheel legs, thereby increasing the wing's AOA on the take-off run (e.g. some F-4 and F-5 variants).

It should be noted that though the reduction in lift slope is detrimental in the above cases, it is in fact extremely valuable for low-altitude, high-speed penetration (see *Variable-sweep wings*, page 66).

Sweepback influences maximum lift in different ways. On relatively thick wings of high aspect ratio it reduces the maximum lift with cosΛ. In the late 1940s wind-tunnel model tests showed that at the high-subsonic Mach numbers made possible by sweep the maximum lift coefficient had fallen to such an extent that it would be impossible to fly straight and level without stalling, particularly at high altitude. The B-47 was a notable example of this effect: at a certain combination of aircraft weight and altitude, known as "Coffin Corner," the low and high-speed stall speeds coincided.

On the thin, low-aspect-ratio wings of subsequent fighter aircraft like the F-100 the maximum lift coefficient increased with sweep. However, the combination of sweep and low aspect ratio yielded very low lift-curve slopes, and well before maximum lift was reached the aircraft were subjected to buffet of increasing intensity arising from wing flow separations. As AOA was increased to squeeze more lift out of the wing, the buffeting became so severe that although the aircraft was still controllable its usefulness as a weapon platform quickly diminished to zero. Beyond this point, but before the AOA for maximum lift, lateral/directional stability and control problems arose. In fact most if not all of the 1960s generation of combat aircraft suffered these difficulties, in the form of nose slice, divergent oscillation in yaw/roll, or wing drop, leading ultimately to a spin if uncorrected. The high wing loadings (W/S) then in use meant that subsonic manoeuvrability was curtailed while stalling speeds became very high. An increase in wing area would have reduced the wing loading, but at the expense of the high-supersonic benefits of sweep.

Higher drag-due-to-lift

For low-speed (i.e. thick) wings, lift-dependent drag is primarily a function of span loading (W/b); that is, it depends on both aspect ratio (b^2/S) and wing loading (W/S). However, at supersonic speed the wingtip influences only that portion of wing lying inside the Mach cone from its leading edge, so that aspect ratio becomes of decreasing importance as the design speed increases. Not so the wave drag due to lift. As implied above, a reduction in aspect ratio is limited by the low-speed case, even for an aircraft with a relatively sharp wing leading edge. Beyond a certain AOA flow separations at the leading edge cause almost total loss of leading-edge suction (i.e. thrust), which can more than double the drag due to lift. Beyond this point, the lift-induced drag is no longer dependent upon span loading but on lift-curve slope. Thus low drag still demands a high aspect ratio and low sweep or manoeuvring flaps.

The combined effects of high sweep and wing loading on the lift-dependent drag of the variable-geometry General Dynamics F-111 can be seen in Fig 38. As the wings sweep fully aft to $72\frac{1}{2}°$ the minimum-drag speed increases rapidly. In addition, at 600km/hr (325kt), for example, the drag (or thrust required for straight-and-level flight) has risen from 31kN for $\Lambda = 50°$ to 53kN at $\Lambda = 72°$. Notice too, in the latter case, that the aircraft is firmly on the back side of the thrust-required curve, i.e. it now requires more thrust to fly slower. A gust under these conditions can raise the drag level more rapidly than the engine can respond to a demand for more thrust, leading to a divergent situation from which recovery might be impossible.

Sustained manoeuvring at transonic speed is limited to the point at which the drag at high g and thrust become equal, i.e. no excess power is available. The designers of the 1960s generation of combat aircraft emphasised 1g flight at lift coefficients less than that required for maximum

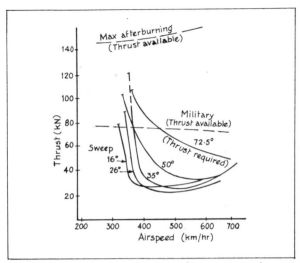

Fig 38 Effect of wing sweep on thrust required. These curves are for a General Dynamics F-111, gross weight 30,000kg, clean, flying straight and level at 600m altitude.[12]

Fig 39 Sweep intensifies roll due to sideslip.

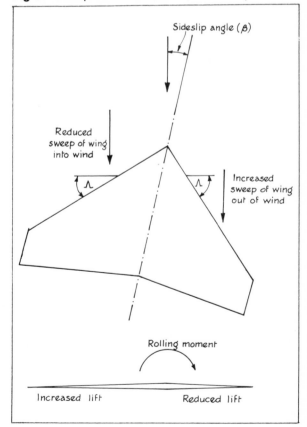

lift/drag ratio. Consequently aspect and thickness ratios were low while sweep and wing loading were high, resulting in aircraft which performed inefficiently at high lift coefficients. The dominant drag term under these conditions is lift-dependent drag. This is one of the critical design constraints for highly manoeuvrable aircraft like the F-15, which was given 45° of leading-edge sweep in an effort to achieve the best blend of transonic manoeuvrability and high supersonic speed.

Sweep intensifies roll due to sideslip

When a swept wing is placed in a sideslip the into-wind wing experiences an increase in lift since its effective sweep is less. Similarly, the out-of-wind wing has increased effective sweep and therefore generates less lift. The result is a rolling moment which tends to lift the one wing and drop the other, and so right the aircraft; this is known as dihedral effect (Fig 39). The effect depends on both sweepback and the AOA of the wing. A highly swept wing operating at high lift coefficients in, say, the landing case can experience such an excess of this lateral stability contribution that handling may be a problem. This has led to some ingenious design solutions. The B-52, for example, has a tandem undercarriage which swivels so that the wheels remain parallel to the runway centreline even though the rest of the aircraft is yawed into the crosswind.

Although objectionable lateral/directional characteristics or Dutch-roll oscillations may affect any aircraft configuration, the use of sweep tends to aggravate them. For example, if the correct level of dihedral effect is achieved for the high-speed, low-lift-coefficient case, the relationship between lateral and directional stability may prove to be unbalanced at low speed and high C_L or even at high speed and high altitude. Since high or low wing position can have a marked influence on roll sensitivity to sideslip, the combination of high sweep and high wing is discussed further in *Vertical wing position* (page 104).

Sweep contributes to tip-stall tendencies

Sweepback alters the lift distribution in much the same way as decreasing taper ratio. All outboard sections of the wing are affected by the upwash produced by preceding inboard sections. Thus sweepback — as well as taper, with which it is always combined — leads to higher local lift coefficients towards the wingtips.

The highly loaded tips, with their elevated outboard suctions, tend to draw the sluggish, slow-moving boundary layer in a spanwise direction, as shown in Fig 40. The isobars are no longer at right

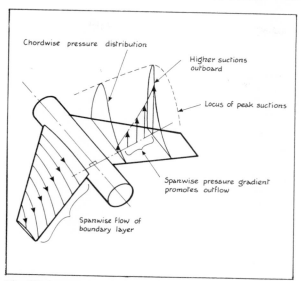

Fig 40 Sweep promotes spanwise flow.

angles to the freestream, so that the line of minimum resistance for the boundary layer is outwards. Growth in boundary-layer thickness is aggravated by an increase in either sweep or AOA, because of the increased tip loading which results.

Ultimately the flow starts to separate in the highly loaded tip region, with progressive increase in AOA causing the separated flow region to spread inwards and forwards. This is the phenomenon of tip stalling, caused not only by taper but, in this case, also by sweepback. The greater the sweepback the more critical the effects of tip stalling. This is partly because the lift loss is greater and partly because the region of lift loss will cause a forward movement of the wing's lift centre, giving an imbalance about the aircraft's centre of gravity and exaggerated pitch-up tendencies. This phenomenon was first encountered at high speed by the Douglas Skyrocket in 1951 and plagued a number of early swept-wing aircraft.

The onset of pitch-up on swept wings generally places an upper limit on the AOA and hence the usable lift coefficient. This may impose limitations both at low speed, rendering unattainable the high lift coefficients needed for low stalling and landing approach speeds, and in air combat manoeuvring at transonic speeds and medium altitudes.

Tip stalling and pitch-up — together with the related problems of buffet, loss of aileron effectiveness and even aileron reversal, wing dropping and roll-off — have been overcome at the expense of an enormous effort. Some of the palliatives employed are discussed in *Aerodynamic crutches* (page 106).

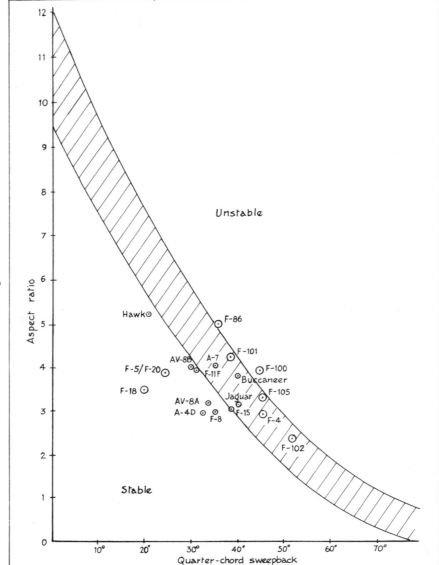

Fig 41 Planform effect on tip stalling leading to pitch-up.

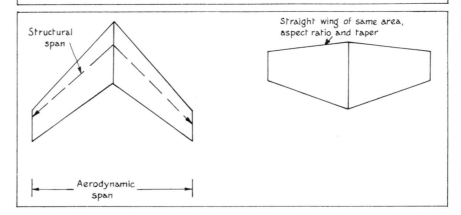

Fig 42 Sweep increases structural span.

The most important feature designed to limit the loss of pitching stability is the low-mounted tail-plane, discussed in Chapter 4.

The combined effects of high sweep and high aspect ratio

The degree to which tip stalling can limit the performance of a wing depends largely on the planform. It has been seen that because the isobars of the swept wing are oblique to the freestream, i.e. direction of flight, the boundary layer over the rear part of the wing drifts outboard as it flows towards the trailing edge. Thus the inboard parts of the wing enjoy the equivalent of boundary-layer suction, with a consequent raising of the stalling lift coefficient, while near the tips the reverse occurs and the local maximum lift coefficient is reduced.

The higher the aspect ratio the worse the boundary-layer drift effect, since the length along which the drift can occur is increased. At the same time the chord length shortens, so that the ratio boundary layer/(thickness/chord) increases, thereby intensifying boundary-layer drift. The shaded area of Fig 41 represents the dividing region between those combinations of sweep and aspect ratio which produce tip stalling leading to pitch-up and those which don't. Some representative aircraft are shown to indicate the wing planforms which have been successfully used. The diagram also demonstrates that delta wings, with their low aspect ratio and high sweep, are unlikely to suffer from pitch-up.

Structural implications of sweepback

As shown in Fig 42, a swept wing has a greater structural span than a straight wing of the same area and aspect ratio. This, together with the greater stiffness needed to counter the bigger airloads generated by the higher speeds, led to a growth in wing weight with the introduction of sweepback. Demands for yet higher speeds soon began to cause wing thickness ratios to drop and, if no resort to the delta was made, a further increase in wing weight was needed to maintain adequate bending strength.

Another effect of fundamental importance was intensified by the introduction of sweepback. All wings, straight or swept, are subject to torsion (i.e. twisting) under aerodynamic loads. Sweepback introduces additional and severe torsion because the applied loads on the wing act significantly aft of the wing root. The loads in the rear spar of a simple two-spar wing are also increased, as seen in Fig 43, which shows the loads reacting the applied wing torsion and shear force. At the rear spar the shear force and torsion reactions are additive, whereas at the front spar they are subtractive. The opposite is the case with the forward-swept wing, in which the front spar is more highly loaded.

The increased torsion introduced by sweep requires more structural material, leading to a further increase in wing weight. In addition, the wing-root torsion box contained within the fuselage is also heavier, since it has to carry the kink loads imposed when the wing loads are transferred to the fuselage. These torsion loads are reduced by the delta planform.

The effect of wing bending on the actual distortion of the structure is discussed in *Forward-*

Fig 43 Sweep intensifies torsional loads. Key: **W** weight, **T** torque, **LE** leading edge, **SF** shear force. (Simplified diagram neglecting drag and pitching-moment effects.)

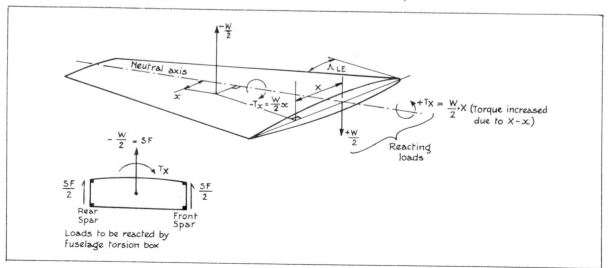

swept wings (page 72). Suffice it to say here that with sweepback the wing, when bent upwards, tends to twist nose-down, thereby offloading the tip. From one point of view this is beneficial, since it eliminates the tendency for the wings to diverge under load. (The opposite is true for forward sweep.) However, the nose-down twisting of the tip can have important implications for pitch stability, since the wing's lift centre then tends to move forward and inboard, increasing the pitch-up tendency. Until the advent of aeroelastic tailoring using composite materials, flutter considerations made it very difficult to build a wing capable of resisting this effect. Flutter resistance calls for the inertia axis of the wing to be kept as far forward as possible. By this means, when the wing deflects upwards due to, say, a gust, the inertia loads tend to oppose the tendency of the local AOA to increase.

Sweep reduces the effectiveness of wing controls and high-lift devices

Though moderate sweep of up to 25° can result in an increase in maximum lift, higher sweep reduces the lift generated by thick wings. At the lower sweep acceptable lift increments can be achieved by using flaps, so that an increase in wing area is not needed to obtain a specified take-off distance. At higher sweepback, however, the lift yield from flaps reduces rapidly. This loss of effectiveness is due to the outflow along the wing. The sweep at the leading edge of the flap becomes a dominant parameter, and the trailing-edge sweep of wings is generally kept low to maximise the benefit from trailing-edge devices. The resulting planform also minimises root thickness ratio and increases the strength of the rear spar and central torsion box.

DELTA WINGS

The birth of the delta planform

As with many advances in high-speed flight, the pioneering work on the delta planform was carried out in Germany during the early 1940s. At the end of the war the results fell into Allied hands, and delta designs soon began appearing on the drawing boards of all the major aircraft design centres. However, the choice of a delta planform was not always being made for the same reasons.

When in 1947 Avro Manchester was designing a high-altitude bomber to cruise at high-subsonic Mach numbers, it was apparent that high sweepback, low thickness/chord ratio and low cruise lift coefficient (0·2) were required. The preliminary

studies centred on a conventional tailed aircraft with quarter-chord sweep of 45° and thickness ratio of 12%. But it was quickly realised that weight would greatly exceed the target value and that neither the specified speed nor range could be achieved. Deletion of the horizontal tail and rear fuselage reduced the engine and fuel requirements, leading to an overall cut in dimensions and weight, with sweepback providing the necessary tail arm. This left the design as basically a lightly loaded flying wing of moderate thickness and normal aspect ratio. These characteristics are however the major culprits in creating a high structure weight. It was this concern that persuaded Avro to propose a delta wing with an aspect ratio of only 2·4, while retaining the original wing loading. The result was the highly successful Vulcan.

An entirely different objective — supersonic performance this time — led Dassault to opt for the delta planform in 1952. At that time the French company was working on a light supersonic fighter and expected that a development of its classic swept-wing Mystère would suffice. More sweep and a lower thickness/chord ratio were required

Dassault Mirage 50, a development of the Mirage III/5, shows off the remarkably low-aspect-ratio, cambered delta wing at which Dassault excels. Outboard of the air intake's splitter plate is the half-cone shock body, which moves fore and aft in concert with local Mach number. (Dassault-Breguet)

for Mach 2; so much so that the conventional swept wing came out with a maximum thickness of only 10cm. This would have been extremely heavy, being almost solid metal, and would have had virtually no room for fuel. Across the Atlantic, however, the Convair XF-92/F-102, with a delta wing of 60° leading-edge sweep, was well advanced. This example, together with limited collaboration with Britain's Fairey Aviation on the FD.2, led Dassault to derive the delta-winged Mirage I and II.

Competing with the Mirage was the swept-wing Etendard, offering a good combination of flight performance, weapon load and airfield performance. The Mirage III needed more field length and carried a smaller load but promised to be much faster. In the event the Etendard was developed as a subsonic ground attack aircraft while the Mirage

III, with a delta wing of 60° leading-edge sweep and 5% thickness ratio was pushed ahead as a Mach 2 fighter. Its increased chord length permitted a maximum wing thickness of around 30cm, making room for useful integral fuel tankage.

These demonstrations in the early 1950s of the fact that the delta was a viable planform for both subsonic and supersonic designs led to the appearance throughout the decade of a succession of tailless and tailed deltas, including the F4D Skyray, F-102A Delta Dagger, Javelin, MiG-21, Draken and B-58 Hustler.

Advantages of the delta as seen in the 1950s

1 Transonic drag rise is more gradual and peak supersonic drag is reduced: the wave drag due to volume is minimised by the high leading-edge sweep and aerodynamically thin sections, that due to lift is reduced because the lift is spread over a broad chord. It was also found that drag was less sensitive to Mach number over a wider speed

range because, compared with a separate wing/fuselage/tail combination, it was relatively easy to obtain a satisfactory cross-sectional area distribution (see *The Area Rule*, page 153).

2 The lift coefficient increases gradually with Mach number to sonic speed and then smoothly decreases with no abrupt variation in lift-curve slope.

3 The leading-edge vortex flows reduce pre-stall buffet levels and give a more gradual lift loss beyond the AOA for maximum lift coefficient.

4 The short span and pronounced taper move the bending forces inboard so that even for the very low thickness/chord ratios typical of deltas, typically 3–4%, the long wing-root chord permits greater depth, giving resistance to bending and better torsional stiffness at lower weight.

5 The greater wing depth provides greater fuel capacity and the stowage of the undercarriage in the wings is less of a problem.

6 The rigid structure aids in the reduction of flutter and control problems; aileron reversal, for example, is eliminated.

7 There is less chordwise movement of the aerodynamic centre over the transonic speed range. (A contrary argument is put later.)

8 The generous wing area gives a lower wing loading. Coupled with a low structure weight, this produces reasonable manoeuvrability and handling qualities of high altitude.

9 The compact dimensions of deltas are of benefit in naval carrier-based applications. In the case of the Douglas A-4 Skyhawk this meant the elimination of weighty and complex wing-folding mechanisms and associated structure.

10 A large underwing area is available for the carriage of external stores, though aircraft like the F-102A were designed with integral weapons bays.

Disadvantages of the delta

By the 1960s the disadvantages of the delta wing planform had begun to make themselves felt as the demand grew for the lifting of larger weapon loads off shorter runways and for greater air combat manoeuvrability. The swept wing had by this time shown itself to be the more versatile, and most designers had dropped the delta. Indeed, even Dassault, the leading exponent of the delta, rejected it when developing an aircraft with reduced landing speeds, improved manoeuvrability and heavier weapon load. This was the Mirage F.1, which, with a swept wing two-thirds the area of that of the Mirage III and only 9kN more thrust, is faster, can loiter subsonically and pursue

supersonically for three times as long, can carry much more offensive load over almost twice the distance, is 80% more manoeuvrable and lands 20% slower.

1 With its high leading-edge sweep and very low aspect ratio, the delta is less efficient as a lifting planform. The low lift-curve slope means that it must be flown at much higher angles of attack to generate the same lift. However, the demands of tail clearance and pilot view limit the usable AOA, as shown in Fig 37. Furthermore, the delta is unable to use trailing-edge flaps unless it has a separate tail to trim out the large nose-down pitching moment. These factors combine to give tailless deltas very high landing speeds and poor airfield performance.

2 The delta's high span loading (W/b) results in very high lift-induced drag in subsonic flight. This

The Sukhoi Su-21 Flagon-F "all-weather" interceptor has a tailed-delta layout. Early Flagons had shorter-span wings lacking the leading-edge kink. The high wing loading and very slender, indented fuselage are typical of early long-range interceptors. (Swedish Air Force)

is a critical drawback in air combat, since very high thrust must be available to avoid a severe drop-off in specific excess power. This is further compounded in manoeuvring by the large trimmed lift loss and associated drag arising from the increasing downloads on the trailing-edge controls as AOA is increased (Fig 44).

3 The low wing loading of the early deltas made them very sensitive to gusts in low-level high-speed flight. This was overcome on the TSR.2 by using, together with a low tail, a very small delta wing of only 65m² area with blown flaps and a high thrust/weight ratio. Low-speed manoeuvrability is however invariably compromised whenever high wing loadings (i.e. greater than 500kg/m²) are used on deltas.

4 Supersonic manoeuvrability is greatly restricted by the relative ineffectiveness of the delta's trailing-edge controls, known as elevons (*elevators/ailerons*), compared with separate tail surfaces. In addition, the aft movement of the aerodynamic centre during transonic acceleration, though reduced by the use of high sweep, is still large in actual distance though appearing small in terms of chord length. Allied to the restricted allowable range of centre-of-gravity position,

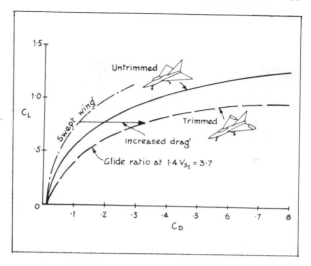

Fig 44 High lift-induced drag of delta wing. Low aspect ratio and loss of lift due to trimming result in a glide ratio of only 3.7 at 1.4 times stalling speed (in landing configuration).

arising from the limited trimming power of the elevons, this means that trim drag is high. An up-elevon deflection is needed to produce the restoring download.

Restricted CG range was a problem with the Convair B-58, in which fuel had to be transferred internally in order to maintain the CG near the aft limit throughout the flight, partly to minimise supersonic trim drag. The elevon deflection required for rotation and lift-off at maximum weight was less than $-5°$, due to the aft CG and the low-slung engines. In supersonic flight at altitude, however, the elevons were never at less than $-5°$.

In Mach 3 cruise the Lockheed SR-71 minimises its trim drag by pumping fuel aft to shift its centre of gravity. In addition, the forebody chines (see Chapter 4) locate the aerodynamic centre well forward.

5 The combination of high wing sweep and the large AOAs necessary for high lift means that the effective dihedral (i.e. rolling moment due to side-slip) can be excessively high at low speed. Thus if a small dihedral effect is achieved at high speed, then the effective dihedral at low speed or high lift, or even high speed at high altitude, disturbs the desired relationship between lateral and directional stability. Dutch roll may then become exaggerated, requiring low-mounted wings and yaw dampers to move the rudder in opposition to the yawing motion. The YF-12, with its 60° leading-edge sweep and high dihedral effect, has approximately zero wing lift when its nosewheel is in contact with the runway during take-off, in order to minimise crosswind effects.

6 Longitudinal (i.e. pitch) damping cannot be as high as for a conventional tailled configuration. Typical resulting problems include the pilot-induced oscillations suffered by the Saab Draken, ultimately remedied by the use of automatic pitch dampers.

Although the addition of a tailplane to a delta would appear to improve longitudinal control and pitch damping, it is in fact the tailplane's vertical position which is all-important. A high-mounted tailplane may improve matters only within the low-AOA pitching envelope, which isn't that troublesome anyway. But at high AOA the separated flow from the wing may actually make a high tailplane destabilising. Aeroelastic problems can also arise from mounting a tailplane on top of a very thin

Dassault Mirage 2000 has a variable-camber wing—the high-lift devices are driven by a quadruplex fly-by-wire control system—and has flown at speeds of less than 100km/hr and more than Mach 2.2. The use of wing/body blending and fuselage area-ruling is apparent. (Dassault-Breguet)

vertical stabiliser. For these reasons all the successful tailled deltas — outstanding examples are the MiG-21 and Su-21 — have featured low-mounted tailplanes.

Artificial stability leads to the renaissance of the delta

Although Dassault rejected the delta planform for its Mirage F.1, the French company could hardly have been expected to stay away from deltas for long. In fact its very next major design, the Mirage 2000, was another delta, an about-face made possible by the advent of full-time fly-by-wire (FBW) control systems incorporating artificial stability. Since then a whole new generation of Western combat aircraft has been designed along these lines. (The concept of artificial stability or relaxed static stability is discussed in more depth in Chapter 4.) By reducing the need for inherent airframe stability and offering a measure of artificial stability by means of a computer-driven control system, FBW offers greater freedom to the designer. Artificial stability helps to overcome the drawbacks of the delta in two ways.

Allowing the CG to be positioned aft in relation to the wing reduces the adverse trimming loads on the trailing-edge elevons to zero if neutral stability is adopted. If negative airframe stability is allowed, then the trimming downloads are not just reduced to zero but actually become uploads (Fig 45). This can improve maximum lift on the aircraft by perhaps 20% or more. In fact the smaller the tail moment arm, the greater the gain in trimmed lift as the CG is moved into the unstable zone. The accepted limit on the amount of negative stability is reached when the full elevon-down travel (upload) used for balancing the wing/body lift at maximum AOA is equalled.

The other very important benefit of artificial

Fig 45 Artificial stability turns elevon download into upload.

stability on a delta is a reduction in supersonic trim drag. The first production aircraft to feature relaxed static stability (RSS) was the B-58, which was difficult to balance at the aft-CG position.

The first delta-winged aircraft to combine fly-by-wire with RSS was the Dassault Mirage 2000. It has neutral inherent airframe stability at subsonic speeds, giving an increase in trimmed lift of 10–15% compared with the stable Mirage III. With a thrust/weight ratio approaching unity, the Mirage 2000 it claimed to have transonic and supersonic performance rivalling that of its competitors. In combat at subsonic speed, however, it is likely still to suffer an inherent disadvantage of the delta, namely high induced drag. Though its span loading is lower than that of the Mirage III, it is higher than the optimum for air combat manoeuvring, which is achievable only with a high-aspect-ratio wing. (see *Variable-sweep wings*, page 71). Moreover, above a certain AOA the induced drag is dependent more on lift-curve slope than on span loading, and this too has traditionally required a high-aspect-ratio, low-sweep wing. The designers of the Mirage 2000, with its very-low-aspect-ratio, highly swept delta wing, solved the problem by using computer-driven full-span leading-edge slats to vary the wing's lift slope (see *Leading-edge devices*, page 85).

The Mirage 2000 also significantly betters the Mirage III in the area of airfield performance, in which deltas have always been deficient. A 16% reduction in wing loading, use of slats and artificial stability have reduced landing approach speed from 330km/hr for the Mirage III to 260km/hr for the Mirage 2000.

Compound-sweep deltas

The supercruiser concept
Experience has shown that even when a combat encounter occurs at supersonic speed, the

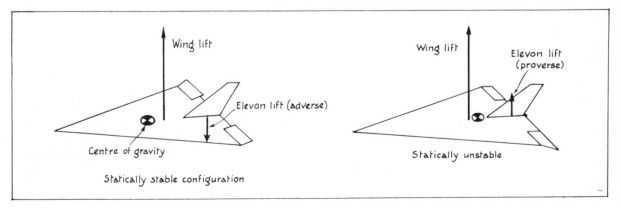

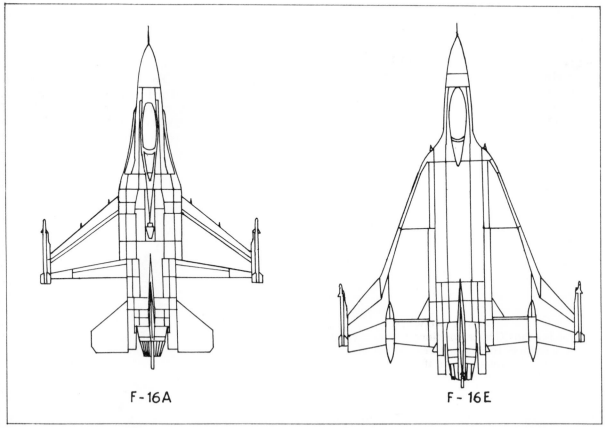

F-16A   F-16E

Fig 46 General Dynamics F-16 design evolution.

reduction in specific excess power as a result of manoeuvring causes a rapid slowing to subsonic speed if the engagement is pursued. NASA research during the 1970s on wing planforms and sections for a second-generation supersonic transport appeared to show how to maintain both speed and manoeuvrability. It was to this end that in the late 1970s the USAF launched the Supersonic Cruise and Manoeuvring Programme (SCAMP). As part of this effort General Dynamics and NASA investigated over 150 different configurations in the course of 3,600hr of wind-tunnel testing before selecting the cranked-arrow (or compound-sweep delta) planform.

Then, in mid-1980, the USAF defined a more immediate requirement for an improved ground attack aircraft to succeed the F-4 and F-111. General Dynamics shifted its sights to this goal and changed certain details of its cranked-arrow wing to meet the new requirement. The changes affected the camber, twist and trailing-edge reflex, optimising the wing for supersonic speed at low level. Remarkably, the new wing was not part of a com-

pletely new aircraft but was married to the existing F-16. As can be seen in Fig 46, the transformation was profound. The new 60m² wing was mated to the basic F-16 structure by means of two fuselage plugs, one 0·91m long and inserted ahead of the undercarriage, and a 0·67m section aft. To provide for ground clearance on rotation the longer rear fuselage was angled up by 3° and the ventral fins deleted. The upsweep puts the thrust line below the CG, helping to improve rotation on take-off. This, together with the very advanced wing, allowed the F-16XL (subsequently known as the F-16E) to be rotated at speeds down to 195km/hr, leading to a field-length requirement only two-thirds that of the F-16A. Flight testing of the F-16E showed it to have a lift/drag ratio between 10 and 45% better than that of the basic F-16A, and it could roll and pitch faster in any configuration. It could also pull an AFCS-limited 9g over twice the Mach-number range. While the F-16E offers no L/D improvement in subsonic manoeuvres, it does retain the subsonic cruise efficiency of the F-16 planform. Where it scores is in supersonic cruise performance: at Mach 2·2 its L/D is over 9. This is due to the improved fineness ratio arising from the

The General Dynamics F-16E's cranked-arrow wing was developed over 3,600hr of wind-tunnel testing in the late 1970s. The high degree of sweep on the inboard leading edge meant that flaps were fitted only outboard of the kink. The absence of a forward cockpit canopy frame is unique to the F-16. (General Dynamics)

increased fuselage length and even better wing/body blending. Even though the wing area is more than double that of the standard F-16, the skin

friction drag is only 22% more, due partly to the deletion of the horizontal tail.

The cranked-arrow planform of the F-16E comprises a sharply swept (70°) leading-edge inboard section lying within the shock cone of the nose and, at 63% semi-span, a 50° outboard section of thin profile and sharp leading edge. This is designed to obtain the low wave drag associated with highly swept or thin wings without the aerodynamic penalties of sweep or structural problems of thin sections. However, the F-16E takes the delta planform much further in that the experience gained with the leading-edge strakes of the basic F-16 enabled General Dynamics to maximise the vortex-lift benefit. The two swept panels of the cranked-arrow planform produce vortex systems which mutually interfere. At low angles of attack the leading-edge vortex from the inboard wing passes over the root chord of the outboard wing panel. In addition, vortex lift is available at the tip as a result of the action of the outboard leading-edge vortex. At high AOA the single primary vortex system acts over the whole of the outer panel. Thus augmented vortex lift occurs at supersonic speed, while at lower speeds the benefits of the primary vortex counter the high induced drag which plagued earlier delta planforms.

The improvements in stability and control with and without stores were such that no limitations due to buffet, wing rock or nose slice, nor spin tendency were encountered during the flight test programme. Angle-of-attack excursions resulted when the airspeed dropped to zero but the aircraft always recovered without any pilot input. 360° rolls at maximum g/maximum AOA similarly failed to cause any departure from controlled flight (Fig 47).

The major difference between the application of vortex flow to transonic fighters (e.g. F-16, F-18) and to the supercruise fighter (e.g. F-16E) is the extent of vortex lift available. The supercruise fighter, having more of the wing highly swept, develops more of this lift. Only a small fraction of the increased lift comes from the potential (or attached-flow) lift; the rest is due to the vortex lift acting over the increased wing area. This extra lift increases instantaneous turn rate, now regarded as more important than sustained turn rate, which largely governed the original F-16 design. Newer gunsights and missiles like the AIM-9L Sidewinder reduce the need to hold the target in the sight for weapon aiming. General Dynamics relinquished a small amount of sustained manoeuvrability in order to double the 9g envelope and move it into the high supersonic regime.

It should not however be forgotten that the F-16E was initially developed for ground attack. In this respect the new wing increased internal fuel capacity by 82%, which eliminated for most missions the weight and drag of external tanks. This gave it a 45% increase in combat radius with twice the weapon load of the F-16A and a more than 120% increase with the same weapon load. The aircraft is equipped with 17 store stations with 29 hardpoints. In the event the F-15E, a development of the two-seat F-15C, was chosen as the dual-role fighter for the USAF, though it remains possible that development of the F-16E will continue.

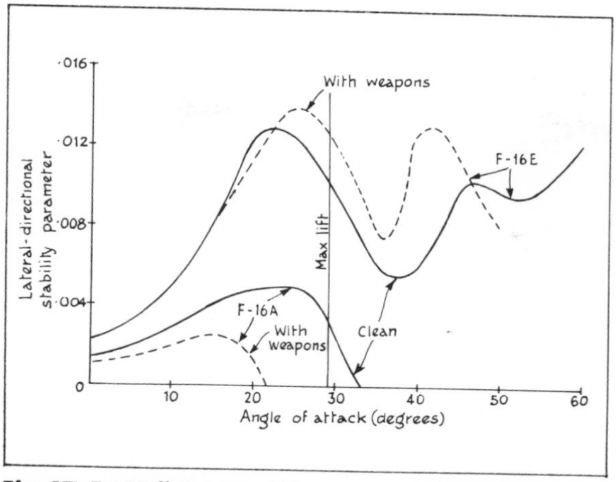

Fig 47 F-16E flying qualities compared with those of the F-16A. Lateral/directional stability is improved; external loads do not adversely affect flying qualities; there are no limitations due to buffet, wing rock, nose slice, deep-stall trim points, or spin tendency; there are no limits on angle of attack, minimum speed and bank angle; and the full range of manoeuvres can be performed while carrying the maximum load of air-to-ground stores.[13]

Air combat fighters

Though the simple delta is in itself a poor choice for the air-superiority role, developments like those incorporated in the Mirage 2000 have transformed this planform into a leading contender. In the early 1980s designs for compound-sweep deltas coupled with foreplanes began to appear in Europe as the next generation of air combat aircraft was defined. Two projects in particular feature compound-sweep wings: the BAe/MBB/Aeritalia ACA now the European Fighter Aircraft (EFA), and the Dassault-Breguet ACX, now named Rafale. The inboard and outboard sweep angles were originally 60°/40° and 55/42° respectively. The high degree of inboard sweep promotes strong vortex formation at high AOA, and low wave drag at supersonic speed. The lower sweep of the outboard panels maximise manoeuvrability by lowering the span loading to reduce the induced drag which has been the drawback of simple deltas. Both projects were designed with automatic leading-edge slats, those on the outboard panels being particularly powerful as a result of the lower sweep. The British precursor for EFA, the Experimental Aircraft Programme (EAP), has subsequently appeared with a curved inner leading-edge panel to further promote vortex formation and to improve the area distribution. Nevertheless, the EFA wing is likely to have a straight leading edge with 53% sweep.

Despite industry's apparent universal enthusiasm for the canard-delta configuration, some

BAe's EAP technology demonstrator on final approach, showing its cranked-delta/canard configuration and programmable leading-edge flaps. Low wing loading is needed to give high turn rates and good airfield performance. The resulting long wing-root chord dictated a low position for the all-moving foreplane. The fairings within the intakes house the actuators for the two independently movable lower intake lips. (BAe)

analysts asserted that it had no inherent advantages over the traditional aft-tail configuration. Specifically, the critics contended that the canard configuration is more critical in the area of high-AOA pitch-up problems and lateral/directional stability. The merits of this argument — which BAe counters by claiming that correct foreplane positioning can solve such problems — are discussed more fully in Chapter 4.

VARIABLE-SWEEP WINGS

Variable sweep leaves the nest

Variable sweep was investigated in the USA in the early 1950s with two aircraft, the Bell X-5 and Grumman XF10F-1. Similar British studies were based on wind tunnel and free-flight model testing, mainly by Barnes Wallis of Vickers-Armstrong. The American results, though indicating significant improvements at both ends of the flight spectrum, did not in themselves suggest that the gains justified full-scale development. This was due largely to the engineering problems associated with the sweep mechanism: hardly anyone wanted to over-complicate aircraft until the improvements offered became essential. Designers were therefore not tempted away from the principal task of overcoming the drawbacks of conventional wings of moderate sweepback.

By 1957, however, advances in propulsion had made it clear that multi-mission aircraft capable of offering both high supersonic speed and good airfield performance were not unrealistic and might well be the next requirement. The mismatch between the two ends of the flight spectrum remained the main obstacle, however. The USAF wanted, as a replacement for the runway-hungry F-105, an aircraft that would combine Mach 1·2 low-level penetration with an unrefuelled trans-atlantic ferry range and the ability to operate from 1,000m unpaved strips. A secondary air-to-air role demanded Mach 2·5 at high altitude. Simultaneously, the US Navy was being urged to consider whether a similar aircraft would meet its need for fleet air defence. With "commonality" the watchword, the US Department of Defence

launched the TFX (Tactical Fighter Experimental) project, which led to the F-111A for the USAF and the F-111B for the USN.

Mission requirements demanding variable sweep

A combination of three performance requirements stimulated enormous interest in swing wings in the 1960s:

1 Long-range subsonic cruise or long-endurance loiter on station

2 High-supersonic interception and transonic low-altitude strike

3 Operation from limited-length runways or aircraft carriers.

Wing size (page 38) describes the widely differing wing designs needed to meet each of these requirements. The following discussion describes in more detail how, by using variable-sweep wings, the apparently irreconcilable demands of the three missions can be met in a single design.

Efficient subsonic cruise and loiter

The variation of lift/drag ratio with Mach number for a range of wing sweep configurations (for the F-14) is shown in Fig 48. Good subsonic perform-

Fig 48 Variation of L/D$_{MAX}$ and C$_{D_0}$ with wing sweep and speed. Smaller graph at top right shows variation of span loading (W/b^2) with leading-edge sweep.[14]

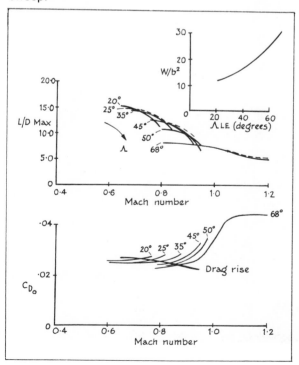

ance requires a minimum-sweep design; that is, a high-aspect-ratio wing of relatively thick section generating high lift, and low span loading giving low vortex drag. Such a configuration cannot be considered as a supersonic or even a transonic design since it is characterised by a steep drop in L/D with Mach number, and very low M_D.

The cruising efficiency of an aircraft is better represented by the parameter Mach number × lift/drag (ML/D). Plotting this against Mach number itself further reinforces the case for minimum sweep, since again a rapid reduction in ML/D occurs beyond the optimum. While an increase in sweep angle will increase the Mach number for maximum ML/D, it also simultaneously reduces the efficiency parameter.

The great value of variable sweep lies in the fact that it allows the wing planform to be changed in order to obtain, within limits, the optimum sweep for each Mach number. This is evident from Fig 49, in which variable sweep is compared with a wing of fixed intermediate sweep. The F-111, for example, uses 26° sweep for low-subsonic cruise and climb and 45° for high-subsonic cruise. Provided that the cruise range required is long enough, the improved aerodynamic efficiency can offset the structural weight penalty, reduced fuel volume and cost, and variable sweep may be justified on these grounds alone.

Supersonic efficiency

In supersonic flight with the wings fully swept, typically to 70°, the shock wave drag due to volume (i.e. that part of the wave drag due to the bulk of the aircraft, which is independent of lift) is minimised. The lift is spread over a wide chord, minimising lift-dependent drag. The variation in section thickness at the two extremes of wing sweep for the F-14 in comparison with the F-4 and MiG-21 is shown in Fig 50.

A clear vindication of variable sweep at supersonic speed is shown in Fig 51. Plotted in this figure are the ratios of drag/weight and thrust/weight against Mach number for two contemporary aircraft, the F-14 and F-15. Because of the greater sweepback of the F-14 (68°) its drag/weight is substantially lower than that of the F-15, with its 45° sweepback. This enables the F-14 to match the top speed of the F-15 despite a 25% lower available thrust/weight ratio.

Wing sweepback angle on the Grumman F-14 Tomcat is controlled by the automatic Mach/sweep programmer; the angle visible here is around the optimum for Mach 0·9. The extent of the wing oversweep for carrier deck parking is indicated by the darkened area ahead of the fins. (US Navy)

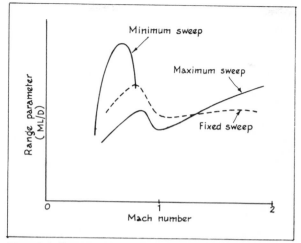

Fig 49 Influence of sweep on cruise efficiency.

Fig 50 Wing thickness comparison.[14]

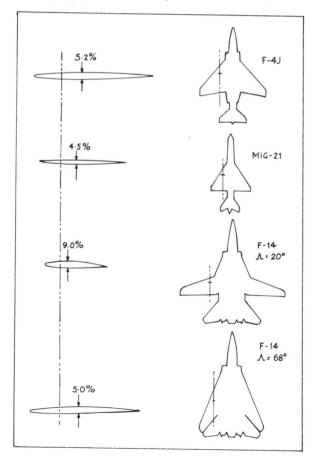

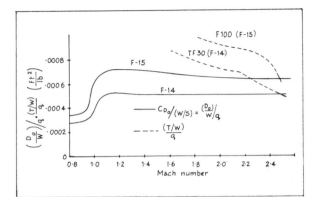

Fig 51 F-14/F-15 thrust and drag comparison. The two broken lines indicate the thrust/weight ratios yielded by the TF30 engines in the F-14 and the F100s in the F-15. Altitude is 10,000m.[14]

Gust response in high-speed, low-altitude flight

If the crew are to have a smooth ride and airframe fatigue life be acceptably long, the aircraft must be insensitive to the vertical gusts likely to be met in the turbulent atmosphere at low altitude. Crew tolerance of gusts falls as speed increases, and about five minutes is the maximum endurance at Mach 0·8 with a high-aspect-ratio wing of low sweep. Fig 52 shows that increasing sweep reduces gust response, so that at maximum sweep the tolerable exposure time may have increased perhaps tenfold as a result of the wing's lower lift-curve slope. The vertical acceleration due to an upgust is proportional to speed × lift slope ÷ wing loading. The most powerful means of reducing lift-curve slope is a combination of reduced aspect ratio and increased sweep. On the F-111, for example, as the wing sweeps from 16° to 72° the aspect ratio falls from 7·56 to 1·34. This obviates the need to increase the wing loading, though for a fixed-sweep aircraft this is the only recourse, even though it adversely affects airfield performance and manoeuvrability.

Aft movement of a swing-wing usually results in an increase in longitudinal stability (i.e. pitch stiffness). This, by definition, increases the nose-down pitching moment upon encountering an upgust and further reduces gust response by a factor of two or three. The combined effect is to raise the tolerable exposure time to something well beyond the likely requirement for sustained low-altitude transonic penetration. The Rockwell B-1 is however probably an exception, incorporating as it does computer-driven delta-shaped vanes on the fuselage side near the cockpit location to improve the ride.

Flight under such conditions is carried out essentially at wing zero lift coefficient, since the wing area actually available is more than required

and the body alone produces sufficient lift. This means that the lift/drag ratio is far from the optimum, a penalty which has to be paid. Minimum drag would be achieved by an aircraft which resembled a flying fuselage, i.e. a body of maximum fineness ratio for minimum wave drag and minimum wetted area for low skin-friction drag. It was this reasoning which gave rise to the "over-swept" wing planforms which appeared in the early 1960s for the TFX in its strike configuration. "Over-sweep" was used on the F-14, though not for the above reasons; sweeping the wings a further 7° beyond the in-flight maximum of 68° reduces the necessary carrier deck stowage space.

Take-off and landing performance

Maximum lift is generated by thick-section, unswept wings equipped with high-lift devices. This is indicated in Fig 53, which shows the varia-

Fig 52 Influence of sweep and speed on ride quality.

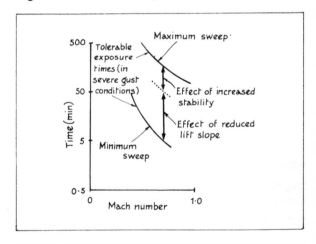

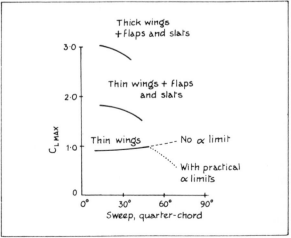

Fig 53 How sweep affects maximum lift.

tion of maximum lift with sweep angle. For the thin, unflapped wing, maximum lift increases slightly with sweepback, though considerations such as pilot view, tail clearance on take-off and landing, buffet and drag mean that it is not usually possible to exploit the wing's full lifting potential. Flap effectiveness decreases with sweepback, since the hinge line also sweeps. Thus a thin wing with sufficient sweep to permit high supersonic speed (i.e. greater than 45°) typically achieves a maximum lift coefficient of about 1·0. Not only does the variable-sweep wing benefit from being able to use thicker wing sections at low sweep, but the extra thickness allows very effective slotted flaps and slats. The F-14, for example, with its single-slotted flaps and leading-edge slats, achieves a maximum lift coefficient of nearly 2·5. Though this capability could be used to shorten the field length required by allowing lower approach speeds, in many current variable-sweep designs the high lift of the low-sweep, fully flapped configuration is used to minimise wing area, which is of great benefit at high speeds.

Nevertheless, the reduction in landing speed available from variable sweep provides a valuable safety margin. The accident frequency for land-based aircraft increases with approach speed squared, while for carrierborne aircraft it is related to the cube of the approach speed. With its wing swept 20° the F-14 has a carrier approach speed of 213km/hr compared with the 239km/hr of the F-4J with its 51°-swept slatted and flapped wing.

The fundamental drawback: excessive longitudinal stability

It was recognised in the early 1950s that although variable sweep had promise, a practical means of employing the technique had yet to be found. The work with the Bell X-5 had revealed that when the wings were rotated aft about a fixed pivot point located within the fuselage, the aerodynamic centre moved significantly aft in relation to the CG. The wing's CG itself moves aft, but since the wing's contribution to weight is small its effect on whole-aircraft CG is minimal. The net result is an excess of longitudinal stability (i.e. increased static margin). For an aircraft at a given weight and speed the required AOA increases as the wing is swept aft due to the reduction in lift-curve slope (lower aspect ratio, higher sweep). With the much larger static margin, the downwards force at the tail for balancing has to increase significantly, thereby increasing its own lift-dependent drag and interference.

Furthermore, the increased distance between the centre of lift and CG (i.e. static margin) at maximum sweep means that the nose-down moment increases rapidly with increasing lift, requiring larger tailplane deflections to balance changes in speed or normal acceleration. With maximum sweep at high lift the consequent large tail downloads result in trim drag penalties, with the wing having to provide additional lift to make up for the downloads on the tail, as well as supporting the aircraft's weight.

A further aft movement of the wing's aerodynamic centre occurs when accelerating through the transonic regime. This causes an additional increase in longitudinal stability which must be countered if a variable-sweep aircraft is to have adequate supersonic manoeuvrability. The much higher available sweep does however ease this problem in comparison with that faced by a fixed and lower-sweep design.

Thus the major obstacle to a viable swing wing was the fact that adequate stability for satisfactory handling at low sweep meant excessive stability at high sweep.

The solution chosen for the Bell X-5 was to mount the whole wing on rails so that it could be translated forward with respect to the fuselage as sweep was increased. This system proved quite satisfactory for an experimental aircraft, but the mechanism was very heavy and the need for translation added extra volume to the fuselage in the vicinity of the wing root. Similar wing translation schemes were studied in Britain, particularly in connection with the TSR.2 requirement.

The real breakthrough came in 1952 when NACA (as NASA was then known) proposed a practical variable-sweep arrangement that avoided the need for wing translation. This is the outboard pivot. It was shown that the lifting area of the wing could be divided between fixed and movable portions in such a manner that the movement of the centre of lift caused by sweep variation need not present a serious excess-stability problem. The markedly different behaviour of the outboard pivot is compared with that of the inboard pivot (i.e. translating wing) in Fig 54. Also shown is the distribution of aerodynamic loading along the length of the aircraft. For the inboard pivot it can be seen that the aerodynamic centre as represented by the lift vector moves rearwards as sweep is increased. When the pivot is carefully positioned outboard, however, the aerodynamic centre at maximum sweep may be located very close to that at minimum sweep.

This highly desirable behaviour is explained as follows. The lift on the movable wing panel decreases as sweep angle is increased; in order to recover this lift the aircraft's AOA must be raised. This increases the proportion of total lift developed

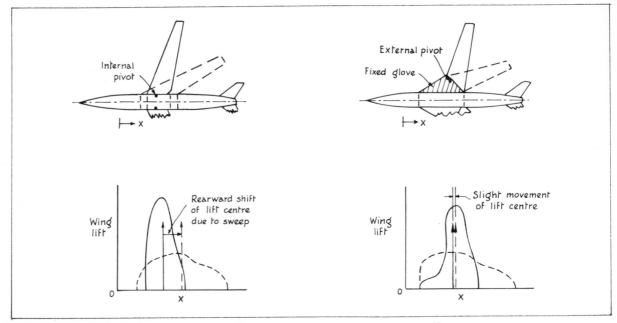

Fig 54 Effect of pivot location on aerodynamic loading. X = longitudinal axis.[15]

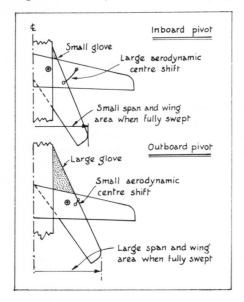

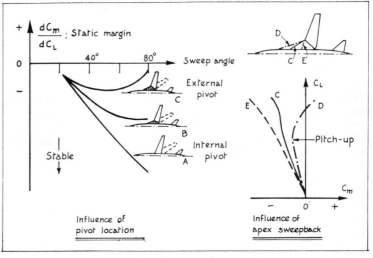

Fig 55 *Left*: Influence of pivot position on wing span and area.

Fig 56 *Above*: Pivot and apex influences on longitudinal stability.[15]

on the forward, fixed, part of the wing. The reduction in size of the movable wing panel, caused by the use of the large fixed apex needed to support the outboard pivot, and the larger proportion of lift carried by the fixed apex combine to limit the aft movement of the aerodynamic centre. This is shown in Fig 55.

An examination of the change of stability for various pivot positions as the wing is swept aft (Fig 56) clearly shows the value of the outboard pivot. In the case of the inboard pivot (A), there is a relatively rapid increase in stability with sweepback. As the pivot is moved out from the fuselage (B), the rate of growth of stability is initially lower and stops altogether at around 70° sweepback. This is because the tailplane's contribution to stability is reduced by the wing's increased downwash. As the pivot is moved farther outboard still (C), with the fixed apex necessarily becoming larger, the rate of change of stability decreases further. In fact it reverses at around 50°, so that for a sweep of 70° the longitudinal stability is approaching that at minimum sweep.

A potentially major longitudinal stability problem can however be encountered near maximum lift by designs incorporating a large fixed apex. The flow over the highly swept apex is dominated at high AOA by a vigorous vortex pattern which increases the lift there even though the outer wing panel at low sweep may have already stalled, leading to the possibility of pitch-up. The vertical location of the horizontal tail has a profound influence under these circumstances. With the tail in the same horizontal plane as the wing, as on the F-111 and Su-24, there can be a severe nose-up pitching moment as the stall is approached, whereas with a low tailplane (e.g. F-14 and Tornado) acceptable nose-down pitching occurs.

In spite of this potential problem NASA researchers felt that they had conclusively shown that an outboard pivot on a well tapered wing and the correct tailplane location eliminated the need for the centre section of the wing to translate fore and aft.

The choice of pivot position was the main difference between American and British designers. The British view in the late 1960s was that an outboard pivot on a large fixed apex was, for a multi-role combat aircraft, merely an interim solution. Indeed, British work suggested that a better solution for such an aircraft was to place the pivots as far inboard as possible. As late as 1969 the British Aircraft Corporation proposal for the Tornado incorporated an inboard pivot and translating wing, whereas German partner MBB favoured an outboard pivot and fixed apex. In the event the requirement for greater manoeuvrability became increasingly important and a compromise position was adopted.

Nevertheless, the arguments in favour of the inboard pivot were substantial:

1 Fully swept wing area and span are smaller, as shown in Fig 55. This helps to maximise the performance gains for the low-altitude, high-speed strike role.

2 The inboard pivot does not need a fixed apex. This gives the highest effective aspect ratio in the unswept condition, which is good for cruise and manoeuvrability. Tail effectiveness is also increased.

3 The effect of aeroelastic distortion on the rearward movement of the aerodynamic centre tends to reduce that movement. In the fully swept position there is a pronounced reduction in wingtip angle of attack due to bending. This causes reduced lift on the outer wing, with more lift on the inner portion. Consequently there is a forward shift of aerodynamic centre compared with the rigid wing. This is greater for a wing with an inboard pivot, and the growth in stability with sweep is not so severe.

4 The trim drag penalty is not particularly acute for combat aircraft using full sweep only for supersonic dash or low-altitude, high-speed penetration of limited duration. It does however become crucial for strategic strike aircraft like the B-1 and Blackjack, and both of these aircraft have large wing gloves containing outboard pivots.

5 Trim-change effects can be effectively hidden from the pilot. For example, whereas the trim change is quite noticeable on the F-111 when the pitch dampers of its auto-trim system are switched off, it is barely perceptible when they are working.

6 The complications of fairing and sealing a fixed apex are avoided, as is the undesirable airflow pattern induced by the discontinuity in the wing leading edge at low sweep. Even more important, deletion of the apex allows the use of full-span leading-edge high-lift devices. The F-111 uses an apex slat to help recover some of the lift loss in this region and to control the vortex formation on its highly swept apex at high AOA.

The extra degree of freedom which the swing wing offers the designer can only be fully exploited by the correct choice of overall planform, wing/body cross-sectional area distribution, and pivot position. These decisions are influenced not only by aerodynamics but also by structural, mechanical and operational factors.

The first operational aircraft to use an outboard pivot was the F-111, which was also the first operational variable-sweep aircraft. However, despite the claims for the outboard pivot, the F-111 did suffer from excessive stability, displaying all the classic faults of large tail downloads for trim, high trim drag and poor manoeuvrability at high lift. When it came to the VFX programme (which led to the F-14), Grumman was fully aware of the F-111's shortcomings. Consequently the F-14 has its pivots noticeably farther outboard than does the F-111, as shown in Fig 57. This relocation of the pivots had one major benefit: whereas the F-111's static margin, which is a measure of stability, steadily gets larger as sweep increases, the F-14's static margin rises to a peak at 50° sweep and then steadily declines. The result is that at maximum sweep the F-14's static margin is little more than a

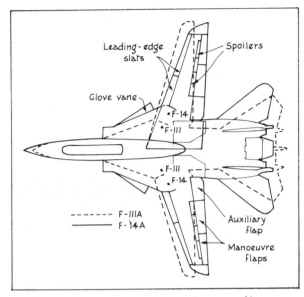

Fig 57 F-14 and F-111 wing pivot locations.[14]

Fig 58 F-14 and F-111 supersonic static margins compared.[14]

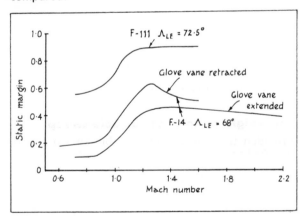

quarter that of the F-111. In coping with the transonic shift of the aerodynamic centre, the outboard pivot on the F-14 again show up to advantage. For example, at Mach 1·6 the F-14's static margin is 40% lower than the F-111's (Fig 58).

It was concern with the additional aft movement of the aerodynamic centre across the transonic regime that persuaded Grumman to incorporate the glove vane (shown in Fig 57) on the F-14. The glove vane is a small delta wing programmed to extend from its slot at Mach 1 to produce a forward lifting force. This has a destabilising influence, reducing the aircraft's static margin by about 10%. Fig 58 shows that at Mach 1·6 the combined

effects of a more outboard pivot and the glove vane cut the F-14's static margin to less than 50% of that of the F-111.

Closer examination of Grumman's data[15] on the glove vane's performance shows why the company valued it so highly. For example, the F-111's maximum manoeuvring load factor is restricted to approximately 2g compared with almost 6g at Mach 1·2 for the F-14, with the glove vane adding another 1g. Other benefits are reductions in tail download by 40% and attendant trim drag by 40 drag counts, which translate into a 5% increase in lift/drag ratio at a lift coefficient of 0·4. The effect on manoeuvrability is strikingly illustrated by comparing the F-14's sustained turning flight envelope at 3g with those of the F-111 and F-4J. At 4g the use of the vane was estimated by Grumman to be equivalent to a thrust increase of 18kN.

It is not known whether Soviet designers independently discovered the outboard pivot as a means of minimising aerodynamic centre shift, but by 1970 both the Su-17 Fitter-C and MiG-23 Flogger were operational with outboard-pivoted variable-sweep wings. The Su-7 Fitter-A was originally designed with a 62° fixed-sweep wing, resulting in a landing speed of over 320km/hr and consequently poor airfield performance. When the type was modified for variable sweep (in the process becoming the Su-17 Fitter-C), the pivots were located at approximately half-span, giving a limited range of aspect ratio: 3 to only 4·9, compared with a more typical 2 to 8. However, with the wing bending and torsion loads at half-span only a fraction of those at the root, this solution was easier than a full redesign and produced a much needed improvement in airfield performance at lower cost. This is an example of the Soviet philosophy of stretching a sound basic design to its limit by progressive improvement.

The MiG-23 Flogger and Su-24 Fencer are comparable in geometry to their Western counterparts, with sweep and aspect-ratio ranges of 20–70° and 2–8 respectively. Both aircraft feature large wing gloves housing outboard pivots. They do however differ in the spacing between wing trailing edge (fully swept) and tailplane leading edge. The dynamic stability of an aircraft is a function of the square of the distance between wing and tailplane aerodynamic centres. It is therefore perhaps reasonable to suppose that the Fencer and Flogger layouts were chosen to avoid risky flight characteristics or because of the Soviet reluctance to rely overly on stability augmentation systems.

Sweep control

Whereas the angle of sweep is manually selected

on the F-111 and the strike version of the Tornado, the F-14's primary sweep control is fully automatic, as is that of the Tornado ADV. The F-14's sweep programmer, part of the automatic flight control system, was originally intended not as a means of optimising aircraft performance but to limit the wing's maximum bending moments, the worst case being at minimum sweep. By limiting the minimum sweep of 20° to a Mach number no greater than about 0·7, Grumman was able to design for a much reduced wing strength, saving an estimated 450kg of structure weight.

By 1968 Grumman had began to realise the significant operational advantages of sweep programming across the whole speed range, recognising that manual selection of optimum sweep was difficult under the best of conditions and well nigh impossible in the heat of combat.

The concept of optimising for either maximum lift/drag ratio or drag-rise Mach number is illustrated in Fig 48. The shape of the individual L/D versus Mach number curves shows the classic reduction in absolute L/D caused by the reduced wing span (i.e. increased span loading: W/b^2) as sweep is increased. The variation of optimum wing sweep to maximise L/D across the transonic region is indicated by the dotted line. The case for M_D is similar.

At the heart of the sweep programmer are the sweep versus Mach number programs, which place limits on the usable combinations of these parameters to ensure the structural integrity of the wing. For altitudes above 6,000m, for example, a straight line on the sweep versus Mach number plot links $\Lambda = 20°$, Mach 0·7 to $\Lambda = 57°$, Mach 0·9. The pilot can if he wishes control the sweep manually, though within strict limits. He cannot command a sweep to the right of the line, so that while 40° at Mach 0·8 is acceptable, for example, 30° is not.

In addition to limiting the wing-root bending moments, the sweep program is also written with maximum L/D and containment of drag rise (M_D) in mind. Grumman data clearly show the performance benefits of the sweep programmer in reducing the lift-dependent drag by unsweeping the wings to below 50° (typically the optimum for Mach 0·9) at Mach numbers less than 0·8. Dramatic improvements in specific excess power during 4g manoeuvres were found. At Mach 0·7, for example, the SEP advantage yielded by 35° rather than 50° sweep is well over 35m/sec. Since an advantage of 15m/sec in SEP is generally regarded as decisive, other things being equal, the value of programmed sweeping during the high stress of combat becomes clear. Similar improvements in SEP are obtained when the sweep programmer selects increasing amounts of sweepback at supersonic speed.

Features specific to variable-sweep aircraft

As the wing sweeps back, the inboard trailing edge must be housed within a cavity in the fuselage. On all current Western designs this is accomplished by means of an air-inflated bag into which the wing retracts. As well as providing an aerodynamic seal around the wing, the bag maintains a smooth external contour at minimum sweep. Wing closure is achieved by means of an overwing fairing of glass-reinforced plastic plates which open and close like a fan. On the F-14 this fairing has external stiffeners which have the appearance of wing fences.

A typical wing-sweep mechanism consists of a pair of actuators which are mechanically coupled to preclude out-of-step operation of the two wings. Weapon pylons mounted on the movable wing panel must be able to pivot to align with the free-stream flow. Each wing of the F-111, for example, has two swivelling pylons inboard and two fixed ones outboard which have to be jettisoned when the wing is swept beyond 26°. The Su-19 Fencer has two pylons on each wing glove, with a swivelling pylon outboard. Tornado features two swivelling pylons on each wing. Wing fences are naturally not used on the moving wing, though dog-tooth extensions formed from the area inboard of leading-edge slats are a feature of the MiG-23.

The weight penalty of variable sweep

Provided that the use of variable sweep can be justified on grounds other than weight, the answer to the question of the weight penalty is simple. There is no weight penalty: on the contrary, there is a significant saving.

For the VFX mission, for example, Rockwell's submission was the only one to feature a fixed-sweep design. The virtues of variable sweep were convincing enough for General Dynamics, Grumman, Ling-Temco-Vought and McDonnell Douglas all to submit swing-wing designs in response to this demanding requirement, subsequently and successfully addressed by the F-14. No-one can dispute the extra weight of the pivot assembly (the extensive use of titanium bears witness to this), the greater weight associated with the trimming necessary with variation in wing sweep, the extra trim drag, and the necessary increased engine thrust leading to more engine weight and larger fuel load. The structure weight may increase by 2–5%, depending on mission. But if a variable-sweep aircraft and a fixed-wing type having exactly the same performance are compared, the weight saving for variable sweep becomes clear.

Grumman in fact pursued a fixed-wing design almost as far as that of the F-14 for comparison purposes. In trying to reconcile the conflicting requirements of high maximum Mach number, subsonic loiter and carrier suitability the designers soon realised that a fixed-sweep aircraft would have a higher wing area and thrust/weight ratio, making it significantly heavier. In the end the fixed-sweep Model 303F would have turned out almost 2,250kg heavier because of the larger wing area of 69m² (compared with the F-14's reference area of 52m²) required for carrier suitability. While the F-14 can land safely with single-slotted flaps, the fixed-wing 303F needed double-slotted flaps and could not achieve the single-engine carrier wave-off rate of climb demanded by the US Navy.

FORWARD-SWEPT WINGS

Aeroelastic tailoring

Although the idea of forward sweep is not new it was impossible to explore its claimed benefits until the advent of recent developments in materials. The major drawback of the forward-swept wing is its tendency to structural divergence, in this case related to the way a wing twists when it is subjected to bending. As has been seen, when an aft-swept wing is subject to bending the wing twists in such a way that the tips twist downwards, reducing the local AOA and offloading the tips, especially during high-g manoeuvring. The reverse is true of the forward-swept wing (FSW): the wing twists in such a way as to increase the AOA at its tips, thereby increasing the tip loading and further increasing the twist until the wing eventually fails (Fig 59).

Conventional metal wings are limited to about 15° of forward sweep before running into the need for wing stiffening, which would impose a prohibitive weight penalty. However, it is now possible to make wing skins from high-strength/low-weight carbon-fibre laminates, which have the combined bending and torsional characteristics needed to counter spanwise twisting without weight penalty. The wing skins are built up in a series of layers typically arranged so that the unidirectional plies which constitute the separate layers lie at 0°, 45° and 90° to one another. Superimposed upon this matrix of layers is a sweep forward, typically of 10° relative to the axis along which the metal wing box naturally bends without twist, i.e. the flexural

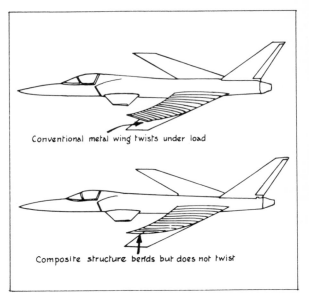

Fig 59 Controlling twist with aeroelastic tailoring.

axis. As the wing bends upwards, its upper skin is compressed while the lower skin is put in tension. The laminated skins, lying at an angle to the bending axis, shear forward under compression and backwards under tension. This shearing action generates a nose-down twist of the wing box as it bends up which opposes the FSW's natural tendency to twist nose-up. Such "aeroelastic tailoring" is the basis of the Grumman X-29 wing and is the driving force behind all other FSW designs.

Advantages of forward sweep

A conventional aft-swept wing (ASW) suffers from increased local lift coefficients on its outer panels which are exaggerated by taper and boundary-layer drift. Pitch-up can occur at high AOA because the longitudinal balance of lift is upset by tip stalling. In addition, the roll-control effectiveness of outboard ailerons is reduced, and uncommanded rolling may also occur, leading to

departure from controlled flight and possible spinning. Another undesirable characteristic of ASWs is that the shock-wave sweep is less than the leading-edge sweep, giving high wave drag. Reduction of the shock strength — by increasing the shock wave's sweep — requires the wing to be more highly swept. The FSW counters these two undesirable characteristics as follows:

High-AOA benefits

The flow over a forward-swept wing is towards the wing root, which increases the local lift coefficient there and, when combined with the inward boundary-layer drift, will cause the root to stall first. The resulting lift loss behind the aircraft's CG makes pitch-up a significant possibility. This could

The Grumman X-29 was built to explore the characteristics of forward-swept wings. An aerodynamically complex aircraft, it is equipped with no fewer than three forms of pitch control, all fly-by-wire: all-moving foreplane, discrete variable-camber trailing-edge flaperons, and rear-fuselage strakes.

be countered by twisting the wing root downwards to reduce the AOA locally or by limiting the extent of the inflow with fences. A limited area of aft sweep on the innermost region of the wing could also be used; this would have the benefit of modifying the sweep of the isobars inboard and improving the transonic area distribution. Such an approach was used on the Grumman X-29 and other FSW designs. The presence of a foreplane can also have a controlling influence on flow conditions at the wing root. Forward-swept wings have to be attached relatively far aft, making the use of a conventional tailplane impractical. The foreplane thus required produces a downwash which helps to offload the inboard wing panels and further acts to suppress pitch-up tendencies.

With flow separation at the wingtips no longer the major hazard, roll-control effectiveness and roll damping are improved at high AOA. At the same time, the dihedral effect (rolling moment due to sideslip) is also reduced. At low speed, when wings need to be held level in crosswind landings, and in combat at high AOA, when wing dropping, wing rock and nose slice may occur, these FSW characteristics are of value. Indeed, it is claimed that one effect of a close-coupled canard configuration is that flow separation on the wing first appears downstream of the foreplane's tip, with subsequent spreading inboard and outboard to give a well-behaved stall. This, along with the improved lateral control available at the wingtips, is claimed to make spin-proofing a possibility.

On the debit side, the aft mounting of the FSW results in close coupling between the vertical stabiliser and the wing root, leading to a possible loss of fin and rudder effectiveness due to their immersion in the separated airflow from the wing root.

High-speed benefits and penalties

If a comparison is made between two swept wings having the same leading-edge sweep (Fig 60) then an advantage for the FSW is apparent at high-subsonic speed. The wing shock wave is more highly swept, giving reduced shock strength and wave drag. This offers improved manoeuvrability.

If on the other hand the two wings are designed to have the same shock-wave sweep (Fig 61), a more realistic comparison, then the FSW needs lower leading-edge sweep. In fact it has lower sweep at all points forward of the shock-wave position, which is typically at 70% chord. This reduced leading-edge sweep increases the lift-curve slope of the FSW, which can give higher usable lift on take-off and landing than can the ASW, with its restrictions related to tail clearance and pilot view.

The FSW's increased lift slope could be a penalty in low-altitude, high-speed penetration, due to increased gust sensitivity. Whereas the ASW loses lift-curve slope due to flexibility at high

Fig 61 Forward sweep allows higher aspect ratio and lower leading-edge sweep for the same wing area, taper ratio, shock sweep and bending moment at the pivot station.[16]

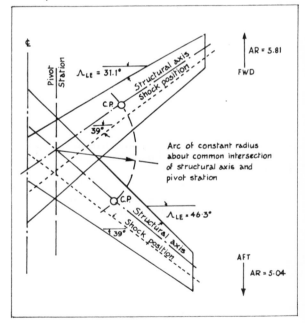

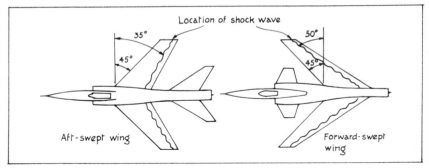

Fig 60 Comparison of shock waves on forward and aft-swept wings.

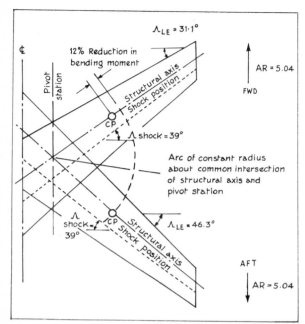

Fig 62 Forward sweep reduces the bending moment at the pivot station for the same wing area, aspect ratio, taper ratio and shock sweep.[16]

subsonic speed, the FSW gains. However, if forward sweep is used to reduce wing area, the consequent increase in wing loading, together with active-control gust-response suppression, could compensate to give a similar attitude response, which is now regarded as more important than g loading.

Reduced leading-edge sweep also offers a reduction in induced drag, thereby improving subsonic lift/drag. This would improve manoeuvrability, particularly sustained turn rate and cruise/loiter performance, or allow a smaller wing to be used. The lower sweep of the FSW causes additional wave drag at supersonic speed, though this may be offset by optimising the wing for transonic flight, resulting in reduced area, or by increasing the leading-edge sweep. The correct option depends on the intended role of the aircraft. A further unexpected benefit of low leading-edge sweep was found. This was the fact that the drag component produced by shock-induced flow separation is a function of leading-edge sweep, i.e. the lower the sweep the lower this part of the total drag.

The FSW also offers, for the same area, span and shock sweep as an equivalent ASW, a shorter structural span (Fig 62) and an aerodynamic centre closer to the wing root. This gives reduced wing-root bending moments, yielding lower structure weight. Alternatively, for a given wing-root

bending moment a higher aspect ratio may be adopted. This allows a further reduction in induced drag.

HIGH-LIFT DEVICES

The need

It is difficult to obtain satisfactory landing and take-off performance from wings typical of those used on combat aircraft, with their low thickness/chord ratio (4–7%), high sweep (40–60°), low aspect ratio (3–4) and high loadings (400–500kg/m²). Their inadequate lifting capability at low speeds must be augmented by means of extendable high-lift devices which then retract at high speed. In spite of the significant increases in thrust/weight ratio and reductions in wing loading introduced in the 1970s, concern over the vulnerability of concrete runways has not waned, although no real inroads have been made into reducing landing distances apart from the thrust reversers used on the Tornado and the Viggen and, of course, the VTOL capability of the Harrier.

Generally speaking, the speed when clearing a 50ft (15m) obstacle after take-off — one of the performance measures used for certification purposes — must for safety reasons be at least 20% higher than the configuration's stalling speed. This is governed mainly by the maximum lift coefficient the wing can generate. The basic goal of the high-lift system is the highest lift/drag ratio at the highest possible lift coefficient, as shown in Fig 63. The interdependence of these two parameters is shown by consideration of the take-off case. A small flap deflection yields a higher L/D ratio, resulting in an improved rate of climb. But take-off distance is increased, since this is inversely proportional to $C_{L_{max}}$ available. A similar argument applies to the landing case.

The demands on the high-lift system depend on the role and specification of the aircraft. For

Fig 63 Take-off lift requirements.

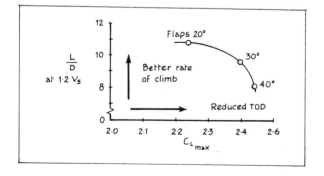

Fig 64 Principal factors contributing to increased lift from the basic wing section. The solid lines show the effect of applying each measure.

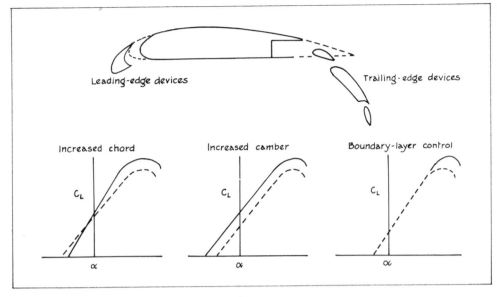

Fig 65 Idealised wing flow in the landing configuration.

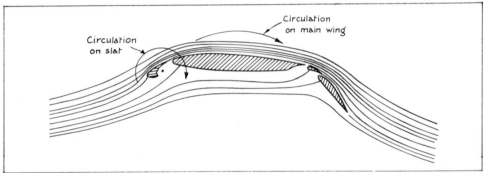

example, when operating from long concrete runways the F-15 can meet the requirement with a simple trailing-edge flap on a fixed swept wing, whereas the carrier-borne F-14 requires a variable-sweep wing equipped with leading and trailing-edge high-lift devices.

As shown in Fig 64, there are three principal ways of increasing the maximum lift of the basic wing section.

1 Increase wing chord length, thereby increasing the wing area.

2 Increase wing camber, thereby increasing circulation. (The large nose-down pitching moments which then arise, especially on the landing approach, have to be trimmed out by tail downloads. See Chapter 4).

3 Improve the state of the boundary layer over the section.

High-lift devices are generally divided into two types, distinguished by their location: leading edge

and trailing edge. Fig 65 shows an idealised flow over a wing with leading and trailing-edge devices deployed in a typical landing configuration.

Leading-edge devices

Leading-edge devices increase the maximum lift of an aerofoil without significantly increasing the drag by: spreading the leading-edge force, and reducing the intensity of the high suction peaks to decrease the adverse pressure gradients and delay leading-edge flow separation. Combat aircraft can incorporate three basic categories of leading-edge device:

A Acts by changing the pressure distribution: leading-edge flap; Krueger flap; slat without a slot; flexible leading edge

B Acts on boundary layer: tangential blowing; boundary-layer suction

C Combined action: slat with a slot.

The three basic types are illustrated in Fig 66.

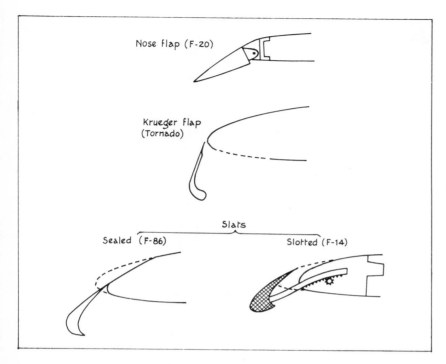

Nose flap (F-20)

Krueger flap
(Tornado)

Slats

Sealed (F-86)   Slotted (F-14)

Fig 66 Leading-edge devices.

Leading-edge flap

The leading-edge flap consists of a portion of the nose of the aerofoil which can be hinged to move downwards. A typical deflection angle is 25°, though the radius of the hinge knuckle is a predominant factor in determining the maximum useful angle. The manufacture of a smooth knuckle is difficult and a significant reduction in the lift increment can result from such irregularities, as well as gaps and leaks. Leading-edge flaps achieve their effect by increasing the camber of the section and are most useful with thin, sharp-nosed sections, on which flap deflection reduces the high peak suctions and separations which would otherwise exist in this region. Leading-edge flaps are also easier to accommodate than other devices, which require more section depth.

They do not combine well with trailing-edge flaps, contributing to a thickened combined nose and main element wake which passes over the trailing-edge flaps, reducing their effectiveness. They have however been found to be more effective than slots on highly swept wings and have been applied on the outer half span to reduce tip stalling. (MiG-23). Leading-edge flaps are also used on the F-5, A-7, Dassault Etendard and Mirage F.1, F-16, F-18 and F-20 (Fig 66).

Krueger flap

This comprises a part of the lower surface rotating forward about a simple hinge (Fig 66). It works by increasing wing chord, or increasing the nose radius, or both. On thin wing sections the first effect lies behind their advantage over the simpler, nose-drooping flap. On thicker sections (t/c ≈ 6%) a further advantage lies in the increased nose curvature, which plays such an important role in the generation of maximum lift. Krueger flaps are used on the inboard fixed apex of the Tornado IDS. Main disadvantage is higher profile drag.

Slat without a slot (sealed slat)

The principal difference between the Krueger flap and the sealed slat is the extension mechanism and its effect on the upper surface of the nose of the aerofoil section. Sealed slats were used on the F-86 Sabre, designed to pop out automatically under the influence of the leading-edge suction. But problems arose in combat when asymmetric deployment occurred.

Slat with a slot (slotted slat)

Though complex, requiring rails and rollers in addition to actuators, this is probably the most widely used leading-edge device for combat aircraft. However, when account is taken of the resulting increase in maximum lift and its favourable effect on lateral/directional flying qualities, the extra complication is amply justified.

The fundamental difference between this and all other leading-edge devices is the incorporation of a slot. The effect of well designed slots, be they incorporated in leading-edge or trailing-edge devices, has been stated by A.M.O. Smith,[17] who discounted the idea that they work as a sort of blowing boundary-layer control. His main conclusions are summarised as follows:

Slat effect
The circulation generated on the slat runs counter to the circulation on the wing section, as shown in Fig 65. Though this greatly reduces the suction peak on the wing section and lessens its lift, the lift on the slat more than compensates. The much reduced adverse pressure gradient on the wing section thus achieved presents a far smaller obstacle to its boundary layer. As a result, the slat delays the stall to higher AOA so that significantly higher maximum lift coefficients may be achieved.

Circulation effect
The circulation generated on the wing section rotates in the sense shown in Fig 65. This flow places the trailing edge of the slat in a region of high velocity and high angle of attack. For the flow to leave the trailing edge of the slat smoothly, in what is known as the "Kutta condition", it has to generate about itself the necessary extra circulation. This increase in circulation produces higher lift on the slat.

Dumping effect
Because the trailing edge of the slat is in a region of appreciably higher velocity, its boundary layer discharges at higher velocity. The increased velocity relieves the pressure rise impressed on the boundary layer as the trailing edge is approached. This

Fig 67 Pressure distribution on wing with slat and flap near the stall.

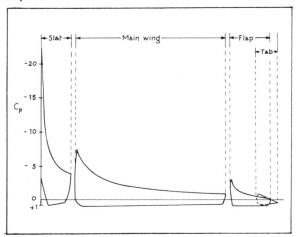

alleviates the risk of flow separation and explains why slats in particular can carry such high loads; the slat shown in Fig 67 is carrying 35% of the total lift.

"Fresh" boundary-layer effect
On each element of a properly designed multi-component wing system (e.g. slat, wing section, slotted flap) the boundary layers start out afresh. Thinner boundary layers can sustain greater pressure gradients than thicker ones. Flow separation is delayed by breaking the boundary layer into several thinner ones.

The slotted leading edge was originally proposed by Handley Page and Lachmann around 1920 and proved extremely beneficial in extending the lift curve, as shown in Fig 64. Designed to operate automatically, it consists of a slat quite free to move on tracks. At low AOA the slat is held flush against the leading edge. At high AOA the high local suctions on the slat create a forward chordwise force, pulling out the slat. The slot so formed allows the wing to continue lifting to a higher AOA, significantly increasing the maximum lift coefficient. A slight chord extension also occurs.

If the operating mechanism imparts a downward motion to the slat, the peak suctions on the slat are reduced for a given lift coefficient and there is a camber increase. Camber at the leading edge is however less effective than its equivalent at the trailing edge; on the other hand, there is only a small change in pitching moment. As will be seen later, the slotted slat's ability to suppress leading-edge and shock-induced separation has made it essential for air combat manoeuvring. The widespread use of the slotted slat on combat aircraft such as the F-14, Tornado, Jaguar, Su-17, Su-24 and F-111 bears testimony to its value. Indeed, the slatted leading edge on the F-111 is claimed to increase the maximum lift coefficient by over 1·2.

The slotted slat has one main disadvantage. Since a slot alone gives no change of camber, the higher maximum lift is obtained only at higher AOA, requiring the aircraft to fly at a high AOA during take-off and landing in order to avail itself of the potential increase in lift coefficient. This can affect forward visibility and may require excessive tail-end upsweep for ground clearance. However, when used as a drooping slat in conjunction with trailing-edge flaps, which increase lift at constant AOA, the slotted slat gives a significant improvement in airfield performance.

Trailing-edge flaps
Trailing-edge flaps increase the effective AOA of

the wing without requiring the aircraft to be pitched upwards. This is achieved primarily by the application of camber where it has the greatest effect, at the rear of the section, which moves the lift curve to the left, as in Fig 64. Lift at any given AOA is increased, and there is a simultaneous improvement in maximum lift coefficient and reduction in stalling AOA. These effects all increase with flap deflection.

The principal disadvantage of trailing-edge flaps is that they intensify the peak suction at the leading edge of the wing, which can restrict the effectiveness of leading-edge devices. On thicker aerofoil sections, characteristically prone to trailing-edge separation, the severe adverse pressure-gradients aft of the intense peak suction can cause leading-edge separation instead. This tendency can be controlled by use of leading-edge devices which either reduce the nose curvature or modify, via a slot, the parent section's suction peak. Thinner sections are prone to leading-edge separation anyway.

It should be noted that flap deflection affects the pressure distribution over the complete lifting surface, not just the flap. Indeed, the lift increase occurs primarily on the main aerofoil section.

Plain flap

This consists of a portion of the rear of the aerofoil which is hinged so that it can be deflected downwards (Fig 68). This causes an increased peak suction at the leading edge of the wing, together with a peak in the region of the hinge. The pressure gradient over the flap is greatly increased. Because the boundary layer, already in an exhausted condition, cannot negotiate this adverse gradient, the flow usually separates over plain flaps at moderate angles, generally 10°–15°. The point of separation remains behind the hinge line up to large flap angles, and the lift coefficient continues to increase although the maximum value is less than that for fully attached flow. Maximum lift is obtained prior to flow separation over the whole wing, which takes the form of the separation point moving upstream of the hinge, or leading-edge separation. As shown in Fig 68, the deflection of the flap also produces a large increase in profile drag. A simple two-position (0° and 30°) plain flap is used on the F-15. Plain flaps are also used on the MiG-25 and AV-8A Harrier.

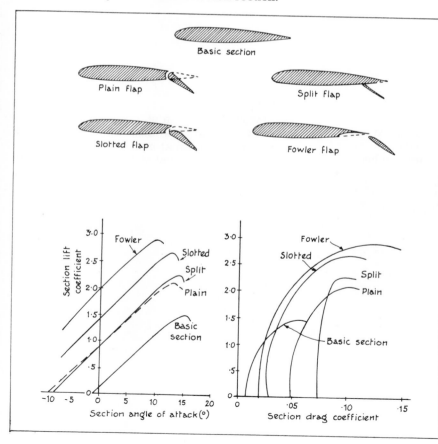

Fig 68 Flap configurations and (graphs) effect on section lift and drag characteristics of a 25%-chord flap of each type deflected 30°.

Split flap

This is formed by splitting the wing trailing edge in a roughly chordwise manner, as shown in Fig 68. The upper surface remains unchanged, thereby helping to keep the flow attached, while the deflected flap increases the pressure on the lower surface upstream of the flap. This pressure rise is due to the increased circulation caused by the increased camber, and leads to a slightly larger lift increment compared with the plain flap. But the most noticeable difference between the plain and split flaps is the large increase in profile drag generated by the latter, a result of the low pressure in the wake region downstream of the deflected flap. Split flaps were used on many of the early swept-wing fighters, including the A-4 Skyhawk and Hunter.

Slotted flap

The slotted flap was introduced to cure the premature separation suffered with the plain flap. As the flap is rotated downwards it also travels rearwards to produce a convergent slot. The pressure difference between the upper and lower surfaces causes air from the wing's lower surface to be injected through the slot to the upper. Thus a slot located towards the trailing edge behaves in much the same way as one at the leading edge: in particular, it reduces the peak suction on the flap and allows a new boundary layer to establish itself on the flap and remain attached for longer. This

allows greater flap deflections and camber to be used before separation occurs. The lift increment is greatly increased, as shown in Fig 68, while profile drag is much lower for comparable flap size and deflection. Not only does the slotted flap allow larger flap angles (up to 45°), but the slight chord extension needed to give the all-important convergent slot shape also gives an added lift bonus.

Typical applications for single-slotted trailing-edge flaps are the A-6, A-7, F-5, MiG-23, Mitsubishi F-1, F-14, Su-17, F-18 and AV-8B. More than one slot can be used with trailing-edge flaps when the demand for high lift is particularly pressing, as in the case of the Etendard, Mirage F.1, Hawk, Su-24, Jaguar and Tornado.

A comparison between the single-slotted arrangement of the F-14 and the double-slotted extendable flap of the F-111 carried out by Grumman[18] showed that the former system is much lighter than its more complex double-slotted counterpart. It also had the advantage of being more easily mechanised for use as a manoeuvre flap in transonic flight.

Used in conjunction with thrust reversal, the Panavia Tornado's full-span leading-edge slats and trailing-edge double-slotted flaps give exceptional landing performance and the ability to haul heavy weapon/fuel/ECM loads. (MBB)

Fowler flap

This is somewhat similar to the slotted flap, the main difference being that the flap moves much further aft along a set of tracks, which increases the chord and therefore wing area (Fig 68). It is thus characterised by large increased in maximum lift for minimum changes in drag. A long over-hanging shroud is required to achieve a good slot profile when the flap deflects downwards. Because of the large rearward motion required, the Fowler is a relatively complex and heavy system and has not found many applications in combat aircraft, examples being the Alpha Jet, Tu-22 and F-111 (double-slotted).

Fowler flaps were considered for the F-14 which needed, in addition to high transonic manoeuvrability, good low-speed performance for operation from aircraft carriers. The following comparison of two competing trailing-edge flap designs reveals the double-slotted Fowler's effectiveness in reducing the wind-over-deck speed needed for a carrier catapult launch.

	$C_{L_{max}}$	WOD speed
Requirement	2.52	13kt
Single-slotted (no chord extension)	2.64	11.5kt
Double-slotted Fowler (20% chord extension)	2.81	3kt

The very marked reduction in WOD speed achieved with the Fowler is due more to the chord-extension effect on lift across the AOA range, rather than to the lift increments generated by slotted devices without chord extension. Such increments are obtained mainly at high AOA, which is not attained during catapult launching.

Sizing of high-lift devices

The chordwise extent of any high-lift device is largely governed by the positions of the main structural elements of the wing, namely the front and rear spars which form the main wing box. High-lift devices can occupy only the area in front of and behind these stations, which are typically at 15 and 65% wing-root chord.

The spanwise arrangement of leading-edge devices is generally designed to produce low drag with moderately high lift coefficients inboard, and a high local maximum lift coefficient outboard to prevent tip stalling. On the F-14, for example, the chord of the leading-edge slats increases from 15% chord inboard to 22% outboard.

The spanwise extent of the trailing-edge devices is governed by the choice of roll-control surfaces. Until recently, ailerons were the preferred form of lateral control. Roll-control requirements sized the ailerons, and hence restricted the spanwise extent of the trailing-edge flaps. Then came the trend towards the replacement of ailerons by spoilers and differential tails (tailerons), freeing the complete trailing edge for use by high-lift devices, as on the F-111, Su-24, Jaguar, Tornado and F-14.

MANOEUVRABILITY

The requirements

Superior transonic manoeuvrability is a prime requisite for a modern fighter aircraft. The high turn rates necessary for combat result in flight at high angles of attack, which normally result in flow separations on the wing. These separations lead to increased drag, buffet, and stability and control problems which degrade combat ability. The recent development of high-thrust/weight-ratio aircraft capable of high sustained and instantaneous turn rates have expanded the flight envelope and given great impetus to the quest for good high-AOA transonic flight characteristics.

Methods of reducing drag, delaying buffeting and preventing flight control problems are important for a variety of reasons:

1 These problems reduce pilot control and weapon-aiming accuracy.

2 Full use of the manoeuvring potential of the aircraft is inhibited or prevented.

3 Inadvertent stalling and spinning is a possible consequence which not only impairs combat effectiveness but has caused the loss of hundreds of aircraft.

4 Increased drag reduces combat effectiveness.

Before considering the methods used to suppress or eliminate these problems it is necessary to consider the flow phenomena which give rise to them.

The flow over swept wings

It is difficult to generalise about the three-dimensional flows which occur on swept wings because nearly every case is a particular one. This is due to the high number of parameters which characterise a wing: aspect ratio, taper ratio, sweep angle, thickness, camber and twist distribution. Nevertheless, wings can be classified by one of the most important parameters, the mean sweep angle. Since most combat aircraft with swept wings have sweep angles of 30°–50°, the flow over such wings is of greatest relevance.

Swept-wing flow is of a highly complex three-dimensional nature, comprising an inextricable mixture of shock waves, vortex systems, strong spanwise flows, and boundary-layer separation and reattachment. The "typical" transonic flow pattern for moderately swept wings at moderate AOA is shown in Fig 69. It is characterised by a three-shock system, development of which is outlined below and detailed fully elsewhere.[19,20]

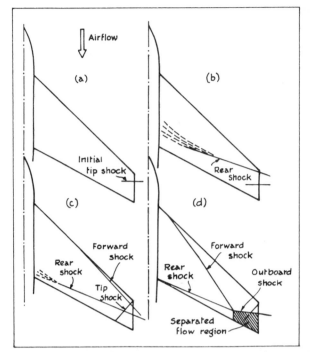

Fig 69 Flow development on a swept wing with increasing Mach number.[19]

Flow conditions near the tip of a swept wing give rise to the early formation of a comparatively weak shock wave called the initial tip shock (Fig 69a). This is overtaken by an aft-moving shock wave which rapidly develops to affect a large part of the wing span. This rear shock (Fig 69b), as it is called, forms as a result of the distorted pressure field which exists at the wing-root junction. The effect of section thickness is to turn the local flow inboard, an effect which near the wing root is constrained by the fuselage side and the need for flow symmetry at the centreline. The inward-turning flow is therefore straightened by a series of compression waves propagating outwards from the wing root which coalesce on the outer part of the wing to form the rear shock wave.

As AOA is increased at constant Mach number, high velocities occur locally near the leading edge. At subsonic speeds flow separation ultimately takes place, rolling up to form a part-span vortex. At higher Mach numbers this leading-edge separation is suppressed and a forward shock appears close to and almost parallel with the leading edge (Fig 69c). The formation of the forward shock depends on local conditions at the leading edge; for example, the blunter the leading edge the lower the AOA at which it will appear. Drooping the leading edge can also delay the forward shock's formation.

As Mach number increases, the forward shock moves inboard and rearwards and eventually intersects the rear shock (Fig 69d). Outboard of this intersection there then forms a strong shock wave called the outboard shock. The pressure rise through this shock wave is roughly the sum of the pressure rises through the other two shocks. Thus while neither the forward nor the rear shocks may separately provoke flow separation, the outboard shock invariably does. As the AOA is increased, the shock moves forward and inwards and the separation increases in severity and extent.

As AOA is increased another form of tip shock appears. This is not the critical tip shock but one which originates close to the tip leading edge and which places a limit on the inboard extent of the wing surface affected by the tip. Initially weak, the tip shock grows in strength with AOA and will provoke leading-edge separation at the tip. This spreads inboard until the entire leading-edge flow separates. The flow pattern on the wing is then dominated by a large part-span vortex and closely resembles that for the wing at subsonic speed and high AOA.

Ideally, as an aircraft is brought to its limiting AOA (or lift) condition it should still have a tendency (inherent or artificial) towards a reduction of the AOA in a pitch down. At all events, the aircraft should remain controllable. Although some deterioration in handling qualities is inevitable, it should be progressive rather than abrupt, and distinctive enough not to mask the fact that a limiting condition is being approached. In practice many aircraft have fallen far short of this ideal. Sources of trouble have been buffeting, lateral/directional instability, excessive drag, and pitch-up.

Buffeting

In the wake of the flow separations, be they leading-edge or shock-induced, come unsteady pressure fluctuations which act on the lightly damped flexible structure of the wing. This vibration, or buffet, is sensed by the pilot as an oscillating normal g load varying from the barely perceptible ($\approx \pm 0.05g$) to the intolerable for more than a few seconds ($\approx \pm 0.8g$).

Buffet is generally reckoned to have set in when $\pm 0.05g$ is detectable at the aircraft centre of gravity. Since buffet onset precedes limiting flight conditions such as pitch-up or stall, it can, provided it is not unduly severe, usefully serve as an indication of impending difficulties. Indeed, pilots have in the past relied upon a mild but increasing level of buffet to warn of approaching stall conditions. Air-

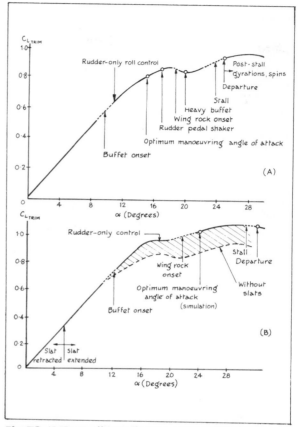

Fig 70 McDonnell Douglas F-4 trimmed lift curves without (A) and with (B) leading-edge slats.[21]

craft which had such a characteristic were well regarded while those which did not were considered tricky if not dangerous. Some modern aircraft such as the A-7 and F-4 have such a large AOA range between buffet onset and stall/departure that buffet build-up cannot be used as a stall/departure warning (Fig 70), making it necessary to give the pilot artificial stall warning.

The flight regimes in which buffet will be encountered are defined by buffet boundaries based on lift coefficient and Mach number. A typical flighter may cruise at well below the buffet-onset boundary but will frequently perform 5g manoeuvres which could take it deep into moderate or even heavy buffet (Fig 71). The moderate buffet limit is sometimes taken as the highest level at which guns can be successfully aimed. Heat-seeking missiles do not require the same tracking accuracy as guns and so can be employed up to the heavy buffet limit, at which the aircraft becomes useless as a weapon platform but is still controllable. Because of the urgency of the pilot's

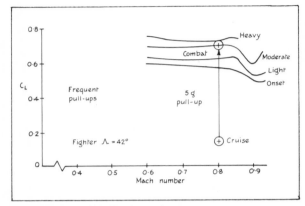

Fig 71 Typical buffet boundaries.

situation, defensive manoeuvres may well be executed at AOAs and buffet levels closer to the stall/departure boundary than are those of the assailant. Even so, it is not unusual for attacks to be pursued well into the heavy buffet region.

Lateral/directional instability

Some of the handling deficiencies which result from high-AOA stability and control degradations are referred to in Fig 70. Other deficiencies encountered are wing drop, pitch-up and nose slice.

Wing rock

This is sensed by the pilot as a rolling motion. It can be subdivided into pure wing rock, roll/yaw wing rock, and plain Dutch roll. Generally speaking, the hard-edged pure wing rock occurs only at high Mach numbers, making precise tracking impossible. Roll/yaw wing rock has a significant yawing content, with roll rates up to 50°/sec and bank angles of 90°. In comparison with the other two motions, pilots seem to tolerate Dutch roll well, and though gun tracking is impaired, missiles can function satisfactorily under these conditions.

Wing drop

This is an uncommanded motion seen by the pilot as a divergence in roll and an incipient departure from controlled flight. Typical roll rates of 10°–20°/sec put the motion beyond aiming limits. Immediate recovery action is required.

Nose slice

This is an uncommanded motion seen by the pilot as a divergence in yaw; it is also an incipient departure. There is no question of gun aiming after its onset, and on the F-4 and A-7 nose slice is followed so rapidly by departure into a spin that the pilot has no time for corrective action.

These characteristics afflicted aircraft designed

The Chance Vought (LTV) F8U-3 Crusader III flew off against the F4H-1 Phantom for major US Navy orders, in the late 1950s. Like its Crusader II forebear, it had a very thin two-position wing, plus flap blowing. Unusual aspects of the F8U-3 were the forward-swept intake and large ventral fins, which folded from horizontal at low speed to near-vertical at Mach 2-plus.

in the late 1950s for service in the 1960s, 1970s and, in some cases, the 1980s. Many of the problems have been shown to be associated with loss of lift on the outboard wing panels, resulting in a loss of effective dihedral.

Improving the high-AOA characteristics of the basic wing

Wing characteristics have been improved in the following ways:

1 Manoeuvre flaps located at wing leading and trailing edges.

2 "Variable camber" devices which articulate the surface of the wing to form a smooth surface.

3 The utilisation of vortex flows by means of leading-edge root extensions.

Manoeuvre flaps and slats

Following the introduction of very thin wings for supersonic flight it was found on aircraft such as the A3J and F8U-3 that subsonic cruise performance could be improved by partially deflecting the leading-edge devices designed for use in landing. Since then efforts have been made to improve air combat manoeuvring by means of leading and trailing-edge devices, and now it is standard practice to design the high-lift devices for use in combat.

Some of the earliest work on manoeuvre flaps was carried out in 1968, when the effects of deploying the high-lift devices of an F-105D at high subsonic speeds were studied. As shown in Fig 72, use of high-lift devices reduces the AOA for a given lift coefficient and flattens the spanwise load distribution to postpone flow separation on the outer wing, resulting in a significant delay in buffet onset. Furthermore, the leading-edge suction is maintained, delaying the drag break and generating worthwhile drag reductions.

In the late 1960s the US Navy launched a major effort to improve the combat effectiveness at high

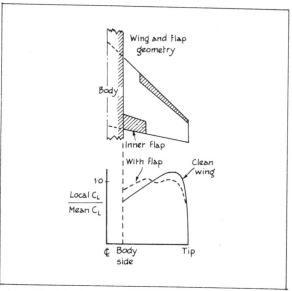

Fig 72 Combat flap redistributes the lift towards the wing root.[22]

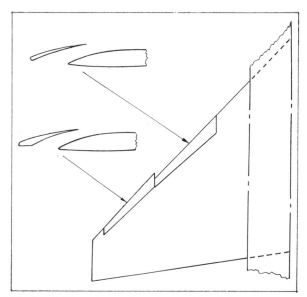

Fig 73 F-4E manoeuvring slat configuration.

Fig 74 Effect of manoeuvring slats on YF-4E lateral/directional characteristics. The broken line indicates the performance of the YF-4E, the solid line that of the standard unslatted aircraft.[23]

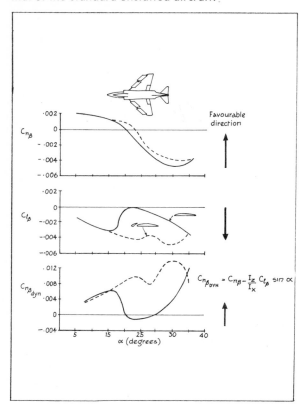

AOA of the F-4, A-7 and EA-6B. The F-4 work is especially pertinent since it had as its three main aims an improvement to the lift capability at high AOA, reduction of buffet levels below the stall, and improvements to lateral/directional stability, so reducing wing rock.

It was found the lateral/directional instabilities affecting the F-4 at high AOA resulted from adverse sidewash created by the wing/fuselage combination, and that directional stability and dihedral effect could be improved by drooping the leading-edge flaps. McDonnell Douglas developed a very promising leading-edge slat system for the mid and outboard wing sections and tested it on the YF-4E development aircraft (Fig 73). Its promise was indeed fulfilled, as shown in Fig 74. The parameter $C_{n_{\beta_{dyn}}}$ is a function of the directional stability and dihedral effect together with inertial characteristics, and experience has shown it to be a good indicator of directional divergence (i.e. nose slice) at high AOA. The results obtained for the slatted-wing YF-4E indicates that whereas the basic F-4E diverges at 21° AOA, addition of slats effectively eliminates nose-slice tendencies. Further improvements were obtained when trailing-edge flap deflections were used.

Graphic evidence of the handling improvements obtained with the slatted wing is shown in Fig 70. The increased lift capability at high AOA is apparent enough, but most noteworthy is the fact that the angles of attack for buffet onset, rudder-only roll control, wing-rock onset, optimum manoeuvring, stall and departure are all substantially increased over those of the basic F-4. Wing-rock onset became much less abrupt and the YF-4E was consistently test-flown to AOAs greater than 30° with only mild wing rock and no stall tendencies.

The results of this very successful programme were incorporated into the F-4J, which, like its YF-4E precursor, has turning performance superior to that of the standard unslatted F-4E (Fig 74).

In the early 1970s all fighter aircraft design terms were under the same pressure to improve high-AOA handling qualities, which experience in the Vietnam War had shown to be inadequate. As an indication of the extent of the problem, the number of US military aircraft lost in accidents linked to high-AOA flight in the period 1966–70 was 225[24]. Thus it was that the use of leading and trailing-edge devices to enhance high-AOA performance and handling was expanded rapidly in the 1970s.

The Northrop F-5, with its excellent record for high-AOA handling, was one of the first types to incorporate a manoeuvre flap system, the essence of which (for the F-5E) is shown in Fig 75. This has

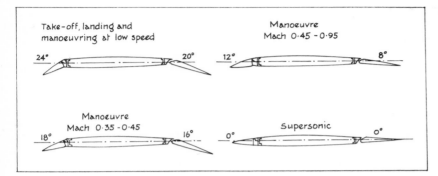

Fig 75 Northrop F-5E wing flaps.

Fig 77 F-18 trimmed drag-due-to-lift. The curve indicated by circles is for leading and trailing-edge flap angles of 0° and 0° respectively; triangles are for 5°/8°; and squares for 10°/12°.[25]

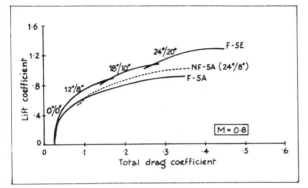

Fig 76 Lift and drag benefits at various flap settings. The angles given are for leading and trailing-edge flaps respectively.[6]

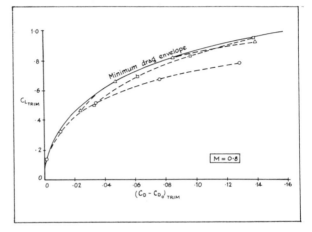

developed via the introduction of a leading-edge flap on the F-5A/B to increase maximum lift, through the single-setting manoeuvre flap on the NF-5, to the advanced arrangements on the F-20 and another Northrop-designed type, the F-18.

The ability to vary the flap deflection can be used to improve the drag polar, as shown in Fig 76. For example, at a representative drag coefficient of 0·2 a 17% increase in lift can be obtained at Mach 0·8. As Mach number increases so this benefit declines — as it does with other manoeuvre flap systems — so that at Mach 0·9 the lift increase is down to 10%. The F-18 and F-20 both incorporate a flap system fully automated through the air data computer so that the flaps deploy automatically to the degree demanded by the prevailing AOA and Mach number. This produces a smooth minimum-drag envelope (Fig 77), resulting in improved manoeuvrability. The typical leading-edge flap deflection is about half that used for landing.

Programmed flap deflection has become the norm for contemporary fighters (e.g. F-16, Mirage 2000). As shown in Fig 78, it allows the effective lift slope of the wing to be increased in a prescribed manner. The reverse is also true, so that for flight conditions in which a reduction in lift slope is

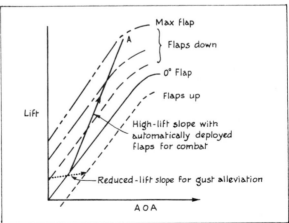

Fig 78 Automatic flaps can be programmed to suit flight mode.

desired — e.g. for gust alleviation — the flaps can be deflected upwards, effectively reducing the basic aerofoil section's camber. This is also used on the F-16 to eliminate the drag due to excessive camber at supersonic speeds, the leading and trailing-edge flaps being programmed to deflect 2° upwards.

The idea of using the F-14's leading-edge slats for high-speed manoeuvring arose from a study of the Dassault Mirage G variable-sweep prototype. Grumman found that partially extended slats worked well on a wind-tunnel model and went on to develop a fully automatic system for the F-14. The air data computer is programmed to co-ordinate manoeuvre-flap actuation with wing sweep to obtain the maximum delay in buffet onset consistent with acceptable wing root bending moments.

All of the aircraft discussed above were developed before the advantages of manoeuvre flap/slat systems became apparent, and thus have

been retrofitted to varying degrees. Future fighters will have them built in from the start, one example of this being BAe's Experimental Aircraft Programme (EAP). The value of leading-edge manoeuvre slats to a canard configuration of this type is shown in Fig 79. With the aircraft model at 10° of sideslip, the leading-edge vortex on the highly swept wing is reinforced on the leeward side by the tip vortex from the foreplane. On the into-wind wing this interaction does not occur, resulting in a strong rolling moment. Fig 79 shows that without an outboard slat the configuration is departure-prone beyond 26° AOA, a situation that is greatly improved by the use of outboard slats.

Smooth-surface variable-camber wings

This is a logical development of the variable-camber devices discussed earlier. A typical design is that shown in Fig 80, in which both the leading and trailing edges articulate to give a smoothly changing wing contour. The necessary degree of deformation has been made possible by advances in materials technology and innovative mechanical design of the linkages which, contained entirely within the wing contour, control the surface shape. Developments of this concept include the Mission-Adaptive Wing sponsored by NASA and the USAF and RAE Farnborough's Variable-Aerofoil Mechanism. If worthwhile gains can be achieved, this approach looks likely to replace conventional slat and flap devices.

Vortex lift

Throughout the development of aerodynamics one of the major wing design considerations has been the avoidance of flow separations. In an effort to oppose adverse compressibility effects, wing-sweep angles have been increased and thickness ratios reduced. These changes have however conspired to make the maintenance of attached flow more difficult, resulting in many performance, stability and control problems and stimulating the development of a range of devices, discussed

Fig 79 Effect of wing slats on lateral/direcional stability of a canard configuration.[26]

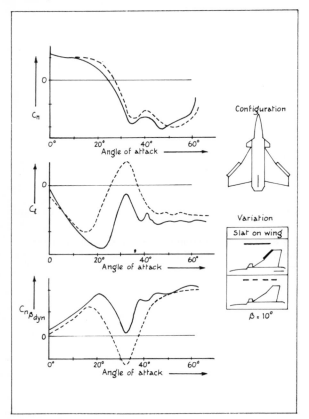

Fig 80 Variable-camber aerofoil section. The angles δLE and δTE refer to the leading and trailing edges respectively. Figures on upper surface represent proportions of chord.

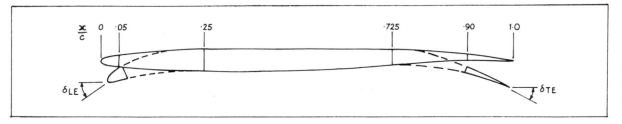

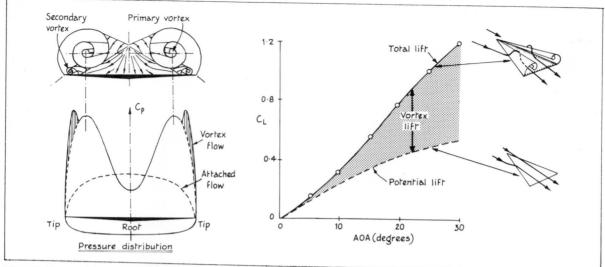

Fig 81 Vortex lift on a slender-delta wing.

above, designed to cope with widely disparate flow conditions.

The time-honoured reverence for attached flow was called into question by one aspect of the design of the supersonic Concorde, and this has left its mark on fighter design since the 1960s. Studies of a supersonic transport carried out at RAE Farnborough in the 1950s were based on a slender delta wing designed to minimise wave drag. Acceptable low-speed performance was to be achieved by making the leading edge so sharp as to actually provoke separation along its entire length. This, it was discovered, could produce a highly stable spiral vortex system which would stream back over the wing and enhance the lift at low speeds. As shown in Fig 81, these twin vortices would produce extra suction over the top of the wing, giving rise to "vortex lift" in addition to that achieved with fully attached flow. If the vortex system could be kept stable over a wide range of attitudes and Mach numbers, there would be no need for high-lift devices. That this was achieved on Concorde by means of "controlled separation" is beyond dispute. But the ability of this novel approach to wing design to improve the high-AOA capabilities of combat aircraft was not immediately appreciated.

Then, in the mid-1960s, Northrop began work on improving the manoeuvrability of its F-5. The company had been the leading exponent of the art of combining moderate sweep and low taper to achieve good flow characteristics and spin resistance, as typified by the T-38 supersonic trainer. When the F-5A appeared in 1963 it differed from the T-38 in having a very small leading-edge exten-

sion (LEX), intended basically to alter the cross-sectional distribution and so reduce wave drag for maximum transonic acceleration. The Northrop designers were aware of the vortices that the LEX would produce and the induced-drag penalty that would result. However, not only was the wave drag reduced, but a 10% increase in usable lift appeared at high AOA (see Fig 82), which markedly improved turning performance. The size of the LEX on the F-5E was increased to 4·4% of the basic wing area when the intakes were extended forward. This further improved the area ruling (see *The Area Rule*, page 53) and, more important

Fig 82 Performance improvements resulting from the application of LEX to the Northrop F-5. Conditions are: Mach 0.3, no leading or trailing-edge flap selected, and centre of gravity at 0.12 of geometric mean chord. S = planform area.[6]

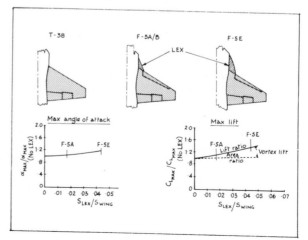

still, increased the maximum lift by 38%. Further development of the F-5E has led to the F-20, which, with increased LEX area and higher thrust/weight, has a 25%-higher sustained turn rate. Both aircraft have instantaneous turn rates comparable with that of the F-15, which achieves 14°/sec at Mach 0.9 at 4,500m, mainly by virtue of its much lower wing loading.

Impressive though the above figures are, the greatest advance in the application of vortex lift to combat aircraft came in 1966, when Northrop began work on the F-5 derivative which became the YF-17 and, ultimately, the F-18. As shown in Fig 83, the basic YF-17 wing planform already displayed the virtues of the classic moderately swept wing (i.e. low induced drag, good stability characteristics, and high spin-resistance). Its combination with a much larger LEX turned it into a truly hybrid wing, with the LEX generating a very strong vortex field not only on itself but also on the parent wing. The maximum lift capability of the hybrid wing is shown in Fig 84, which reveals a 50% increase in lift at subsonic speed for just 10% more wing area.

Fig 83 Hybrid wing planform.

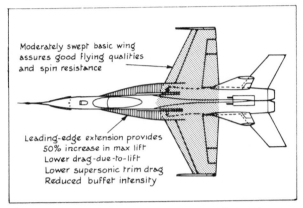

Developed by McDonnell Douglas and Northrop from the latter's YF-17 Light Weight Fighter, the F-18 has a high degree of twist built into its carbon-fibre-skinned wing. Note the unusual location of the twin vertical fins between wing and tailplane, and the excellent cockpit visibility. (McDonnell Douglas)

Fig 84 Effect of hybrid wing and variable camber on maximum lift.[27]

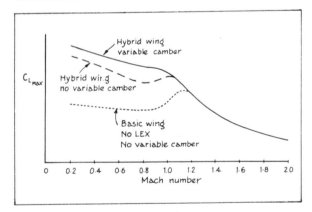

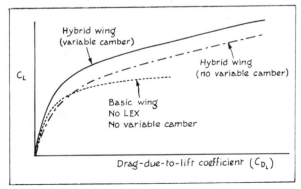

Fig 85 Effect of hybrid wing and variable camber on drag-due-to-lift at Mach 0.8.[27]

On the debit side, the separated nature of vortex flow results in a loss of leading-edge thrust, leading to increased drag at low AOA. As shown in Fig 85, however, this can be rectified by the use of manoeuvre flaps. The combination of LEX and manoeuvre devices produces very large drag reductions at typical manoeuvring AOA, giving an improvement of as much as 25% in sustained turn rate. In addition, aileron effectiveness is maintained up to much higher AOA, as shown in Fig 86.

Other advantages of LEX include reduced AOA at the under-strake air intakes (see Chapter 2) and reduced transonic aerodynamic centre shift, giving lower supersonic trim drag at high g. In its test programme the YF-17 demonstrated a far wider range of flying attitudes than had ever before been attained by a comparable aircraft: designed to remain fully controllable up to 45° AOA, it was in fact flown to 63° without showing any sign of departure tendencies. It also achieved a manoeuvre combining sideslip and AOA of 36° and 40° respectively.

General Dynamics — Northrop's main competitor in the Light Weight Fighter programme,

which gave rise to the YF-17 — initially took a more conventional approach to the problem of obtaining high lift. The original designs relied on the established virtues of a 45°-swept wing with a relatively blunt leading edge, intended to maintain attached flow and retain leading-edge suction for lower

Fig 86 Effect of hybrid wing on lateral control effectiveness at Mach 0.2.[27]

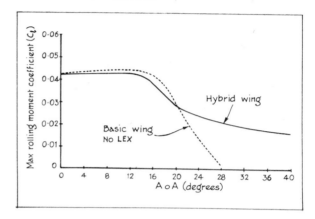

General Dynamics F-16 at high AOA, with leading
and trailing-edge flaps deflected. Vortices are
streaming back from its highly swept strake, which
at Mach 1·2 effectively reduces wing loading by 30%.
Note also the degree of wing/body blending and the
shelves aft of the wing.

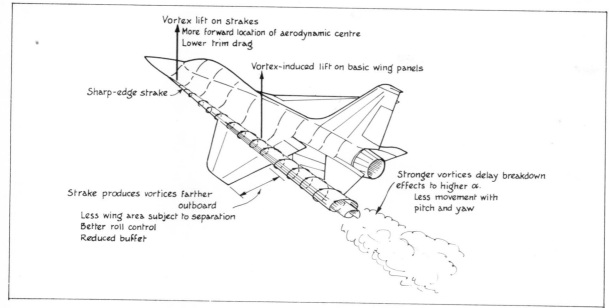

Vortex lift on strakes
More forward location of aerodynamic centre
Lower trim drag

Vortex-induced lift on basic wing panels

Sharp-edge strake

Stronger vortices delay breakdown effects to higher α.
Less movement with pitch and yaw

Strake produces vortices farther outboard
Less wing area subject to separation
Better roll control
Reduced buffet

Fig 87 Controlled vortex lift generated by forebody strakes on the General Dynamics F-16.[28]

drag. But previous work for the FX (F-15) competition had shown the high-lift value of a wide forebody, and this was incorporated. Twin vertical fins were used to maintain directional stability at high AOA. In spite of this, early wind-tunnel testing showed the design to suffer from poor directional stability, as well as high induced drag. The problem was traced to a combination of unforeseen wing flow separations and the forebody flow separation streaming back over the fins and reducing their effectiveness as stabilisers (see Chapter 5).

At this point NASA aerodynamicists suggested that the lift of the wide forebody could be increased by sharpening its leading edge. This would strengthen the forebody vortices rather than weaken them, as General Dynamics had attempted to do. The reasoning behind this was that since forebody flow separation was inevitable at very high AOA anyway, the lift advantages offered by the sharp leading edge's ability to control the separation should be exploited. This would also allow the forebody vortices to dominate and hopefully stabilise the flow field over the entire aircraft, even the outboard wing panels, at high AOA. The benefits to the F-16 of what General Dynamics describes as forebody strakes are shown in Fig 87.

A wide range of combinations of strake planform, size and location, forebody shape, and leading-edge flap deflection were tested to determine the best configuration. In particular, it was found that the use of large leading edge flap deflection was very beneficial at high AOA (Fig 88) and also improved lateral and directional stability.

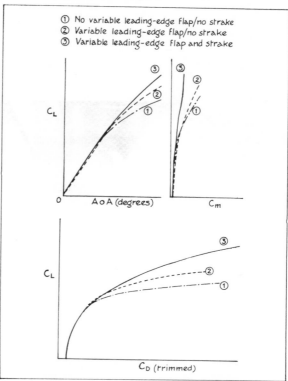

① No variable leading-edge flap/no strake
② Variable leading-edge flap/no strake
③ Variable leading-edge flap and strake

Fig 88 Aerodynamic improvements produced by leading-edge flap and forebody strake on General Dynamics F-16. C_m is coefficient of pitching moment around quarter-chord.[29]

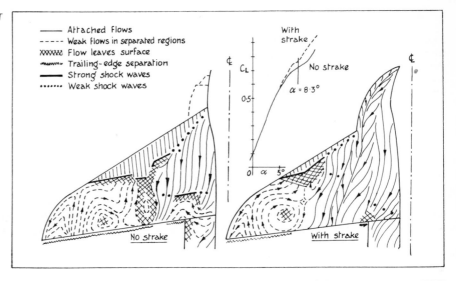

Fig 89 Effect of strakes on wing performance at high speeds. Speed is Mach 0.9 and AOA 8.3°.[30]

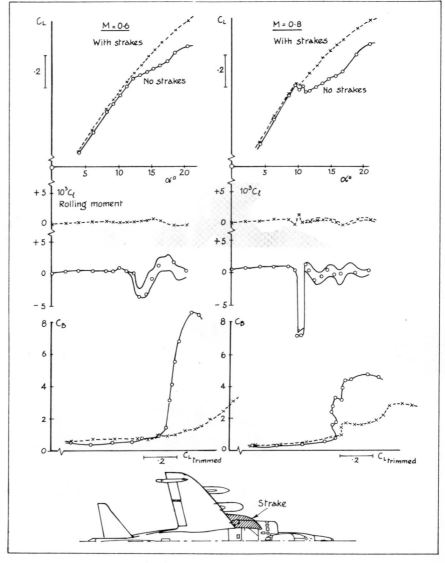

Fig 90 Effect of strakes (LERX) on Harrier wing buffeting and unsteady rolling. C_B = root mean square of wing-root bending moment.[30]

Another virtue of the strakes is the fact that though their use does not always delay the onset of buffet, the progression to higher intensities is slowed down, particularly when strakes are combined with programmed leading-edge flap.

The development of the vortex-flow generators on the YF-16 and YF-17 created worldwide interest. For example, a good deal of effort has gone into increasing the BAe Harrier's maximum usable lift at high speed. Fig 89 shows just how complex is the flow field of such a wing under these conditions, with unsteady separated flows having deeply imbedded shock waves. The influence of a leading-edge root extension (LERX), the British Aerospace term for a strake, is evident. Without the strake, 70% of the wing leading edge has attached high-suction flow. Further aft, however, weak shock waves are found inboard, with strong shocks outboard intersecting the leading edge. These strong shocks cause the flow to separate locally, and at mid-span there is flow separation fully to the trailing edge. The strake reduces the area subject to high suction ahead of the strong shocks, causing a loss of lift which is more than offset by the increase in wing area inboard over which the flow is attached. A further gain in lift arises from intensified suctions on the area lying

under the path of the vortex leaving the strake. In addition there is a marked weakening of the aft inboard shock. Though the wingtip region is largely unaffected, the extent of the trailing edge subject to flow separation has been reduced. This could allow the use of manoeuvre flaps inboard to further increase lift.

Some results of wind-tunnel tests carried out on a Harrier model are shown in Fig 90. Major improvements in lift and buffet response are evident at high AOAs. More significant however is the vastly improved rolling-moment curves, which for the unstraked wing are indicative of the wing rock from which the configuration was found to suffer at high AOA. Although the large strake shown was found when flight-tested to give unsatisfactory pitch characteristics, a smaller version has been incorporated into the wing of the AV-8B Harrier II.

Vortex bursting

One of the factors which can limit the amount of performance improvement from a wing-plus-strake combination is known as "vortex bursting". This is a fundamental fluid mechanics phenomenon in which at some point downstream from its origin the vortex loses stability and "bursts" into a completely unstable flow with no aerodynamic value.

Vortex bursting can occur symmetrically or asymmetrically. In the symmetric case the vortex burst point moves forward with increasing AOA and can adversely effect the tailplane flow, giving

BAe's active control technology (ACT) development work centres on a Jaguar fitted with a quadruplex digital fly-by-wire control system and massive leading-edge root extensions (LERX). (BAe)

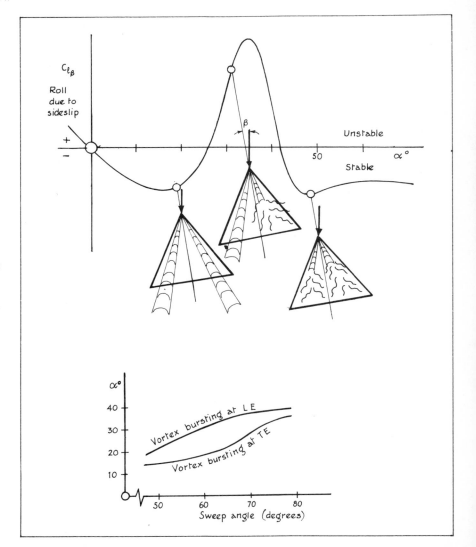

Fig 91 Roll stability versus angle of attack for a pure-delta wing.[31]

rise to an unstable (i.e. nose-up) pitching moment. Asymmetric vortex bursting occurs in a sideslip and is caused by the resulting effective increase in sweep angle of the leeward strake/wing combination and the corresponding reduction of the windward sweep angle, as shown in Fig 91. This can lead to lateral instability, and when the vortex breakdown is in close proximity to the vertical tail an abrupt loss of directional stability can also be experienced. Thus while it is relatively simple to achieve high manoeuvring lift with strakes, if the increased lift is to be usable the strake/wing/empennage combination must be tailored to increase moderate-to-high-AOA lateral/directional stability. One method which has proved effective in reducing lateral instability is the use of large leading-edge flap deflections.

The loss of leading-edge suction resulting from separation on the strake was the major disadvantage of the first applications of vortex lift. Northrop attempted to minimise this by building in a high degree of camber on the YF-17's LEX, which was further developed for the F-18. This effectively delays the formation of the vigorous vortex to lift coefficients beyond those developed in the cruise or supersonic manoeuvre, and so maintains a small amount of leading-edge suction, according to Northrop. The future use of strakes, particularly for supersonic manoeuvring, is expected to take this further. Camber will be variable, by means of a flapped strake or vortex flaps, since too much fixed camber can cause flow separation on the underside of the strake at low AOA.

LATERAL CONTROL

Rolling motion of an aircraft

Lateral (i.e. roll) control of aircraft has traditionally been achieved by means of differential lift on the wings. This is generally produced by some form of aileron or spoiler, though since the 1960s tailplanes which operate differentially as well as symmetrically have been used to generate rolling moments. However it is created, the rolling moment is used to accelerate the aircraft into rolling motion or to control the aircraft in a sideslip by opposing the dihedral effect.

When an aircraft is rolling the wingtips move in a helical path. For example, when an aircraft rolls to the right, the right wingtip has a downward velocity component and the left wingtip an upward component. The resulting angle between the flightpath vector and the resultant path of the tip is known as the helix angle of roll. If the roll velocity is p radians/sec and b is the wing span, then the wing has a tip velocity of p × $\frac{b}{2}$. The helix angle is formed by the ratio tip velocity ÷ flight velocity $\left(\text{i.e. } \frac{Pb}{2V}. \right)$

The roll rate due to the rolling moment increases until an equal and opposite moment is created by the resistance to rolling, or "damping in roll". In the case above this resistance develops as follows. The downgoing right wing experiences an increase in angle of attack, whereas the upgoing left wing has a reduced AOA. For flight below the stalling angle, the downgoing wing therefore experiences an increase in lift while the upgoing wing has a lift reduction. The resulting rolling moment opposes the rolling motion, and a steady-state rolling motion occurs when the damping moment equals the control-induced moment. The response of the aircraft to the control deflection can be seen in Fig 92.

The effect described above can be complicated by a sideslipping motion, which may arise because the wings are no longer level and cannot support the aircraft's weight. The motion will then be modified by the aircraft's dihedral effect (roll due to sideslip) and directional stability (yaw due to sideslip). When rolling most aircraft will, for various reasons, develop adverse yaw, which tends to turn the aircraft away from the rolling direction. This can produce sideslip, despite resistance by the aircraft's directional stability, which creates a rolling moment opposing the desired roll. The effect on roll rate is shown in Fig 92, which indicates that high directional stability and low dihedral effect is the preferred combination.

Rolling performance requirements

The rolling performance required of an aircraft is often specified in terms of $\frac{Pb}{2V}$, though in certain conditions of flight it may be more appropriate to specify the minimum acceptable roll rate. It is argued that a maximum roll rate of 150°–180°/sec is generally acceptable, though this does depend on the aircraft's role.[32] Too low a rate of roll can mean an inadequate ability to track evading targets and to avoid debris and collisions. Too high a roll rate

Fig 92 Aircraft response to roll-control deflection.

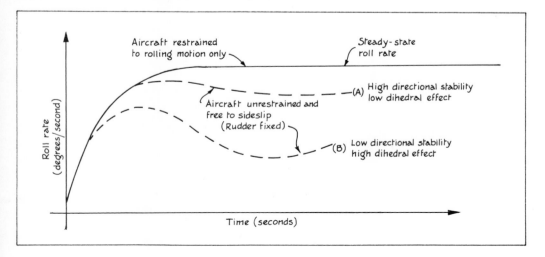

can lead to inertia coupling problems, which in any case place a limit on the number of consecutive rolls an aircraft is allowed to perform.

Low-speed requirements

High speeds are necessary for high roll rates (neglecting for the moment the effects of compressibility and aeroelastic distortion), and the low rates obtaining at low speeds can lead to handling problems. Take an aircraft with high effective dihedral (high wing, large sweepback) and low weight, and hence low approach speed, landing in a strong crosswind. This combination of factors gives large sideslip angles which could severely tax the ability of the pilot to keep the wings level at touchdown. It is thus usual to specify minimum roll rates for the approach, a typical requirement being 30°/sec.

Adequate control at high AOA is important but difficult to achieve with conventional devices. They all suffer a loss of effectiveness at the stall which can be quite sudden as a result of the close proximity of the control surface to the source of flow separation. In addition, the adverse yawing moment produced by aileron deflection can have a profound effect even when the actual rolling moment produced is quite small. In fact the rolling moment due to sideslip resulting from the adverse yaw can overpower the rolling moment commanded by the aileron. This is known as roll reversal. The yawing moments themselves can provoke departure tendencies. Both of these effects have led to restrictions being placed on the use of ailerons at high AOA on certain aircraft.

Roll control at high speed

Rolling ability is influenced by two basic effects arising from high-speed flying. One is due to air compressibility, the other to aeroelastic deformation of the wing structure.

Compressibility

In transonic flight a conventional trailing-edge surface loses effectiveness for several reasons. With a region of supersonic flow existing ahead of the control surface, its sphere of influence is limited to the surface aft of the shock wave which terminates the supersonic flow. A shock wave strong enough to cause flow separation will inevitably place the control surface in a flow field over which it can exert little if any influence. These two conditions may cause an almost complete loss of control effectiveness over a narrow speed range, as shown in Fig 93. One way of overcoming this, providing the control surface hinge line is not excessively swept, is to make the trailing-edge

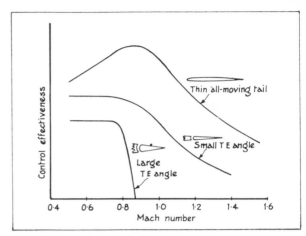

Fig 93 Loss of control effectiveness due to compressibility.

angle very small, either by reducing the thickness of the surface or by making the trailing edge blunt.

Aeroelastic distortion

The deflection of an aileron mounted, as they conventionally are, along the outboard wing trailing edge inevitably causes twisting of the wing. At low speeds and hence low dynamic pressures the aerodynamic loads cause relatively insignificant twisting. But at high dynamic pressures the downward deflection of an aileron can cause the leading edge of the wing to be twisted downwards so much that the anticipated effect of the aileron is negated (i.e. the aileron deflects the wing rather than the airflow). Such aeroelastic distortion may be so severe that the rolling moment is in the opposite direction to that desired. This is the phenomenon called aileron reversal, and all aircraft should be designed so that the aileron-reversal speed is beyond the maximum speed attainable (Fig 94).

The B-47 suffered from too low an aileron reversal speed. This high-subsonic strategic bomber, with thin, high-aspect-ratio swept wings, was designed in 1945, when practically nothing was known about building such wings. Two things were certain, however. First, the wing would be very flexible; indeed, it turned out to have a tip deflection of 10m between maximum positive and negative loads. Second, this flexibility would have a serious impact on stability and control. Lacking digital computers, the designers used a simplified method to calculate the wing twist in response to aileron deflection and so establish the degree of stiffness needed to keep the aileron-reversal speed above the design limit speed. Unfortunately, the

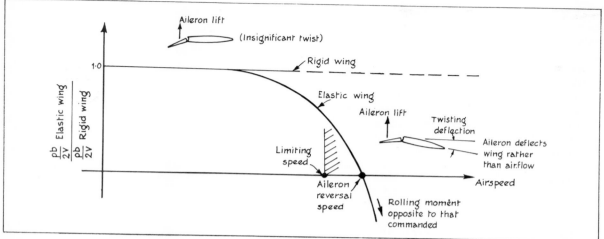

method did not allow for the fact that when the aileron deflected the wings also bent. When bent, swept wings twist, and this was added to the known degree of twist. As a result the wing was insufficiently stiff in torsion, giving too low an aileron-reversal speed. This placed a limit on the maximum speed at low altitudes, since above the reversal speed the aircraft would roll in the opposite direction to that intended. This effect can be countered

Fig 94 How aeroelastic distortion can cause aileron reversal.

Fig 95 Variation of control effectiveness with sweep, Mach number and AOA for three different types of roll control.[32]

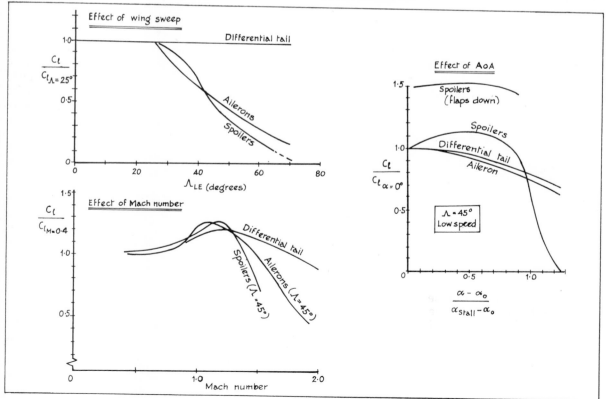

with spoilers or by moving the ailerons inboard, as in the case of the F-100. Though this aircraft had a relatively short-span, highly tapered wing, very large two-piece ailerons were fitted to the trailing edge, leaving so little span for flaps that none were fitted on the earliest models.

More than 30 years after the design of the overflexible wings of the B-47, problems with aeroelastic distortion still arise despite an enormous increase in understanding and the powerful analytic tools available. The F-18, for example, was found to suffer from a marked loss of roll rate in transonic flight, in spite of having a differential tailplane and inset ailerons. The cause of the shortfall was aeroelastic distortion of the wing, ultimately remedied by rewriting the control system computer's software to phase in both the trailing and leading-edge flaps differentially to give extra roll-control muscle.

Ailerons

The traditional roll-control device, the aileron is well understood in most operating regimes. It has linear characteristics and produces small yawing effects at low AOA. Its main disadvantage is its

ineffectiveness on a highly swept wing at high AOA, when the wing's rolling moment due to sideslip can be excessive (Fig 95). With the tip region of such a wing already prone to separation, downward deflection of an aileron, which increases the local camber over the rear part of the wing, will worsen the already adverse pressure gradient, provoking separation. When flow separation is already taking place, aileron deflection will aggravate it. Placing the ailerons inboard can delay the onset of this problem.

The adverse yaw produced by ailerons at high AOA, when the aircraft's directional stability is low, can produce nose slice (Fig 96). If lateral control is applied to keep the wings level, adverse yaw can overwhelm the low directional stability and provoke divergence. Differential ailerons, with the upgoing aileron deflecting more than the downgoing, are a common way of reducing the adverse yaw. The designers of recent combat aircraft have exploited the fact that rudder displacement causes a rolling moment, directly through the sideforce created on a high fin and indirectly through the

Fig 96 Variation of yawing moment due to roll control with sweep, Mach number and AOA for three different types of roll control.[32]

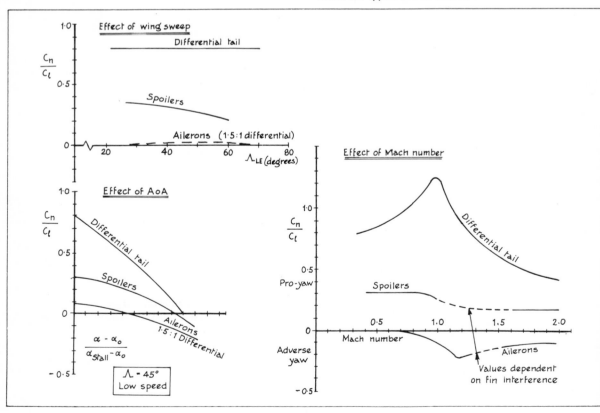

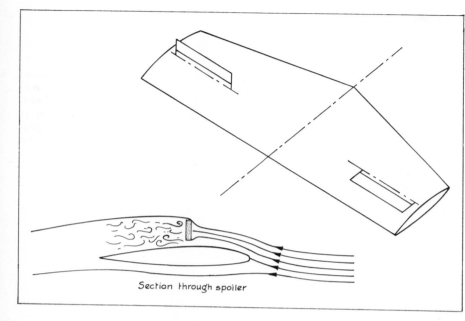

Fig 97 The use of spoilers for roll control.

Section through spoiler

dihedral effect. On the F-4, for example, the rudders are the only form of roll control allowed above 12° AOA, and on the A-7 the roll augmentation system is turned off at 18·5° AOA to preclude pro-spin aileron inputs, again leaving the rudder as the sole roll control. A further development of this trend has been aileron-rudder interconnect (ARI), used on the F-15, F-16 and F-18. This gradually phases out the ailerons in favour of rudder as AOA is increased.

Another increasingly important drawback to ailerons is their occupation of part of the trailing edge which could otherwise be used for flaps. This has been overcome to some extent by making it possible to droop the ailerons so that they become "flaperons". On the F-16, for example, the ailerons are given a 20° downward bias when the landing gear is lowered, thereafter operating up and down about this new datum position. This can however aggravate the adverse yaw due to ailerons, and was a problem on the Buccaneer as a result of its limited rudder control during landing.

Spoilers

A spoiler is a surface usually mounted flush with the upper surface of the wing which when deflected upwards on one wing causes the flow to separate and "spoil" the streamline flow (Fig 97). By dumping lift it also increases profile drag, introducing a beneficial proverse yawing moment (i.e. one in concert with the roll). This contrasts with the adverse yawing moment associated with ailerons.

One of the first combat aircraft to be equipped

with spoilers was the F-105, which had a four-segment system for use at high speed and conventional ailerons for low speeds. They were mounted inboard, leading to a reduction in the aeroelastic distortion of the wing at high speed. The F-4 also has a spoiler/aileron system, with the spoilers mounted directly in front of the ailerons. This is acceptable since on a given wing only one control surface operates at a time: either a spoiler goes up (45° maximum deflection) or an aileron goes down (30° maximum deflection).

Because spoilers are not mounted along the trailing edge of the wing, full-span flaps can be used. This is particularly valuable on low-aspect-ratio wings, on which flap span is scarce. On the Jaguar, for example, spoilers are the primary roll control, backed up by a differential tail. The benefits to airfield performance are particularly significant for swing-wing aircraft, all of which use spoilers for roll control at low and intermediate sweep angles. This is where spoiler effectiveness is greatest, as shown in Fig 95. There is also a bonus in the flaps-down case which is very useful for crosswind landings.

Used asymmetrically for roll control, spoilers can also be used symmetrically as lift dumpers on the ground to cut the landing distance. On the F-14, for example, the four-segment spoilers deflect 50° when a switch on the undercarriage senses weight-on-wheels. The F-14's spoilers are put to further use as direct lift control (DLC) devices during the landing approach. If this mode is selected by the pilot, the spoilers deflect symmetrically 7° up, about which datum they can impart vertical accelerations of 0·13g up and 0·07g down without changing the pitch attitude of the aircraft. Operated symmetrically, the spoilers can also be used to supplement the airbrake in giving drag modulation in the event of a carrier wave-off.

One of the main drawbacks to spoilers is their abrupt loss of effectiveness near the stall, as shown in Fig 95. This is due to the fact that to work they must act on a streamline flow. Leading-edge devices to delay flow separation ahead of the spoilers can help to maintain spoiler effectiveness to high AOA. Like ailerons, spoilers become ineffective at high sweep angles, as shown in Fig 95. All swing-wing aircraft therefore lock down their spoilers beyond a certain wing sweep angle (e.g. F-111 45°, F-14 57°). Beyond this angle a differential tailplane is the only form of roll control available. The tendency of spoilers to aggravate the pitch-up tendency of swept wings can be countered by positioning them on the span so that they favourably influence the wing's downwash over the tailplane.

Differential tailplanes (rolling tails, tailerons)

The differential tailplane is an all-moving tail, both elements of which can operate either symmetrically for pitch control or differentially for roll control. The North American A3J Vigilante was the first operational aircraft to use a rolling tail (along with many other features now commonplace on combat aircraft). The concept has the advantage of allowing full-span flaps to be used, a facility fully exploited on the TSR.2, which, having a very small delta wing, needed blown flaps to meet its airfield performance requirement. The wing was unable to accommodate any roll-control devices, and so a large differential tailplane with interlinked all-moving fin served this purpose.

The differential tail retains its effectiveness to very high AOA (Fig 95), giving high proverse yaw at low AOA due to the induced sidewash-on-fin, which reinforces the yawing moment (Fig 96). Seeking departure-resistant very-high-AOA flight for the F-14, Grumman developed a taileron-rudder interconnect which phases out the differential tailplane in favour of the twin rudders.

Rolling tails retain their effectiveness at high Mach numbers and are hardly affected at all by wing sweep angle. This could be a problem for swing-wing aircraft, since in sweeping from 20° to 70° the roll damping reduces by a factor of about 7:1. This is due to the diminishing lateral moment of the wing area and the reducing lift-curve slope of

the wing. With constant roll power the rate of roll would increase in inverse proportion i.e. 1:7, giving excessive rates of roll. Though the roll inertia decreases when wings are swept aft, the change is small because most of the mass is in the fuselage. However, the roll power does not remain constant because all swing-wing aircraft use spoilers as well as rolling tails at low speed, and with increasing sweep and speed the spoilers become less effective and are eventually dispensed with. The differential tail is left as the only roll-inducing device, the initial roll acceleration being relatively sluggish.

The corollary of using a differential tail of adequate roll power at high speed on a swing-wing aircraft is that the same tail is quite inadequate at low speed when the wings are unswept, the small lateral moment of the tail surfaces being so much smaller than that of the wing. Out of an F-14 approach roll requirement of 30°/sec, the differential tail delivers 8°/sec while the spoilers provide the remaining 22°/sec. In combat at Mach 0·9 with wings swept back to 42°, the tail provides 52°/sec while the spoilers contribute 38°/sec (though 60°/sec is available). In contrast to the F-14, the very large span of the differential tailplane on the YF-17 lends credence to Northrop's claim that its rolling power is sufficient to allow landings with the ailerons inoperative.

DIHEDRAL/ANHEDRAL AND VERTICAL WING POSITION

Lateral stability

Lateral stability is markedly different from pitch or yaw stability, there being no direct mechanism by which the aircraft tends to return to its equilibrium position when it is disturbed laterally. Although the aircraft may have no restoring moment acting on it in the disturbed, banked, condition, it does have weight and lift vectors which are unbalanced. The resulting motion is a sideslip, and it is that which yields the aircraft's lateral stability. As shown in Fig 98, positive rolling moment is conventionally expressed as right wing down and a positive sideslip as one to the right. Thus an aircraft having static lateral stability will produce a right-wing-up rolling moment (i.e. negative) when it sideslips to the right. This is shown on the plot of rolling moment versus sideslip as a negatively sloping line, the slope of which is given the symbol C_{l_β} (roll due to sideslip). This rolling moment due to sideslip is created in various ways, the most important of which are due to the dihedral of the wings, the

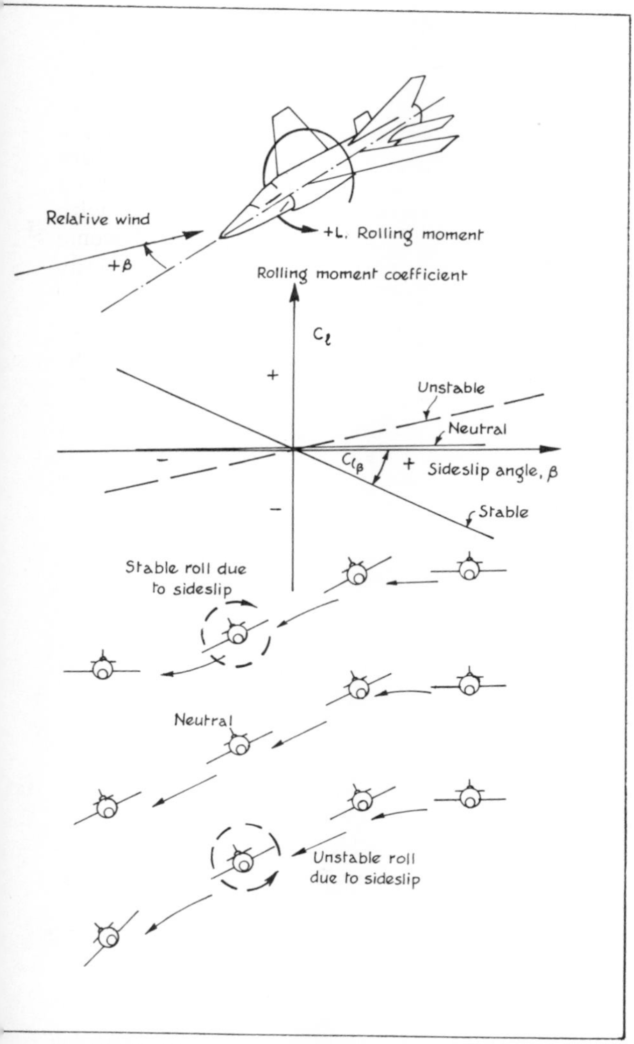

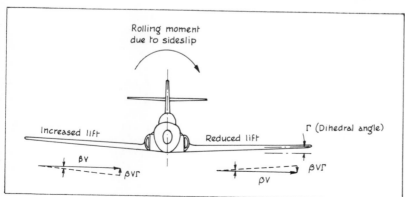

Fig 98 Rolling moment due to sideslip (dihedral effect).

vertical location of the wings on the fuselage, and the sweep of the wings (dealt with separately in the section on sweepback).

Dihedral and anhedral

Viewed from the front, aircraft generally appear to have their wings inclined either upwards, with the tips being higher than the roots (this is called dihedral), or downwards, with tips lower than their roots (anhedral or negative dihedral). So important was this design feature to the lateral stability of older, high-aspect-ratio, straight-winged aircraft that in their context lateral stability was often loosely referred to as "dihedral effect". Dihedral works in the way shown in Fig 99 for an aircraft sideslipping to the right (positive sideslip angle). The windward (right) wing experiences an upward component of velocity while the leeward (left) wing has a downward component. The angle of attack of the right wing is increased, giving more lift, while the AOA of the left wing is reduced, giving less lift. The combined effect is a right-wing-up (i.e. negative) rolling moment. This provides the restoring moment, or lateral stability. The opposite is true for anhedral wings.

If anhedral produces lateral instability, why do some aircraft incorporate it? As noted above, lateral stability can be provided in two other important ways, while too much can be an embarrassment, for the following reasons:

1 A large amount of roll control is required to counteract the effect of sideslip during a crosswind landing.

2 Severe Dutch roll can occur if directional stability is relatively low.

3 Excessive roll response to lateral gusts arises.

4 A large variation of rolling performance with change of AOA is experienced with a swept wing, on which lateral stability increases with AOA.

Fig 99 Influence of wing dihedral angle.

As will be seen later, anhedral has often been used to counteract the excessively high levels of effective dihedral inherent in aircraft with shoulder-mounted swept wings.

Vertical wing position

The vertical positioning of the wing on the fuselage can contribute significantly to dihedral effect by virtue of wing/body flow interaction. The two extreme cases of low-wing and high-wing position are shown in Fig 100. In a sideslip to the right, the sideslip velocity component is deflected both up and down in flowing around the fuselage. In the high-wing case the upward flow on the windward side increases the angle of attack and lift locally on the wing, whereas on the leeward side the wing has its angle of attack and lift reduced locally. This produces a right-wing-up rolling moment, or a positive dihedral effect. The opposite is true in the low-wing case. Thus high wings increase lateral stability while low wings decrease it. The magnitude of the effect depends on the length of fuselage ahead of the wing and its cross-sectional shape,

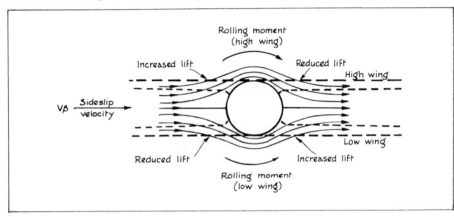

Fig 100 Influence of wing height.

Fig 101 (*Below left*) Contributions to rolling moment due to sideslip (BAe Harrier).[33]

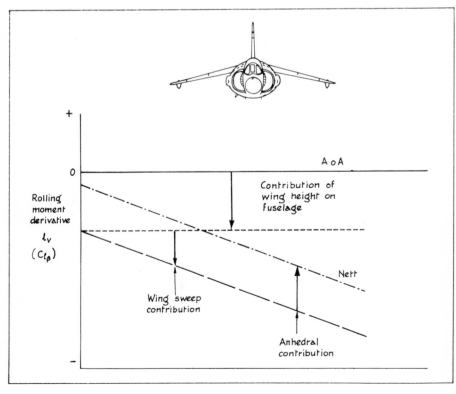

and the planform and location of the wing. A high wing may contribute the equivalent of several degrees of wing dihedral, while a low wing usually produces slightly more effective anhedral.

Combined effects

A particularly good example of the combined effects of wing dihedral, vertical location and sweepback is the BAe Harrier. The Harrier's unique engine type, with its four rotatable exhaust nozzles, means that a high-mounted wing had to be used. This, combined with a relatively large body, gave a large dihedral effect. When the wing's 40° sweep contribution (which increases with AOA) was added to this, an excessive level of lateral stability arose. To avoid Dutch roll instability at high AOA a large amount of anhedral (12°) was therefore incorporated (Fig 101), incidentally yielding the benefit of a shorter outrigger undercarriage.

Another example was the TSR.2, with its shoulder-mounted, 60°-swept delta wing. Use of straight anhedral to avoid Dutch roll at high lift was considered but would have placed the tailplane in the adverse flow field arising from the very strong trailing vortices shed from the wings. The wing could not be mounted higher nor the tailplane

lower, so the wing was kept flat to the outermost 1.2m and then bent down through 30°.

Other design factors influencing wing position

The discussion until now has concentrated upon the stability and control implications of wing dihedral and vertical position. There are however several other considerations which may decide the placing of the wing, as in the case of the Harrier. The amount of dihedral or anhedral is then adjusted to provide acceptable handling characteristics. Among the factors which may predominate are: ease of engine removal; avoidance of breaks in the wing centre-section structural box; height of the wing relative to the tail; length of the undercarriage; intake ducting; and weapon carriage. An unusual example of this is the F-4, which had a low wing to keep the undercarriage reasonably short while allowing enough clearance for fuselage and wing-mounted fuel tanks and ord-

The British Aircraft Corporation TSR.2 of the 1960s taking off (note tailplane angle) with auxiliary intake doors open and reheat on. The very small delta wing with anhedralled tips was essential for high-speed, low-level penetration but required BLC for acceptable airfield performance. (BAC)

nance. The main wing structure carries straight through the fuselage to yield ease of assembly and preserve structural integrity for low weight. But the negative dihedral effect from the low wing had to be offset despite the 48° of wing sweep, and this was achieved by giving 12° of dihedral to the tips at the wing-fold line.

If factors other than stability and control predominate in governing wing position, the designer has little freedom to alter dihedral effect other than through the choice of dihedral angle. It should however be emphasised that the influence which this has can be quite small compared with the effects of wing sweep and wing/body height, as shown by the case of the Harrier. It is then often left to the flight control system to suppress the undesirable consequences by means of control interconnects and autostabilisation.

Fig 102 Effects of wing fence.[34]

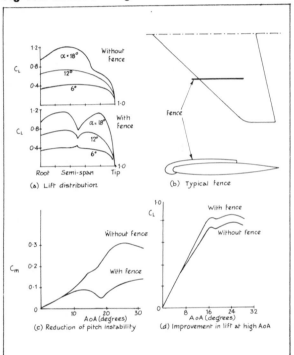

(a) Lift distribution

(b) Typical fence

(c) Reduction of pitch instability

(d) Improvement in lift at high AoA

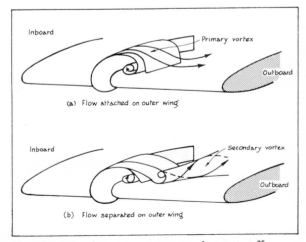

(a) Flow attached on outer wing

(b) Flow separated on outer wing

Fig 103 Wing fence causes vortex formation.[35]

"AERODYNAMIC CRUTCHES"

Having a component of velocity along the wing, swept wings can suffer drift and thickening of the boundary layer towards the tip, where premature

Wing of the BAe Hawk has two stall-breakers on the leading edge, a single fence and a row of vortex generators. Function of the fillet at the wing/body junction is to reduce drag by delaying flow separation. The flattened rear fuselage prevents leakage at the root of the all-moving tailplane. (BAe)

flow separation will occur. Various palliatives have been used to delay separation or at least make it predictable. The most common among these are fences, sawteeth, notches, and vortex generators. Apart from the fact that they all work by producing vortices, their exact functioning is not fully understood.

Wing fences

These were used on the earliest swept-wing fighters — the MiG-15 had two large fences on each wing — and continue to be employed 40 years later (e.g. Hawk 200). The action of a fence is more subtle than a superficial examination might suggest. The fence does represent a physical barrier to the spanwise boundary layer flow and, at higher AOA, to the inwards spread of separation. More important though, the local distortion of the flow due to the fence's projection forwards of the leading edge causes the formation of a separated flow region just inboard of the fence and a vortex (or vortices) just outboard. The separated flow region does not generally lead to a signi-

ficant lift loss nor drag penalty except in the case of multi-fence installations, which are no longer commonplace.

The flow outboard of the fence is very profound in its effect on the wing pressure distribution, since the vortex formed flows back over the wing surface. The high rotational velocity within the vortex produces increased suction on the surface beneath its path, which restores the lift lost on the inboard side of the fence. In addition, the streamwise drift has to build up again, so that outboard the lift loading increases (Fig 102). The flow outboard of the fence has been found to depend greatly on the occurrence of tip separation. At moderate AOA with attached flow outboard a single vortex forms, as shown in Fig 103a, whereas at higher AOA any tip separation spreads inboard to the vicinity of the fence and primary vortex. This causes formation of a secondary vortex, which rotates in opposition to the primary one (Fig 103b). This new vortex grows in strength with AOA and produces high suctions. This, it is argued, is the main factor in improving the lift curve at high AOA (Fig 102).

The use of fences has in the past been very much a matter of trial and error, since apart from shape other variables such as number and position have to be considered. Two fences were used in an effort to improve the roll steadiness of the Harrier at moderate to high AOA, and it can be seen in Fig 104 that spacing proved critical.

Not all fences are on the scale shown in Fig 103. The BAe Hawk 60 series and T-45A, for example, feature a large fence at two-thirds span (a commonly favoured position) and three small fences inboard. These replaced two triangular-shaped "stall breaker" strips, maintaining control at the stall without creating lift loss associated with the earlier solution.

Sawteeth

Sawteeth are usually located beyond mid-span and are formed by locally extending the leading edge, as shown in Fig 105. They serve a dual function, producing vortices similar to those generated by fences and giving a reduction in the wing section thickness/chord ratio to minimise drag at high Mach number. They also often introduce leading-edge droop to the outer wing panel.

Sawteeth were incorporated on the Saab Viggen to overcome a reduction in longitudinal stability caused by the flow around large underwing stores, which protruded in front of the wing and disturbed the main delta wing vortex. The introduction of the sawtooth effectively divided the wing vortex

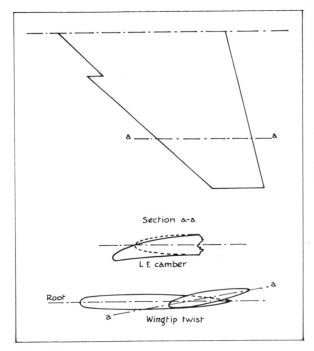

Fig 105 Sawtooth and leading-edge camber on LTV F-8.

system into two smaller vortices. This improved longitudinal stability and reduced buffet levels (Fig 106).

Notches ("ingrowing fences")

Notches are axial cuts in the wing leading edge which generate vortices intended to locally improve wing flow. On the Lightning, for example, they were located directly upstream of the ailerons to cure wing drop and stick shake.

Vortex generators

These are small vanes situated in roughly spanwise rows on a wing upper surface or in any region where a local flow improvement is sought. Set at an angle to the local flow, they produce vortices which draw in air from the external airstream and mix it with the sluggish boundary layer. This re-energises the boundary layer and so delays its separation. Though they inevitably cause drag, their efficient use results in an overall saving. There can however be a large wave drag penalty, which usually precludes their use on highly supersonic aircraft. As shown in Fig 107, the two types in common use are co-rotating and counter-rotating. Their typical height is about 2–3cm, though this depends on the local boundary-layer thickness.

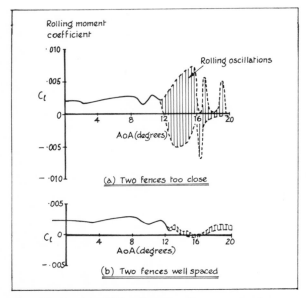

Fig 104 Harrier GR1 roll unsteadiness varies in response to fence location.[36]

A row of vortex generators placed in front of ailerons will improve control effectiveness. At high AOA, however, separation is likely to have occurred upstream of them, in which case they have no effect. In transonic flow the effectiveness of a row of vortex generators depends very much on its position relative to a shockwave, since if they are to perform well the boundary layer must be re-energised before the shockwave is traversed. Because the shock position varies with Mach number and AOA, the optimum position and spacing of the vortex generators has to be found largely by trial and error.

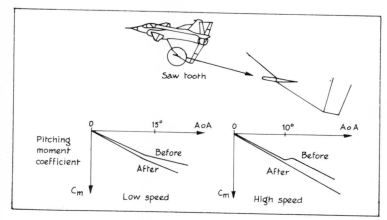

Fig 106 Effect of Saab Viggen main wing sawtooth.[37]

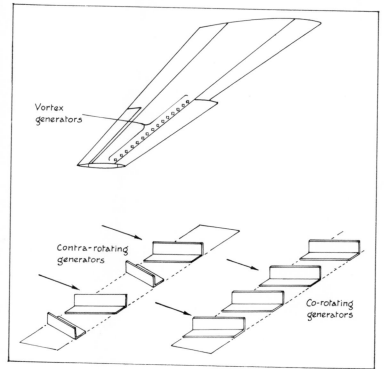

Fig 107 Co-rotating and contra-rotating vortex generators.

CHAPTER 2
AIR INTAKES

INTRODUCTION

Air intakes are frequently overlooked by the casual observer, who imagines that they are simply holes in the aeroplane to let the air into the engine. In fact their function is a great deal more complex and crucial than that, with the result that they are often extremely complicated, very difficult to design and develop, and costly. The success or failure of an aircraft can depend upon their efficiency. This chapter aims to explain the function and vital importance of good intake/airframe/engine integration by examining intake design criteria and the design features to be noted when analysing a modern combat aircraft. Particular attention is given to the way in which overall aircraft shape is influenced by intake location and type, with special emphasis on supersonic intakes. Finally, intake design is related to powerplant type, location and number.

THE FUNCTION AND IMPORTANCE OF AIR INTAKES

All conventional combat aircraft use air-breathing engines. The function of their intakes is complex. The intake has to deliver to the engine the correct air mass flow at an acceptable velocity, and ensure that it arrives at the engine face at the right angle. All this has to be accomplished for a very wide range of aircraft speeds and attitudes, with minimal losses and at the lowest reasonable weight and cost.

Some of the characteristics of a typical air intake are shown in Fig 108. Principal aspects are the intake position; its shape and components including the inlet cross-section, intake lips, sideplates, compression ramps and actuators; the length and variation of the duct cross-section leading to the engine; and the provision for handling the external and internal boundary layers.

Fig 108 North American RA-5 air-intake system.

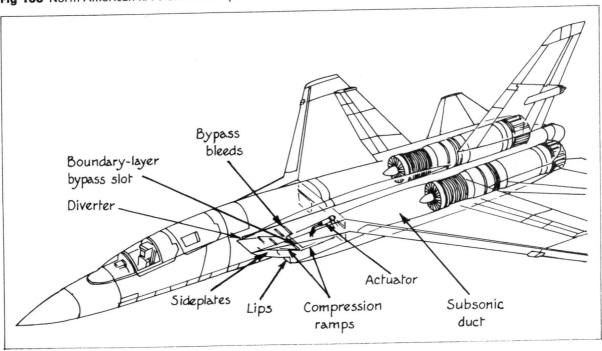

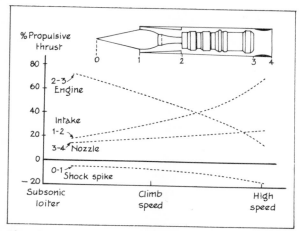

Fig 109 Lockheed YF-12A thrust and drag distribution.[38]

The importance of the air intake may be assessed from Fig 109, which apportions the thrust and drag arising from the components that form the powerplant package. This comprises the compression surfaces, the internal duct, and the engine and nozzle. The example shown is for the Mach 3 Lockheed SR-71, and though the numerical values are specific to this aircraft, the chief conclusion is that as aircraft speed increases so does the thrust provided by the intake. At cruise speed the thrust developed by the engine, as measured on the engine mounts, is only 17% of the propelling force of the aircraft. The remainder of the thrust comes from the pressure distribution around the inlet, which provides a huge 70%, and the ejector nozzle. The entry spike balances the sum with a drag term of 14%.

For a more typical installation the inlet's function as a compressor may be judged from the following values. In the high-subsonic regime the engine compressor generates five times the pressure rise of the inlet. At Mach 1·2 the intake and engine contribute about equally. At Mach 2·8 the engine contribution to pressure rise is negligible, while the pressure ratio of the inlet may be as much as 40:1. This does not however fairly represent the thrust distribution, since this comes also from temperature rise, the primary source being the engine combustor.

The above example highlights the intake's role as a thrust producer. What follows will show that intakes for contemporary and future combat aircraft also have other, sometimes conflicting tasks to perform.

INTAKE DESIGN CRITERIA

Several parameters influence intake performance. They include total pressure recovery (p_r); flow distortion and turbulence at the intake face; spillage drag; boundary-layer diverter and bleed drag; bypass drag; buzz avoidance; and flight safety.

Not only must the intake be closely integrated with the engine but the whole question of inlet/engine/airframe compatibility, indicated in Fig 110, must be satisfactorily addressed.

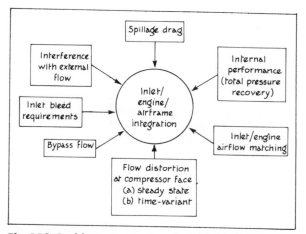

Fig 110 Problems encountered with inlet/engine airframe integration.

Total pressure recovery

Since the intake serves to slow the airflow to a speed acceptable to the engine face, and in consequence raise the pressure of the flow, the smaller the pressure losses within the intake, the greater the thrust. Every 1% loss in pressure represents an equal or greater loss in thrust at static conditions and a proportionately higher loss at forward speed. Typically, at Mach 2·2 an 8% loss in pressure recovery ($p_r = 0·92$) reduces net thrust by 13% and increases specific fuel consumption by 5%.

The efficiency of an intake is expressed in terms of pressure recovery, defined as the ratio of the mean total pressure across the engine face ($\bar{p}_{t_2}$) to the freestream total pressure (p_{t_1}). This is always less than unity (i.e. $\bar{p}_{t_2}/p_{t_1} < 1$), though great efforts are made to minimise the losses of total pressure which arise through surface friction, the intake shock-wave system, and shock-wave/boundary-layer interaction. Each shock wave slows the airflow and converts some of the kinetic energy by increasing the pressure and temperature of the air. Since the temperature gain can be only insignificant compared to that introduced in the combustor, the inlet designer is concerned with maximising the pressure rise. Hence the importance attached to pressure recovery.

Distortion

Distortion is the term for the pressure-recovery pattern across the engine face, which takes the form of pressure peaks and troughs varying in location and magnitude. It is felt by the compressor blades as a pattern of varying velocities. The velocity distribution across an engine face fed by an axi-symmetric (i.e. circular) intake at zero angle of attack will be fairly even over the whole annulus.

Small changes in intake attitude (i.e. AOA or sideslip) can cause local velocity peaks to develop, leading to flow separation from the intake lips or centrebody. With the intake in this condition the compressor blades will pass through alternating high and low-speed regions, which may cause blade vibrations and subsequent failure. The velocity variations result in local changes in blade angle of attack which, if large enough, will cause them to stall in much the same way as a wing. This may spawn stalling not only of the fan stage or first compressor stage but of other stages downstream, leading to a violent disruption of the entire engine airflow. This is engine surge, a phenomenon varying between an unpleasant rumbling and a sharp bang, and which can threaten an engine with flameout.

Flow distortion thus causes a downward shift of the engine surge line, as shown in Fig 111. All engines are therefore designed to have a surge margin beyond their normal operating line to ensure surge-free operation under all likely airflow conditions. These include high angles of attack, and the ingestion of the gases from gun and missile

firing. Sometimes the conditions that the engine is asked to tolerate can be extreme indeed. Aircraft designers have a habit of demanding maximum thrust when the wing is deep in buffet and the intake is at an angle far beyond that generally regarded as the limit for uniform flow. If the aircraft can recover from a spin in which AOAs may reach 60°, they demand, why can't the engine continue to co-operate?

Dynamic distortion

Also known as instantaneous distortion or turbulence, this is a measure of how the distortion pattern varies with time. The duration of local peaks can be less than one engine revolution, i.e. about five milliseconds. Acceptable combinations of distortion and turbulence can be achieved without great difficulty at a specific design point. It is not so easy to do so at high AOA throughout the altitude/Mach number envelope without undue complexity, weight or loss of combat performance. Generally speaking, high distortion levels accompany low pressure recovery and are typical of high intake mass-flow conditions, notably at high AOA subsonically and high supersonic Mach numbers.

During prototype flight tests of the F-111A it became obvious that manoeuvres at high subsonic and supersonic speed were limited by a rapid increase in both steady and dynamic distortion. The resulting compressor stalling proved extremely difficult to remedy. The aircraft designer should thus always strive to offer the engine the smoothest possible airflow even when it is known to be tolerant of distortion. Particularly in need of smooth airflow are the multi-shaft high-compression bypass engines (like the Pratt & Whitney TF30 as used on the F-111A), which have tended to be more sensitive to dynamic distortion than their pure turbojet predecessors.

Spillage drag or cowl lip suction?

The amount of air ingested by a jet engine does not depend directly on intake size or forward speed. The engine doesn't have air forced into it, but takes in what it needs. At low forward speed and high engine RPM the capture stream tube (see Fig 112) is larger than the intake and must converge and thereby accelerate into the intake, giving a sucking condition. At high forward speeds with the engine throttled back (i.e. reduced RPM) the capture stream tube is smaller than the intake, provoking some of the air to spill around the intake lips (Fig 112).

The momentum loss of the excess air as it is

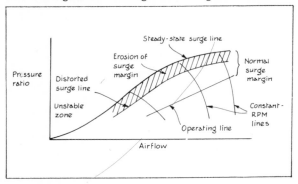

Fig 111 Erosion of engine surge margin due to inlet flow distortion.

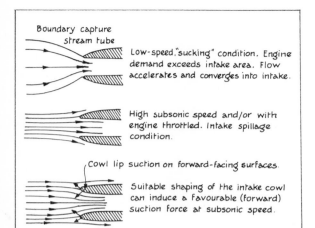

Boundary capture
stream tube

Low-speed,"sucking" condition. Engine demand exceeds intake area. Flow accelerates and converges into intake.

High subsonic speed and/or with engine throttled. Intake spillage condition.

Cowl lip suction on forward-facing surfaces.

Suitable shaping of the intake cowl can induce a favourable (forward) suction force at subsonic speed.

Fig 112 Intake operating conditions.

diverted around the intake is the cause of spillage drag. This can be eliminated by lip suction as the deflected air accelerates over the intake cowl, causing a low-pressure region to form on a forward-facing surface (Fig 112).

Boundary-layer diverter and bleed drag

It can be crucial to prevent the fuselage and intake boundary layer from entering the engine. Boundary layers impair pressure recovery and give rise to intensified distortion, especially if they separate from the walls of the intake ducts.

The diverter systems used to prevent ingestion of fuselage and/or wing boundary layers generate a drag component called diverter drag, defined as

the momentum lost when airflow is deflected by the diverter. Those systems which remove the boundary layer formed on the entry surfaces of the intake create boundary-layer bleed drag. This is defined as the momentum lost by these flows from the time they enter the inlet until they leave the aircraft, plus the exit-door pressure drag. Care must be taken in the design of both types of system to ensure that the drag they generate does not exceed the thrust recovery that they yield.

Intake buzz and bypass drag

Both of these topics are dealt with later in the chapter, since they are better explained in context.

Flight and operational safety

This is a key influence on intake design, the main related hazards being foreign object damage and radar reflectivity.

Foreign object damage (FOD)

Combat aircraft are very prone to FOD if the intake is mounted low on the aircraft or just behind the nosewheel. Under these circumstances the intake will suck in anything lying on the surface over which it rolls. Typical foreign objects are stones,

MiG-29 Fulcrum air combat fighter with leading and trailing-edge devices deployed. The wings have large wing/body strakes which shield the overhanging variable-geometry intakes. The intakes appear to have doors which close off the main inlets during ground operation, allowing air to enter via louvres on the upper surface of the strakes and protecting the engines from objects thrown up by the nose gear. (Hasse Vallas)

nuts and bolts, sand and ice. Nonetheless, only around 10% of all FOD is reckoned to be caused by the nosewheel, the remainder being either personnel-induced (e.g. spanners left in intakes) or unrelated to intake position (e.g. exhaust jet spraying debris into the intake of a following or parked aircraft). Another destructive source of FOD is birdstrike, to which low-flying strike aircraft are especially prone. Intake guards have been proposed, but they are heavy and then to direct the remains into the engine once they are retracted after a birdstrike.

Radar detectability

Some intakes are particularly effective at reflecting radar emissions. This is a drawback in a combat aircraft, and is being tackled by means of radar-absorbing materials and intake shaping and positioning.

INTAKE DESIGN FEATURES

Intake size

The size of an intake depends principally on the intended use of the aircraft, though it should be recalled that the engine takes in what it needs rather than having air forced into it. On aircraft designed to cruise at high altitude and high Mach number (e.g. the XB-70 and SR-71), the intake is sized for this condition. Excess airflow is then inevitably experienced at transonic speed, even when account is taken of the airflow required for boundary-layer control, environmental control systems and engine cooling. On the more common run of supersonic aircraft, which have no specific design point, the intake is usually sized for high subsonic speed, the emphasis being on maximum acceleration in the transonic phase. Any excess airflow again has to be diverted back to the free-stream as efficiently as possible. As a case in point, the Lightning's intake was greatly undersized in order to minimise the spillage drag's effect on the slender thrust margins available from the early Rolls-Royce Avon turbojets. The extent of the undersizing meant that at high RPM the intake was increasingly full of strong shockwaves down to zero forward speed. These were intensified when the engine mass flow was increased after the intake design was frozen for manufacture. The later F-4 Phantom underwent a series of intake size increments to allow for increased mass flow as more powerful engines were introduced. The original F-4A had J79s requiring 75kg/sec airflow, whereas the Spey engines of the F-4K needed 100kg/sec. More recently still, the YF-16's intake

was deliberately sized to allow for a 10% airflow increase in the course of engine development.

Cowl lip shape

Thick, rounded lips are needed to avoid lip flow separation at low speeds. At higher subsonic speeds, or at moderate speeds with the engine throttled, the intake is likely to spill flow around the outside of the cowl, though careful design can avoid a drag penalty. As aircraft speed increases into the high-subsonic regime, the flow, in spilling, will accelerate locally to supersonic speed. A shock wave will form on the blunt lip, terminating the supersonic flow and causing turbulence over so much of the flow that the drag increases severely. Further spillage strengthens the shock wave and eventually the boundary layer separates, giving even more drag. At supersonic flight speed the shock-wave drag resulting from a very blunt lip would be quite prohibitive. It is clear that some compromise is necessary in the form of sharper lips, variable lip shape, auxiliary intakes or some combination of these.

Fixed profile

Reduced lip blunting to restrict the deviation of the flow calls for a lip with a small external radius, and thin enough to limit the flow Mach number at the intake throat. The subsonic Harrier's intake was designed for a throat Mach number of 0·7.[36,39]

The problem of cowl flow separation with fixed lips at low forward speeds is duplicated to an extent at the high angles of attack encountered in combat. Under these conditions flow separation brings in its wake acute distortion, leading to a reduced engine surge margin. The trouble is compounded by the large engine power off-takes demanded by the hydraulic system as it works to give the large tailplane angles required for high AOA and possible wing sweeping. These off-takes raise the engine operating line, further eroding the surge margin.

To combat this condition, increased AOA tolerance can be obtained by blunting the cowl lip, though at the expense of supersonic intake performance. This arises partly because of increased cowl wave drag, and partly because of reduced intake airflow and pressure recovery when the terminal (i.e. normal) shock stands off from the intake lip (see *Intake location*, page 123). Despite these difficulties, cowl lip blunting is a feature of the F-14, F-15 and Tornado.

The benefits to pressure recovery and distortion of cowl lip blunting on the F-15 are shown in Fig 113. The cowl lip blunting and decambering performed on the Tornado also substantially reduced the dynamic distortion. It appears that

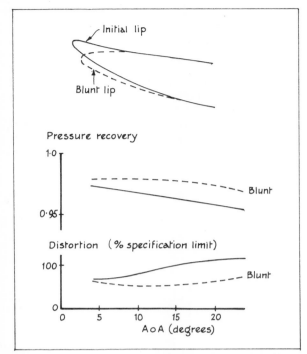

Fig 113 Effect of blunt intake lip on F-15 at Mach 0.9.[40]

dynamic distortion reaches a plateau at very high AOA, possibly because the increasing AOA reduces the effective stagger of Tornado-type intakes. This could cause the flow turning to be more equally balanced between the compression ramps and cowl, thereby suppressing the cowl separation. Nevertheless, it appears that for aircraft without some form of high-AOA shielding (discussed later), cowl lip separation is inevitable.

Variable-radius inlet

Efficient low-speed operation, with the flow converging into the inlet, requires a large lip radius, whereas high supersonic speed demands sharp lips. Variable geometry can be used at low speed to increase the effective radius of relatively sharp lips. The prototype P.1127 (Harrier precursor) was originally flown with a metal lip of bulbous shape for very-low-speed efficiency. But a variable-radius lip was subsequently fitted to achieve a compromise between this and the sharper lip flown successfully at high speed (but unsuccessfully at low speed). Rubber bags fitted to the intake were inflated at low speed and sucked down for high speed. This was a limited advance, recourse being eventually made to suck-in doors.

Another means of enlarging the effective radius is the intake leading-edge flap, proposed for the cancelled Hawker P.1154 and fitted in modified

form to the MiG-25 Foxbat. On the Rockwell B-1 such flaps form a movable cowl lip, the two positions (open and closed) being linked directly to the landing-gear handle. Opening of the lip increases pressure recovery by $7\frac{1}{2}$% at take-off and reduces engine face distortion. Suck-in doors were originally proposed but their close proximity to the main wheels presented a FOD problem.

Suck-in doors

These are auxiliary intakes which admit part of the engine's airflow demand, thereby reducing the primary intake flow and convergence, and suppressing separation. Lateral mounting of the doors (usually at the intake sides) does not add to the thickness of the main lips (Fig 114). Normally they are simply hinged, sucking in when the pressure within the inlet is less than that outside (as in low-speed flight) and closing against stops when the internal pressure rises. Their apparent simplicity (no actuators or springs) belies their value. To ensure an adequate range without prejudicing hovering performance, first 12 and then 16 suck-in doors were fitted to the Harrier. The V/STOL fighter's critical requirement for high pressure recovery resulted in the main intake and auxiliary intakes being designed for a pressure recovery of 97%. This required very well shaped

Fig 114 Harrier suck-in intake doors.[41]

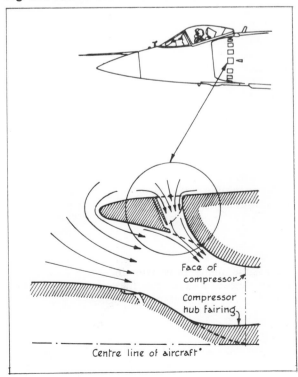

Left: The Dassault Rafale's forward fuselage is highly sculpted to accomodate the semi-ventral fixed-geometry intakes with offset boundary-layer splitter plates. Like the EAP, Rafale has a delta/canard layout, though with less obvious compound sweep and a foreplane located aft of the cockpit.

passages to minimise the mixing losses when the various intake streams merged, something particularly difficult to achieve in the Harrier since the length of the intake duct before the engine face is extremely short (Fig 114). A double row of suck-in doors was originally designed for the AV-8B, and the YAV-8B development aircraft actually flew with them. Though the modification was claimed to offer a thrust increase of 2,700N, a subsequent revision to the intake required the removal of the aft row of doors.

Since the Harrier, suck-in doors have been used on many aircraft, including the F-111. Mirage III, Tu-26, Jaguar, MiG-23, Su-19, Mirage F.1 and Tornado. The YF-16 also incorporated suck-in doors as an insurance against inlet/engine incompatibility during the prototype test programme, but they were found to be unnecessary.

Intake shape

Broadly speaking, intakes are classified as either two-dimensional (rectangular) or axisymmetric (circular or part-circular). Circular intakes have the advantage of efficient structural shape for low duct weight and minimum wetted area per unit of flow area, and were used on the earliest jet fighters (e.g. Me262, He126 and Meteor) and on many of the next generation of fighters with swept wings and nose intakes (e.g. F-84, F-86, MiG-15).

The reasoning behind the positioning of engines and their intakes has evolved over the years, resulting, together with advent of supersonic flight, in a metamorphosis in intake shape. For example, while axisymmetric intakes are still used, the demands of supersonic operation require the insertion of a cone-shaped spike. This in turn raises many difficulties when intake geometry needs to be varied, as described later.

Half-round inlets fit nicely along the fuselage side and have been employed, with and without spikes, on many aircraft. In fact the earliest US operational jet fighter, the Lockheed F-80 Shooting Star, had low-mounted half-circular intakes; the same solution was subsequently used on the subsonic F3D Skyknight, F7U Cutlass and F-89 Scorpion. The Mach 2 Lockheed F-104 first flew with spiked half-round intakes in 1954, and Dassault favoured this approach for all its fighters from the Mirage III to the Mirage 4000.

Like the half-round intake, the D-shaped intake blends well into the forward fuselage sidewall and has been used successfully on many supersonic aircraft, including the Grumman F11F Tiger, Convair F-102A and Northrop F-5, F-18 and F-20 (Fig 115). Probably the most famous example of the D intake is that of the F-4 Phantom, with its variable-geometry compression ramp and slight downward tilt to provide better flow alignment at higher AOA. The Grumman Super Tiger's D intake incorporated a bump on the fuselage just ahead of the inlet to pre-compress the air through a series of oblique shockwaves. The bump also washed out most of the fuselage boundary layer around the inlet. This private-venture aircraft, which flew in the competition for European orders eventually won by the F-104G, achieved Mach 2 with fixed geometry. A similar "speed bump" appears to have been used ahead of the shock cone on the Mirage 2000 (Fig 116).

Rectangular intakes were featured on several combat aircraft which appeared in the 1960s, including Jaguar, Sukhoi Su-15 and MiG-23. Probably the most important development of two-dimensional intakes is the incorporation of horizontally mounted compression ramps. This offers a good combination of performance and operational characteristics. Because it requires the simplest mode of variable geometry — the opening and

Fig 115 Intake shapes past and present.

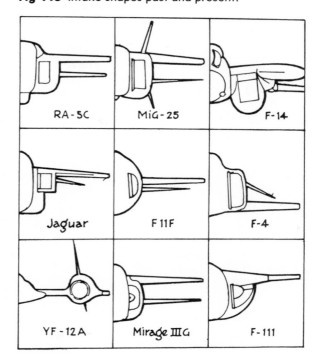

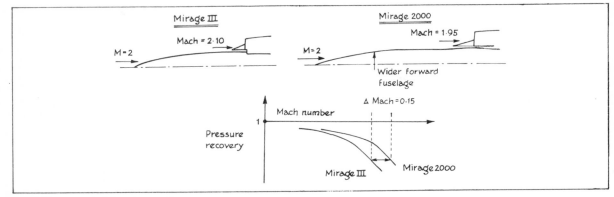

Fig 116 Forward-fuselage effect on pressure recovery.[42]

closing of flat ramps — and because its over-hanging upper surface gives good airflow regulation at high AOA, it has been selected for several very notable aircraft, including the A3J (RA-5), MiG-25, F-14, F-15, Tornado and MiG-31 Foxhound. The vertically mounted ramps of the Rockwell B-1 may appear to be a retrograde step, but with two engines suspended side-by-side in pods toed-in by $\frac{1}{2}°$, vertical ramps were found to reduce the risk of flow interaction between the intakes.

Sideplates

These are a feature of all supersonic aircraft having horizontally mounted compression ramp surfaces, the first of which was the North American A3J (A-5) Vigilante. The sideplate's function is to contain the flow as it is slowed down and compressed by the shock waves generated by the ramps. The inboard sideplate also acts as a boundary-layer splitter plate (see *Intake boundary-layer management*). The A-5 had cut-back sideplates, and the fullest examples yet to appear are those on the MiG-25 and MiG-31.

Variations in sideplate shape were investigated by McDonnell Douglas for the F-15, and some studies showed that partially cut-back sideplates could improve pressure recovery during yawed flight. One explanation of this suggests that without the cutback the sideplate behaves like a slender delta wing in producing a vortex which enters the intake, degrading the flow. Cutting back the leading edge is claimed to give a deviation to the flow, which then approaches the intake in the opposite sense to the sideslip and suppresses the vortex.

Intake boundary-layer management

Boundary layers, being the slow-moving region of flow immediately adjacent to any surface exposed

to airflow, contain relatively little kinetic energy. They are therefore incapable of producing much pressure rise within the intake and are particularly troublesome when confronted by shock waves. Under all circumstances they cause a reduction of pressure recovery and increase distortion, with intake performance decreasing rapidly as more of the fuselage boundary layer enters the inlet. Worse still, as soon as the airflow enters the duct, boundary layers form on its internal surfaces and interact with the intake shockwaves to create further difficulties.

The problem of boundary-layer management thus has two aspects. First, what to do about the fuselage boundary layer ahead of the intake; second, how to handle the internal boundary layer.

Fuselage boundary layer

Almost all modern combat aircraft have their intakes offset from the fuselage to a greater or lesser extent. The two-dimensional intake of the F-4 has its first compression ramp set 5cm away from the fuselage side; the partially axisymmetric F-111A intake has a large splitter plate; and the F-15's inboard sideplates act as splitter plates. The exaggerated offset of the F-14's sideplates (20cm) is a side effect of the podded nature of the engine installation and requires no extra provision for the fuselage boundary layer. Subsonic aircraft also suffer from boundary-layer ingestion, the BAe Hawk's diverter being typical of the designs used to cure it. A rough rule of thumb for the offset of the diverter on such aircraft is 1% of the distance from the aircraft nose.

The penultimate scheme used to improve the inlet performance of the F-111A was the Triple Plow I design, which first flew in 1966 (Fig 117). The name refers to the very large splitter plate used to remove the fuselage boundary layer; a sub-inlet to remove the boundary layer built up on the splitter plate itself; and another sub-inlet for the wing glove boundary layer. The large splitter plate

Rockwell B-1A with wings in the fully swept position. Combined with the forebody vanes, this gives a smooth ride at high speed in turbulent air. Originally designed with variable geometry, the intakes' vertical compression ramps were fixed to reduced complexity, weight and cost. Extensive wing/body blending contributes significantly to the B-1's small radar cross-section. (USAF)

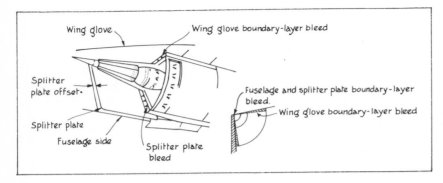

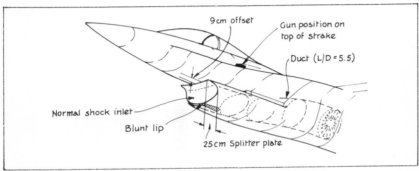

The intakes of the subsonic AMX are characterised by rounded lips and small boundary-layer diverter offset. The launcher rails extend ahead of the wingtips to place the centre of gravity of the Sidewinder AAMs close to that of the aircraft.

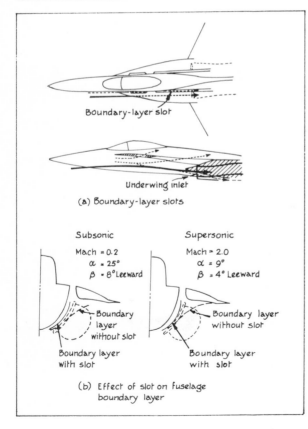

(a) Boundary-layer slots

(b) Effect of slot on fuselage boundary layer

Fig 117 (*Top*) External boundary-layer handling for F-111A intake.[43]

Fig 118 (*Above*) Features of the General Dynamics F-16 intake. The simple design of the normal shock inlet results in low weight and cost, and the blunt lip permits high angles of attack. The underfuselage location gives shielding from wing-induced effects and avoids gun-gas ingestion.[29]

Fig 119 (*Left*) Fuselage boundary-layer removal on Northrop YF-17.[27]

was deleted when the F-111 intakes were eventually offset further from the fuselage and enlarged for the F-111D/E/F. But since the EF-111 electronic warfare version is based on refurbished F-111A airframes, Triple Plow I intakes will still be flying in the 1990s.

The underfuselage intake of the F-16 has a splitter plate, the leading edge of which is a relatively short 25cm ahead of the cowl lip to isolate the intake's normal shockwave from the fuselage boundary layer. The splitter plate is curved to follow the body contour, though with a slightly greater radius of curvature to provide efficient diversion of the boundary layer above the splitter plate, not into the inlet. The offset and other details

of the diverter are shown in Fig 118. The initial half-vertex angle of the diverter is 8°.

The YF-17 featured not only a splitter plate but also a longitudinal slot through the wing root, as shown in Fig 119a. With the nose of the aircraft fully 7·6m ahead of the intake, the slot allowed a passage for the fuselage boundary layer and relieved the wing's adverse pressure field to suppress the growth of the boundary layer. Convincing evidence of the effectiveness of the design can be seen in Fig 119b. On the F-18 the slots were deleted to minimise drag, but the splitter plate has bleed holes to remove its boundary layer ahead of the intake throat.

The subsonic Harrier's large intake has no

splitter plate, since the length of the fuselage ahead of the inlet is quite short. Nevertheless, the large amount of spillage at high speed tended to cause the boundary layer to separate, so flush-mounted bleed ducts with spring-loaded doors are used. These close on take-off to prevent flow from coming out of the slots when the intake is sucking.

Internal boundary layer

The use of intake compression ramps to generate the complex shock structure needed to slow the air-flow efficiently induces shock-wave/boundary-layer interactions. The boundary layers will certainly thicken and are likely to separate from the intake walls unless preventative measures are taken. Two commonly used ways to remove, or at least thin down, the boundary layer are porous surfaces and the throat slot bypass (Fig 120).

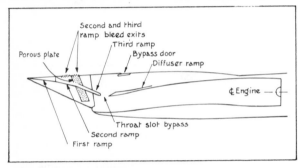

Fig 120 F-15 engine inlet.[44]

The first production aircraft known to use both methods was the F-4, on which the boundary layer is sucked through a gap between its two compression ramps and through perforations (12,500 per side) on the second moveable ramp. The air is expelled through louvres above the intakes.

The F-15 has porous regions on its second and third ramps and on its sideplates in the region of the terminal shockwave, the combined removal being 30% of the total; the remainder is achieved in the throat slot. The B-1 uses a similar arrangement but without a throat slot. The BAe EAP incorporates porosity on its primary compression ramp.

Compression ramp suction is not restricted to planar ramps, having also been used on the F-111 quarter-cone shock body and on the SR-71 inlet spike. The SR-71's porous surfaces are located near the throat, where the final shockwave normally sits. The spike boundary layer is bled away through its support struts to louvres which discharge the air overboard. The duct boundary layer is removed through 33 bypass tubes into the bypass annulus of the nacelle and then to the

exhaust ejector nozzle; in so doing it helps to stabi-lise the normal shockwave and cools the engine and nozzle.

Engine bypass systems

As the engine will accept only a given amount of air, the excess which does not spill around the intake and is actually captured can be bled off by the systems already incorporated for boundary-layer bleeding. However, the quantity of air involved is much larger, and the air must be handled carefully if drag is to be minimised. But some pressure drag on the spill vents and exit downstream is inevitable, as is drag due to the momentum loss between the intake face and spill-vent exit.

Injudicious use of boundary-layer bleed and bypass can have a very severe effect on drag. Preli-minary flight testing of the YF-12 revealed that boundary-layer bleed and bypass flows from the engine nacelles caused a large separated area at the wing/nacelle junction. Wind-tunnel tests showed that bypassing 37% of the intake air, a realistic value for some flight conditions, caused an increase in overall aircraft drag by an amount nearly equal to its zero-lift drag.

The variable bypass slot featured on F-14, F-15 and Tornado is located at the trailing edge of the last supersonic compression ramp, just in front of the subsonic ramp, which blends into the subsonic diffuser. When engine airflow demands are low, the slot opens wide to direct the excess air over-board (Fig 120). These aircraft have intake systems controlled independently by digital computer to optimise inlet/engine matching over a wide range of supersonic flight conditions, engine throttle settings and ambient conditions.

Intake duct length and shape

After the air enters the intake and passes through the shock-wave pattern, further diffusion is needed down to the Mach number of about 0·4–0·5 which is acceptable to current engines. This takes place in the section of duct called the subsonic diffuser. The velocity seen at the engine face is maintained into the combustor, where there is a limit to the speed at which combustion of the air/fuel mixture can take place.

To secure the minimum possible supersonic drag, the cross-sectional area of the aircraft in the centre-fuselage section must be closely controlled, and the intake duct turned into the centre fuselage as rapidly as is compatible with good duct lines. The Tornado is a good illustration of the elongated "S" shape commonly employed. Inlet/engine com-

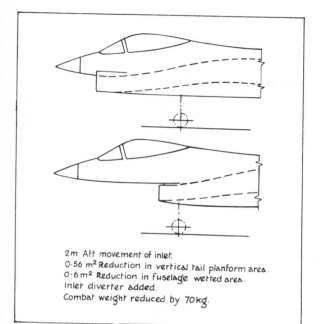

2m Aft movement of inlet.
0·56 m² Reduction in vertical tail planform area.
0·6 m² Reduction in fuselage wetted area.
Inlet diverter added.
Combat weight reduced by 70 kg.

Fig 121 Advantages of a shorter inlet duct on the F-16.[1]

patibility can be affected quite significantly by the design of the subsonic diffuser, which may either reduce or amplify flow distortion. The critical parameter is usually duct length, though using extra length to achieve compatibility is expensive in weight. Nevertheless, when the intake and duct shape require large geometry changes (e.g. the F-111, which also lacked adequate boundary-layer handling), then increasing duct length may be the only acceptable way of reducing flow distortion if vortex generators are inadequate.

The F-16 has a relatively long diffuser, the duct length from inlet throat to engine face being 5·4 times the engine face diameter. It has large-radius turns and an area variation to produce a near-linear Mach number change along the duct, resulting in reduced diffuser losses. The aircraft was originally proposed with the much longer duct shown in Fig 121, but shortening it not only saved duct and fuselage weight (18kg/m) but also offered a saving in vertical tail weight, a result of the reduced destabilising effect of the smaller forward side area. The weight savings more than offset the added drag of the boundary-layer diverter, the mission radius increased by 40km and the area distribution improved.

The curvature of the Tornado's inlet duct was one of the causes of the swirl which showed up early in the programme. At high AOA, cowl-lip flow separation combined with the curvature of the duct to produce severe flow rotation of up to 210° at the engine face. For the left-hand intake the swirl was counter to the rotation of the engine compressor, and when allied to the dynamic distortion it led to engine surging. The right-hand engine received co-rotating swirl and so was surge-free. The cure was to introduce a simple fence on the intake centreline, which works by preventing the effects of lip separation from interacting with those of duct curvature.

A similar swirl condition arose at high supersonic speed, but affected only the right-hand intake. This was induced by flow separation from the third, subsonic, intake ramp, which at high Mach is approaching its maximum angle, made deliberately large to reduce the ramp's length and power requirement. To reduce the swirl content of the duct flow two fences were fitted, one on the bottom centreline and the other on the inboard centreline.

INTAKE LOCATION

Since most combat aircraft powerplants are mounted either within the fuselage or in closely adjacent pods (e.g. the F-14), the intakes are closely tied in to the body side, nose, belly, wing root or upper surface. The range of possible locations and shape is nevertheless very wide.

Nose intakes

Many of the early jet fighters (e.g. F-84, F-86, MiG-15, Ouragan, Saab J29, Mystère, etc) had intakes in the nose, which was the natural place when engines were mounted mid-fuselage, with long jetpipes. The lack of airframe ahead of the intake meant that boundary-layer diverters were not needed, and the long inlet duct helped to attenuate the flow distortion occurring at extreme attitudes. The F-100, with its sharp cowl lips, must have benefited in manoeuvres from its long subsonic diffuser. An overlong duct is however subject to high pressure losses from wall friction and would not be suitable for the aft-mounted engine position currently favoured. The shock-wave centrebody used on the Lightning and MiG-21 was a convenient location for the small radar dishes of the time but would be incapable of housing the equipment currently in use.

Wing-root leading-edge intakes

These were popular with the designers of a number

of subsonic fighters, notably those from the de Havilland, Grumman and Hawker stables. Reasonably tolerant engines were required, the main drawbacks of the location being the small depth of the intake face and rapid changes of cross-section and flow direction. Trying to blend such an intake into the thin wings of the early supersonic fighters proved tricky. Two notable exceptions were the F-101 Voodoo and F-105 Thunderchief, the latter having unique reversed-sweep, variable-ramp intakes.

Side intakes

These have been adopted for most of the combat aircraft designed since the late 1950s, freeing the nose for the installation of radar. Side mounting introduces many extra variables, as the flow field in which they operate is influenced by the shapes of the nose, fuselage underbody and canopy, nose droop and fuselage camber. They are in general subject to magnified AOA effects as a result of upwash around the fuselage contours. This is strongest at the bottom corner, diminishing as it moves upwards and outwards from that point. This may either require fuselage reshaping, as on the F-15, or alterations to the inner lower lip of the intake to avoid separation at high AOA. Alternatively, high mounting of the intake on a flat-sided fuselage, as on the Jaguar, may alleviate the upwash effects. The extended upper lips featured on the A3J (RA-5), MiG-25, F-14, F-15 and Tornado are very helpful in guiding high-AOA airflows into the inlet. This is a form of inlet shielding, but without the use of wings or leading-edge extension.

Central to the success of a side-mounted inlet, shielded or not, is the need for adequate handling of the fuselage boundary layer, which will suffer from the combined effects of AOA and sideslip. It may be thought that protection from sideslip is afforded by the body, but it has been found that the growth of the fuselage boundary layer can produce adverse flow at the inlet. Hence the very wide diverters seen on aircraft with side-mounted intakes.

Shielded side-mounted intakes

Intake shielding by the wing may be used to reduce intake AOA during manoeuvring flight, effectively turning the flow before it reaches the intake. A comparison of pressure recovery with AOA for four different designs is shown in Fig 122. Judging from this alone, both wing-shielded intakes (B-3 and B-4) would appear to have significant advantages. But when account was taken of behaviour in sideslip, it was found that the performance of

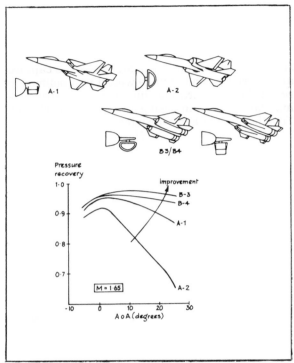

Fig 122 Effect of intake shielding at supersonic speed.[45]

intake B-4 dropped off sharply with leeward sideslip, a result of massive flow separation on the inboard sideplate. The half-axisymmetric B-3 faired better because the inboard part of the flow was deflected into the intake by the spike. The technique of wing-shielded intakes is not at all straightforward, as the following examples show.

Chief among the distinctive features of the Republic F-105D Thunderchief are its unusual forward-swept wing-root intakes. Designed in the 1950s, the big fighter-bomber had the "coke bottle" fuselage characteristic of types built in conformity with the area rules for minimum supersonic drag. (Republic)

Wing shielding was attempted on the F-111, on which the inlet is located in the fuselage/wing root junction. This was chosen to minimise wetted area and to benefit from the wing shock pre-compression, thereby reducing the intake capture area. A reduction in intake weight was claimed to result from integrating the supporting structure into the fuselage and using a relatively short duct. Together with other characteristics of the F-111's quarter-cone inlet mentioned elsewhere, this degree of integration was the undoing of the design and is not likely to be attempted again.

A very successful degree of shielding has been achieved on the YF-17/F-18. The shielding is provided by the highly swept wing leading-edge extension (LEX). Intakes under the wing encounter flow at an angle significantly less than the aircraft's AOA as a result of the flow-turning effect of the wing. The effectiveness of the LEX in reducing intake flow angles at subsonic speed is shown in Fig 123. The flow angle at the intake is around 60% of the aircraft's AOA, while intakes mounted ahead of the wing experience AOAs higher than that of the aircraft. Similar advantages are realised at supersonic speed, with the added bonus

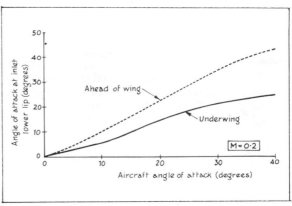

Fig 123 How inlet location affects flow angularity at low speed.[27]

of wing pre-compression. Benefiting also from careful lip shaping, this underwing intake achieves high pressure recovery and low distortion to give a 5% thrust improvement at Mach 1·6. Used on a twin-engined aircraft, the short ducts, which require no abrupt change in cross-section, mini-

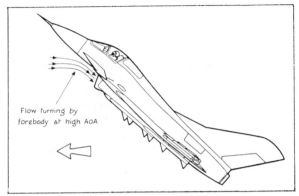

Fig 124 How forebody assists EAP ventral inlet flow at high AOA.

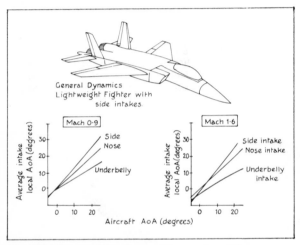

Fig 125 Effect of intake position on local flow AOA.[46]

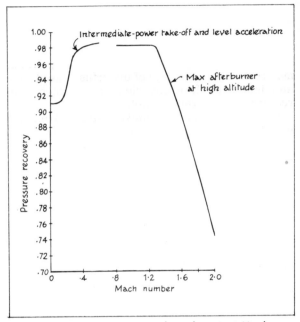

Fig 126 Pressure recovery plotted against Mach number, from YF-16 flight tests.[46]

mise weight and cost. However, the YF-17 required a complicated boundary-layer diverter design with its splitter plate mounted 13cm from the fuselage side, together with splitter-plate bleeding.

Ventral intakes

A ventral intake was originally used on the F-86D as a means of allowing a nose radar to be fitted. This type of intake has subsequently appeared, moving aft, over the years, on the F-8 Crusader, Fiat G.91, Nord 1500 Griffon, Hawker P.1121, F-16 and the BAe EAP (Fig 124).

Ventral location shields the intake at high AOA (Fig 124). The aircraft forebody is an efficient flow straightener which helps in maintaining high pressure recovery and low distortion, especially when the fuselage is locally wider than the intake.

It can also produce pre-entry compression at supersonic speed.

Disadvantages include magnified sideslip characteristics; enforced location aft of the nose-wheel (for stowage and FOD avoidance), which may restrict the carriage of underfuselage stores; and increased forebody side area, which may require a larger vertical tail.

In arriving at the F-16 intake, General Dynamics investigated the flow field properties of nose, side and ventral locations. Some of the results are shown in Fig 125. At an aircraft AOA of 25° in the transonic regime the local flow angle of the ventral intake is only 15°, whereas the side inlets are receiving air at 33°. At Mach 1·6 and $\alpha = 25°$ the respective angles are 12° and 30°. In addition, the flow straightening provided by the fuselage minimises the cowl lip bluntness required and reduces the spillage drag. Compared with the alternative side inlets, the ventral intake was found to have 6% less drag in cruise and 20% less during Mach 0·8 manoeuvres; it was also 180kg lighter.

The precompression at supersonic speed increased pressure recovery significantly (Fig 126). With the intake located 4m from the air-craft nose a thinner boundary layer is encountered, allowing a smaller diverter height with less drag and without the fuselage-corner effects met with side-mounted inlets. The intake lower lip is 1·2 equivalent intake diameters above the ground, and though small vortices of water have been seen to enter, the intake is 25cm higher off the ground than those of a Boeing 737, which is relatively free of FOD. Though General Dynamics concedes that side inlets could have been made to work adequately, they represented a more complex problem and a greater technical risk.

Dorsal intakes

Until recently dorsal intakes have been poorly regarded on account of the inferior quality of the

The need to reduce radar cross-section has led the designers of many of the contenders in the USAF Advanced Tactical Fighter contest to select dorsal intakes. One of the first aircraft with such an intake was the North American F-107A, which first flew in 1956 in competition with the F-105. The absence of a rudder indicates the use of an all-moving fin. (North American)

flow at the intake face at even moderate AOAs. In fact only one fighter is known to have flown with a dorsal intake. This was the North American F-107A, a development of the F-100 which had a central splitter plate and twin variable-compression ramps. The Boeing Model 188, a TFX contender, had twin dorsal intakes but never flew. Two Soviet designs have a form of dorsal, or at least high-mounted, intake, these being the Tu-22 Blinder and Tu-98 Backfin.

Because the AOA capability requirement for strike aircraft is not as demanding as that for fighters, and because dorsal intakes minimise ground-based radar reflectivity, they have been proposed for several future strike aircraft, including the USAF's Advanced Tactical Fighter, due for service in the mid-1990s. It has been argued that careful integration of the inlet on top of the fuselage to take maximum advantage of the sweeping action of the vortical flows from, for example, a leading-edge extension of the wing can control pressure recovery and dynamic distortion to give intake performance comparable to that of more traditional locations. The subsonic Handley Page HP.115 slender-delta research aircraft of 1961 exploited vortices to give a good entry flow and hence pressure recovery to a dorsally mounted engine. The wing vortices were very powerful, being generated by the sharp, 75°-swept leading edge. No intake problems were experienced, even though an AOA in excess of 45° was reached.

Underwing intakes

Though mounting the intakes and therefore engines under the wings is not appropriate to fighter aircraft because of the resulting high roll inertia, this arrangement does have several advantages. Chief among these are:

1 The underwing Mach number is less than the freestream value, so that the potential pressure recovery is increased.

2 Incident flow angles due to aircraft AOA are greatly reduced. Care must however be taken to ensure that the changes in the local wing flow field with AOA do not provoke a growth of the wing's boundary layer, which might then be ingested by the intake.

3 The forces associated with intake spillage and flow turning in the compression process may be used to give lift components which improve the lift/drag ratio of the installation.

4 Access to the powerplant for maintenance is straightforward.

Against these must be set the problem of FOD and the yawing moments arising after engine failure. All in all, the location is more appropriate to multi-engine aircraft such as the B-1 (which has its nacelles toed in by $\frac{1}{2}$° to align the intakes with the local flow at cruise Mach numbers) and Soviet Blackjack bombers.

INTAKE TYPE

Compression surfaces

While the rounded-lip intake is good for subsonic and manoeuvring flight, the intense shock wave which would form just ahead of the lips at supersonic speed would result in a huge loss of pressure recovery. The earliest supersonic aircraft, typified by the F-100, used sharp lips on the simplest form of intake. Known as the pitot intake, this was an oval opening with a very long subsonic duct. Variations on this theme led to the cone-shaped spikes which appeared on the Lightning and MiG-21. Though one function of these spikes was to house small radar dishes, their effect on intake performance at supersonic speed is very significant.

The only means of decelerating a supersonic airstream is by means of a shock wave, which causes a loss of stagnation pressure. The higher the Mach number ahead of the shock, the lower the Mach number behind it and the greater the loss of total pressure. This loss is reduced by generating a number of weaker shocks rather than a single strong one. For intakes, the supersonic deceleration or compression (because it involves an abrupt rise in static pressure and density) upstream of the throat is achieved more efficiently by a surface inclined against the flow. This generates an initial oblique shock wave, so that the second normal shock (i.e., one right angles to the flow, with subsonic flow downstream of it) is comparatively weak. Without any precompression surface (spike or wedge), there is a single normal shock, with its very large loss of pressure recovery at high supersonic speed. This is shown in Fig 127, which compares the intake efficiency of a simple pitot intake (single normal shock wave) with one incorporating a wedge so that two shock waves are generated (one oblique plus one normal shock). The figure shows that the crippling 27% loss at Mach 2·0 for the pitot intake is reduced to 9% when a wedge is introduced. This was precisely the reason for the appearance of shock cones on the F-104, Mirage III, Tu-28 and Northrop P530 and of wedge surfaces of the F-106 and F-4 in the 1960s and F-14, F-15 and F-18 in the 1970s.

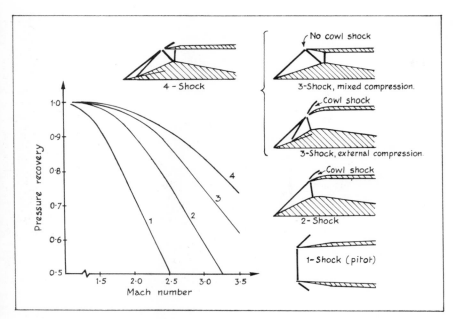

Fig 127 Various types of intake geometry and their effect on pressure recovery.[47]

Fig 128 Shock structure of F-14 intake.[48]

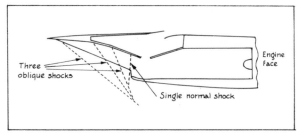

Further improvements can be achieved by using more sloping surfaces, though at the expense of extra complexity, cost, weight and drag, the last of which penalises transonic acceleration. Whether the effort is worthwhile depends on the emphasis on supersonic performance in the design specification. If the design Mach number is less than 1·5, a simple pitot intake is probably the best choice. Even above Mach 1·5, if it is acceleration rather than top speed that is wanted the addition of compression surfaces may not be justified. For example, the Jaguar was originally designed with fixed 7° wedges which were subsequently deleted when wind-tunnel testing revealed that a straight-forward pitot intake allowing some interaction between the shock system and fuselage boundary layer improved the thrust-drag margin (particularly in low-altitude cruise) up to Mach 1·5.

More recently, the normal shock-type inlet has been used on the F-16, which is capable of reaching Mach 2. The selection process for the intake included studies of a pitot, single-shock intake in competition with a Mach 2 fixed wedge and a Mach 2·2 variable-geometry inlet. The Mach 2 fixed inlet showed no benefit in air combat, with a significant deficiency in acceleration time and Mach 1·2 turn rate as a result of increased weight and drag of the larger inlet. This inlet also required a bypass system for intake/engine airflow matching at supersonic speeds. The only benefit from the variable-geometry intake was in specific excess power at Mach 1·6. General Dynamics concluded that for the F-16 mission requirements the fixed

normal-shock inlet was the best, even without taking cost into account. Pending a requirement for higher speeds, the inlet was designed into a 2·4m-long module to provide for enlargement of the inlet to accommodate engine airflow growth or for incorporation of variable geometry.

If high supersonic speed is the driving force, then increasing the number of wedges is the way to improve pressure recovery. The best intake in this respect is the isentropic type, a curved wedge giving an infinite number of infinitely weak shocks terminating in a weak normal shock. But this has never been a design aim, for three reasons: high cowl-lip drag, poor off-design performance, and shock/boundary-layer interactions. The largest number of wedges so far flown on large-production-run aircraft is three, typified by the F-14 and F-15 (Fig 128).

The benefits to pressure recovery of using multiple wedges are indicated in Fig 127, which shows the maximum values achievable, assuming optimum geometry for the various configurations.

An increase in the number of wedges results in the flow being turned through a large angle relative to the freestream. Consequently, lip angles and hence cowl drag are high. Furthermore, as the number of wedges increases, so the extra-to-shock losses increase. These losses are in part due to the inter-action of shocks on the wedge boundary layers and on the side of the inlet, which can rapidly negate the benefit of the increased compression efficiency. Herein lies the need for careful boundary-layer removal.

External versus external/internal intakes

The two three-shock intakes shown in Fig 127 have the same theoretical performance. The first is an all-external-compression type, which has high lip drag. By removing the second wedge from the lower surface and putting the same compression on the upper surface, the cowl lip angle can be reduced to zero, implying no lip drag. As a result some of the supersonic compression occurs within the duct, hence the name external/internal (or mixed) compression intake.

When aircraft missions require extended flight at Mach numbers above 2·5, all-external intakes become much less desirable in spite of their inherent stability and relative simplicity. At Mach 3, for instance, a typical external-compression inlet might have a final ramp angle of 40°, with a cowl lip angle of up to 30°. The shock-induced cowl drag would then be prohibitive. On the other hand, the mixed-compression inlet can accomplish, by means of a series of shock waves reflected within the duct ahead of the throat, the same efficient flow diffusion while giving low cowl drag. Two-dimensional and axi-symmetric designs have been used for mixed-compression intakes on the XB-70 and SR-71 respectively. The rectangular intake tends to be heavier but is less sensitive to AOA and easier to integrate with the airframe. The axi-symmetric is lighter and relatively short for a given application.

In order to produce high performance the mixed-compression intake must operate at a slightly "supercritical" condition (i.e. with the terminal, normal shock just downstream of the throat, see later). The shock structure includes several reflected shocks, and some idea of its complexity is given by Fig 129, which shows the structure for the XB-70 during cruise at Mach 3. This shock system will not establish itself unless the duct contraction

The largely stainless steel North American XB-70 was remarkable in many ways, not least of which was the intake system for its six turbojets. Designed to permit cruise at Mach 3, the mixed-compression intakes developed the most complex and sensitive shock-wave system ever.

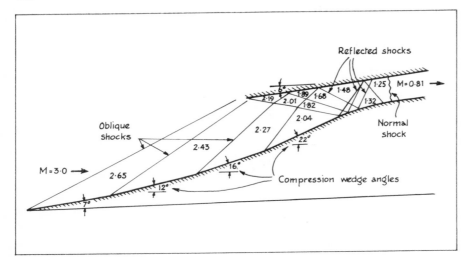

Fig 129 Complex shock structure of XB-70 intake.[49]

is reduced sufficiently. This implies variable geometry, and once the shock system is established — i.e. the intake is "started" — the geometry is adjusted until the optimum compression is achieved. Should some disturbance such as aircraft manoeuvring or a gust push the normal shock forward of the throat, it will immediately move to a position forward of the intake lip and remain there until the geometry is altered in the manner just described. This is known as inlet "unstart" and results in a very rapid deterioration of performance, usually to the level of a pitot intake with a detached shock wave. YF-12 unstarts were so violent that the pilot's helmet would hit the canopy as a result of the sudden yaw caused by the asymmetric loss of thrust.

The basic geometry of these intakes would be sufficient if the airflow entering them was uniform and ambient conditions standard. Neither of these conditions are met in practice, however, and both the XB-70 and SR-71 required a number of auxiliary doors and bleed-air passages to handle variations from design conditions. On the XB-70, for example, the intake was unable to tolerate even a 0·1° error in the setting of its large bypass doors, even though this variation was barely within the limits of accuracy of its door control system. As a result, what happened in practice was a back and forth movement of its terminal shock, known as a "buzz" and sensed by the pilot as violent buffet, while the control system hunted for the correct setting. Being an unstable mode, this could lead readily to an unstart.

Despite this degree of intolerance, a mixed-compression intake was originally designed for the Rockwell B-1 because its lower drag permitted a slightly smaller engine, which favoured the sub-

sonic mission. However, as the design and development programme proceeded, it became apparent that worthwhile reductions in complexity and weight could be obtained by relaxing the requirement and using a simple all-external intake. The resulting saving was more than 540kg per aircraft. Eventually the USAF, seeking to cut costs, agreed to accept fixed inlets, which limited the maximum Mach number to 1·6.

The reflected nature of the internal shock system and the highly sensitive nature of the required intake control system make the mixed-compression intake uncompetitive for aircraft other than those designed to cruise above Mach 2·5. In comparison, the all-external intake is lighter, has lower off-design drag levels, avoids the need for fast-acting variable-geometry control systems, and can tolerate larger AOA excursions at high supersonic speed. The all-external intake is fighter-oriented, providing a far wider stable airflow range with equal or better distortion levels than does a good mixed-compression type.

SUPERSONIC VARIABLE-GEOMETRY INTAKES

Means of altering the capture area of intakes were, until the 1970s, provided on highly supersonic aircraft to accommodate the large variation of engine airflow requirements and to maximise the pressure recovery across the supersonic region of the flight envelope. Then came a need to handle the demand for enlarged manoeuvre envelopes. This section is therefore divided into two parts, with the latter part examining how variable geometry contributes to enhanced manoeuvrability.

Contribution to pressure recovery

With the normal shock wave standing at the throat in the "critical" condition, improvement in pressure recovery can be obtained by altering the angle of the compression wedge. As the angle of the wedge is increased, the total pressure loss across the oblique shock increases. But as the Mach number behind it is reduced, so the strength of the terminal normal shock decreases and with it the total pressure loss across the normal shock. Up to certain angles this procedure yields an overall gain in pressure recovery and therefore a gain in thrust.

Mass-flow control

The engine airflow requirements of a combat aircraft vary greatly across the flight spectrum. For high thrust at take-off and rapid climb and acceleration at subsonic speed a typical supersonic engine may require an inlet opening of say 0·5m². In the lower-thrust transonic regime perhaps only 0·25m² will suffice, whereas at Mach 2·5 the intake may again be required to capture 0·5m². The intake must be capable of adequately handling the full range of airflows. Whether this demands variable geometry depends largely on the maximum design speed.

Intake behaviour as mass flow is varied

Before examining the range of options open to the designer it is worthwhile briefly examining supersonic intake behaviour as air mass flow is varied. The characteristic curve of the simplest type of multi-shock intake, the single-wedge two-shock system, is shown in Fig 130. At low mass flow, as at Point A, the normal shock is expelled forward to enable the excess air to be spilled over the outside of the lip. Some of the air entering the intake in this condition passes through the single shock formed by the fusion of the normal and oblique shocks and therefore enters the diffuser at a lower total pressure than the air nearer the wedge, which has passed through the two shocks. There is therefore a lower pressure recovery at this point. In such conditions of flow spillage the intake is said to be "subcritical".

As mass flow is increased, the pressure recovery improves slightly and reaches a maximum as the normal shock passes into the throat (Point B). At this point the mass flow has also reached a maximum and the intake is said to be running "full" or "critical". Any further increase in engine speed would only reduce the back pressure downstream of the normal shock, causing the wave to move into the diverging diffuser. There is no increase in mass flow as the stream tube, now at the lip, cannot be influenced by further changes in intake condition.

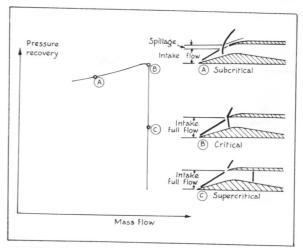

Fig 130 Characteristic curve for mass flow versus pressure recovery for the simplest type of multi-shock intake.[47]

There is however a reduction in pressure recovery, since the normal shock now has a higher Mach number in front of it than it did when sitting at the throat. The intake is now said to be "supercritical".

Intake buzz

At some subcritical mass flow the normal shock will begin to oscillate violently. Known as subcritical instability or "buzz", this condition is to be avoided since the instantaneous peak pressures can be twice as large as the steady-state pressures. At a low mass flow the shock will move rapidly forwards (i.e. upstream) along the wedge and, because it is an abrupt pressure rise, will cause the surface boundary layer to lift. This reduces the flow area and effectively chokes the intake, thereby reducing the mass flow, forcing the shock further forward. The momentum of the air already in the diffuser downstream of the shock wave reduces the pressure at the throat, however, so reversing the pressure gradient at the top of the wedge and re-attaching the boundary layer. With the back pressure on the shock reduced, the wave moves rearwards (downstream) into the diffuser, putting the intake into the supercritical condition. This increases the mass flow to beyond the level that the engine will accept. To adjust matters the shock is expelled and the cycle repeated. The amplitude and frequency of the oscillations depend upon the mass flow and duct length, with typical values ranging from 20 to 200Hz. One of the duties of intake control systems is to ensure that intake buzz is avoided by means of appropriate sequencing of bypass systems.

Coping with mass-flow variations

The range of required mass flows can be accommodated in three ways:

1 Bleeding excess air through bypass doors after it has entered the inlet. This has already been discussed.

2 Arranging the intake geometry to set up an oblique shock wave in front of the inlet so that air is spilled around it. This implies fixed geometry, as on the Lightning and F-106, which gives a reduction of overall thrust minus drag, except when the shock is focused at the intake lip.

3 Physically reducing the freestream opening of the inlet by using a variable-angle ramp(s) or expanding spike.

At supersonic speed intake spillage results in an increasingly severe drag penalty as speed increases. This can only be alleviated by reducing the amount of air to be spilled. This means adopting a variable-capture-area inlet, as described in **3** above.

Means of varying inlet capture area

Capture area can be varied in a number of ways. The MiG-21 has a three-position nose spike; the Mirage III, of similar vintage, has translating half-cones; and the half-cones on the TSR.2 pivoted outwards to reduce flow area. The F-111 variable-geometry intake is unusually complex, featuring both a variable second cone angle and translation of the fore-cone, as shown in Fig 131. This high-lights one of the main drawbacks to the axi-symmetric intake on highly supersonic aircraft: the cone cannot collapse enough to provide the large

Fig 131 F-111A variable-geometry intake.[43]

subsonic flow area required. As seen in the figure, the second conical ramp can vary from 10·5° to 24°, with the first ramp angle fixed at 12·5°. At low speed the spike is forward and the cone collapsed; at high speed the spike is aft and the cone fully expanded. The positions of the intake components are normally controlled by the automatic inlet control system (AICS), which senses local Mach number ahead of the inlet and duct exit Mach number and shapes the control input as a function of engine airflow. The computation is done by a 3-D cam which mechanically stores the functional relationship. The other major user of axi-symmetric variable geometry inlets is the YF-12/SR-71, the spike of which is fully forward and locked for maximum capture area below 9,000m. Above that altitude the spikes unlock and start receding at Mach 1·6 to reduce capture area, and are fully aft at Mach 3 (Fig 132).

Variable geometry for two-dimensional intakes was first used on the F-4 Phantom, which features a vertical fixed ramp, followed by a movable ramp creating a variable throat area and engine bypass slot. Similar intakes can be seen on the Soviet Su-15 and MiG-23. The two aircraft which succeeded the F-4 — the F-14 for the US Navy and F-15 for the Air Force — feature two movable horizontally mounted supersonic compression wedges. The intake of the F-14 is shown in Fig 133, in which the ability of the wedges to over-collapse for low speed and open up for high speed to expose the ramp bypass void is apparent. A similar intake is pre-sumably used on the MiG-25, MiG-29 and MiG-31. The Tornado has only a single movable supersonic compression ramp.

The weight, complexity and life-cycle cost of variable-geometry intakes are such they can be

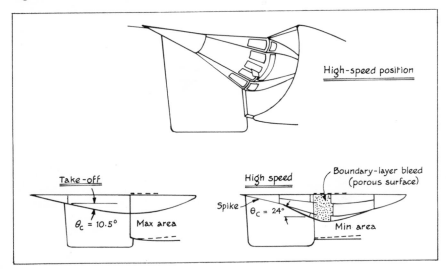

High-speed position

Take-off

$\theta_c = 10.5°$ Max area

High speed

Spike $\theta_c = 24°$

Boundary-layer bleed
(porous surface)

Min area

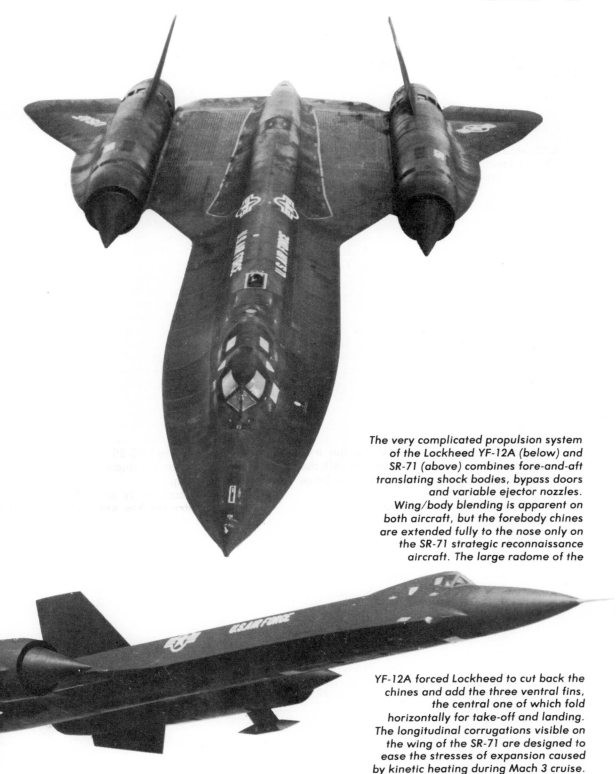

The very complicated propulsion system of the Lockheed YF-12A (below) and SR-71 (above) combines fore-and-aft translating shock bodies, bypass doors and variable ejector nozzles. Wing/body blending is apparent on both aircraft, but the forebody chines are extended fully to the nose only on the SR-71 strategic reconnaissance aircraft. The large radome of the

YF-12A forced Lockheed to cut back the chines and add the three ventral fins, the central one of which fold horizontally for take-off and landing. The longitudinal corrugations visible on the wing of the SR-71 are designed to ease the stresses of expansion caused by kinetic heating during Mach 3 cruise.

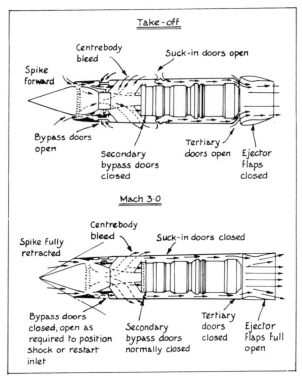

Fig 132 SR-71 variable-geometry intake and engine nacelle airfloor.[38]

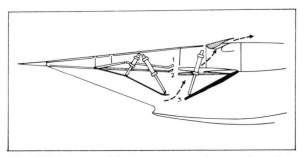

Fig 133 F-14 variable-geometry intake. **1** Take-off **2** Mach 0.5–1.2 **3** Variable above Mach 2.[18]

justified only when there is a clearly identifiable and worthwhile performance improvement. Broadly speaking, variable intake area is unlikely to pay off unless the design Mach number exceeds about 1·7. The Rockwell B-1 is restricted to Mach 1·6 with its fixed intakes, and neither the F-16 nor F-18 has a variable-geometry intake, though both are capable of Mach 2.

Variable geometry for high-AOA flight

Formidable difficulties in integrating propulsion system and airframe were overcome to produce the very wide AOA ranges of contemporary highly manoeuvrable fighters. The intake has to supply air of relatively low distortion to avoid encroachment on the surge margin of the engine, while maintaining a low level of dynamic distortion is the primary requirement at high AOA. When AOA passes 40° it becomes virtually impossible to prevent massive flow separation at the intake. It is argued that the key to low distortion at the engine face is not to delay separation but rather to control the separated region's development. A long inlet duct can help to attenuate distortion originating at the intake lip.

A high pressure recovery may also be demanded in order to maintain thrust. But the parallel effort to limit distortion at high AOA can lead to conflicting requirements or a highly complex variable-geometry intake that tries to satisfy both demands. It is argued that low levels of pressure recovery at high post-stall AOA have a negligible effect on specific excess power. The negative SEPs encountered at extreme attitudes are dominated by airframe drag-due-to-lift, which is typically four to five times greater than the available thrust. Providing that enough pressure is developed at the engine face to ensure satisfactory engine operation, high pressure recovery matters only up to the AOA at which a constant-energy turn can be performed.

The next generation of combat aircraft, featuring advanced aerodynamic design and thrust vectoring, will have greatly expanded manoeuvre envelopes, with AOAs reaching 70°. Innovative intake designs have already been proposed (Fig 134) to meet the resulting engine airflow requirements, and there is every likelihood that some of them will fly operationally, along with the various forms of intake shielding already discussed. Indeed, the rotating forward intake shown in Fig 134 has been flying on the F-15 since 1972. Unique to the F-15, it enlarges the capture area to avoid the need for auxiliary intakes at low speed and reduces it in the transonic region to avoid gross spillage. It also reduces the local AOA around the lip of the intake. The included angle of the intake's leading edge is fixed so that changing the capture area also changes the first ramp deflection angle. The total available rotation range is 15°. The inlet is fully up (maximum capture area for take-off) at − 4°, or fully down at + 11° for landing and high AOA. The objective behind the variable-capture-area inlet was the maintenance of a well-behaved shock structure (three oblique and one normal shock of approximately equal strengths) over a wider range of AOA at mid-supersonic speed. That this has been achieved is evident in Fig 135, in which the fixed-capture-area

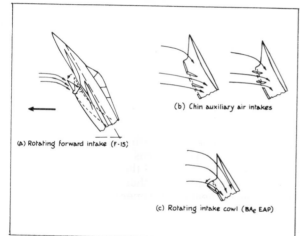

(b) Chin auxiliary air intakes

(a) Rotating forward intake (F-15)

(c) Rotating intake cowl (BAe EAP)

McDonnell Douglas F-15 prototype, with its intake upper lip drooped as if for landing and high-AOA flight. Also apparent is the wing's conical camber and the mounting of weapons in tandem to reduce drag. (McDonnell Douglas)

Fig 134 (*Left*) Variable-geometry intakes for high-AOA flight.

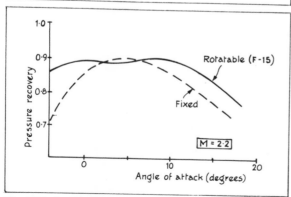

Fig 135 At Mach 2.2 the F-15's rotatable intake permits high pressure recovery over a much wider AOA range than a fixed design.[40]

pressure recovery is seen to peak in the 1°–5° AOA range, compared with the F-15's range of −2° to 12°. Comparing SEPs for a fixed-capture-area intake and the F-15's intake at Mach 1·6, 11,000m, and 5g, the fixed inlet achieves only 21% of the SEP obtained with the variable inlet.

The rotating forward intake offers an attractive means of avoiding cowl lip separation at extreme AOAs, provided that a sufficiently large radius can be achieved for the internal contour at the pivot axis. The rotating intake cowl of Fig 134 is featured on the BAe Experimental Aircraft Programme design. Like that of the F-15, its capture area can be varied as much as 10% below the maximum. An EAP-type intake could also incorporate auxiliary air intake doors of either suck-in or Venetian blind type (Fig 134), which have been shown to be very effective at high angles of attack. With doors open extremely high pressure recovery is achieved up to 70° AOA, even at Mach 0·5, because of effective fuselage shielding, and a 10% improvement in pressure recovery could result in a 15% increase in net thrust.

ENGINES

The chapter dealing with air intakes in a book concerned with the shape of aircraft must make some mention of the engine, without which the combat aircraft can do nothing. For reasons of brevity, however, the discussion is limited to engine location, number and type, all of which make a significant contribution to the layout of an aircraft.

Engine location

The advent of the jet engine forced aircraft designers to rethink the whole question of engine installation, and in the first decade of the jet era a number of solutions were tried. The first British jet, the Gloster E28/39, demonstrated a layout which subsequently became a classic on the F-86 and MiG-15 and many others, with air being taken in at the nose, devoured by the engine just aft of the pilot, and exhausted through a long jetpipe clear of all structure. The Me262 and Gloster Meteor had two wing-mounted pods, which kept intakes and jetpipes short. Other methods of minimising the volume of the installation included that of the de Havilland Vampire, with its bifurcated intake and twin-boom structure. The Hawker Sea Hawk took this a stage further by bifurcating both intake and exhaust. Bifurcated root intakes were convenient because the aircraft of the day had relatively thick wing roots.

Many aircraft appeared in the 1950s with engines tucked into the wing root in pods, as in the CF-100 and Buccaneer. This was not feasible with the delta-wing Javelin, in which the jetpipes were continued fully to the rear. These aircraft had their engines fully forward, with the CF-100 having virtually zero-length intakes but very long tailpipes. Other designers shortened the tailpipe and decreased structure weight by arranging for the engine to exhaust beneath the mid or rear fuselage, as on the early Yak-15, MiG-9 and Saab 29. This proved very popular, subsequently being applied to

twins like the F-89, F-101, F-4 and Jaguar. Twin-engined aircraft tended to have their engines further forward because a shorter intake duct is permissible in the absence of the bifurcation of single-engine types.

With the maturing of supersonic flight, the demands for variable-geometry intakes and longer intake ducts gradually pushed engines further back, allowing more room in the centre fuselage for fuel over the CG. The supersonic aircraft were generally bigger — particularly in length, for reasons of wave drag due to volume — and this made room for the aft movement of engines, along with the now inevitable afterburner. One of the aircraft which set the trend to fully rear-mounted engines was the MiG-21, with its short afterburner. Since then aircraft like the F-111, MiG-25, F-14, F-18 and Tornado (the latter two having extremely compact engines) have featured this location, which ensures that the exhaust is aft of the empennage, yielding low drag when the reheat is off and reducing heating and acoustic effects when reheat is on. The VTOL Harrier is a special case in which the engine and thrust-vectoring nozzles must straddle the aircraft CG.

Podded designs were very popular in the 1950s for US high-altitude bombers, which did not have to display the low roll inertia demanded of fighters. Wing-mounted pods relieve the wing bending moment, though at the cost of exaggerated engine-out fin and rudder requirements.

A range of podded designs was studied for the four-engined B-58. Production aircraft ultimately had pods spread across the wing, with the inboard engines about midway between root and tip and the outboards near the wingtip and inclined downwards to be aligned with the incident flow. The exhausts were then clear of the trailing edge, so avoiding scorching to the structure, a problem encountered with the twin-pod design. The total package also had a more acceptable area-ruled layout.

Podded installations are inappropriate for fighters, appearing only on a few interceptors in which high agility is not a primary aim. Pods are

A compact propulsion system and under-tail exhaust were characteristic of three McDonnell generations: the F3H Demon, F-101 Voodoo (shown here) and F-4 Phantom.

used on the F-12/SR-71 mainly to distance the complex intake and ejector nozzles from wing/fuselage interference. The problems of high asymmetric thrust and drag caused by engine failure and unstart were faced by using a stability augmentation system which rapidly provides the appropriate corrective action. Excess wetted area is the main drawback, offset by accepting a lower design load factor of only 3g and by the structural weight savings of wing bending relief.

A semi-podded design was chosen for the F-14 and considered for the F-15. Both design teams recognised the structural weight penalty as the primary drawback, with excess drag being a secondary factor. But the issue was settled by this installation's superior growth potential; smaller horizontal tail for roll control, a result of the increased moment arm about the roll axis; cleaner intake with no need for a boundary-layer diverter; and Grumman's bitter experience with the F-111's highly integrated propulsion system. When the pods were moved closer together to reduce wetted area and give better single-engine control, and the wing box was kinked to lower the fuselage, the result was "rolled inlets", with the pods canted outwards. This maintained the flow-straightening effect of the channel between the pods while providing the 10° ejection clearance required by the belly-mounted stores.

On larger swing-wing aircraft like the B-1 and Soviet Blackjack the choice of engine location is limited. Fighter-style rear mounting produces very long intake ducts, a characteristic of the Tu-26 Backfire. These produce unacceptable pressure recovery losses and create CG problems as fuel is burned and weapons released. Underwing nacelles have shorter ducts but demand a high tail position to avoid thermal and acoustic effects.

The high-mounted pods of the Tu-22 Blinder are unique, with the pods helping to fill in the area-rule gap between wing and tailplane. They are also well located for radar shielding of the intakes, and such pods are featured on at least one of the current designs for the USAF's Advanced Tactical Fighter and on Northrop's Advanced Technology Bomber.

Engine number

One of the fundamental decisions to be taken during, or perhaps before, the formative stage of a design concerns the number of engines. To a large extent, this is a policy decision influenced by considerations of safety, cost-effectiveness and availability. The aircraft manufacturer's experience of single and multi-engined installations also plays a part. The number of engines has a profound influence on fuselage shaping, dictating the dis-

position of intake ducts and fuel tanks, and having a direct influence on fuselage cross-section shape.

Safety and survivability

In the debate over the number of engines most disagreement has arisen over the likely survivability of each layout. It has been argued that few twin-engined aircraft return from battle on one engine, and that the loss of one engine often involves the loss of the other. Various studies have however shown a large number of peace-time returns on one engine, a significant proportion of which arose from engine difficulties which would have made the return of a single-engined aircraft extremely hazardous. The extra volume of a twin appears to be insignificant when account is taken of the chances of being hit, and many military users appear to favour twins on grounds of survivability. There are statistics to show that at least two single-engined aircraft are lost for every twin.

The use of a single engine on one of the most recent military types, the F-16, was partly prompted by General Dynamics' inconclusive studies of the apparent better survivability of twins. But Northrop, with its wide experience of the T-38 trainer and F-5 in combat, countered this with the view that when engines are effectively isolated a hit on one engine does not permit FOD or fire to spread to the other. One of the reasons the US Navy chose to develop the YF-17 into the F-18 was its twin-engined safety advantage when operating over water. The very hostile environment of the battlefield support role prompted both Northrop and Fairchild-Hiller to choose twins for the AX programme, as exemplified by the highly separated podded layout of the A-10.

Cost-effectiveness

When considering cost-effectiveness, there is a single question to be asked: which configuration meets the operational requirement at least overall cost. The overall cost of an aircraft breaks down into four primary areas: initial purchase cost, maintenance and operation cost, replacement of lost aircraft cost, and pilot training cost.

The USAF Light Weight Fighter programme of the 1970s is a good example of the way cost-effectiveness is argued. The General Dynamics YF-16 (single F100 turbofan) and Northrop YF-17 (twin YJ101 turbojets) were engaged in a fly-off competition. On the face of it, this would appear to be an impartial way of choosing an aircraft. Indeed, in selecting the F-16 the USAF could point to its greater agility (sustained turn rate 0·5°/sec better at Mach 1·2, 9,100m), acceleration (15secs faster from Mach 0·9 to 1·6), and endurance (370km greater radius of action in the air-superiority role, 650km greater ferry range). More influential still perhaps were Pentagon calculations showing the flyaway cost of the F-16 to be 8% less because of the extra development cost of the newer General Electric YJ101 turbojet. In contrast, the Pratt and Whitney F100 engine had already been developed for the F-15 and engine costs could therefore be spread over more units. This factor, together with the prospect of a nominally common engine for its two front-line fighters and the 36%/hr fuel saving yielded by the admittedly more complex F100 turbofan were estimated by the Pentagon to save $1·3 billion over 15 years at 1975 prices.

Northrop countered the performance shortfall argument by asserting that the YJ101 was in fact a prototype engine and that the F-17 with developed engines would match the F-16. In fact one performance area in which the YF-16 and YF-17 were equally matched was the air/ground support role, and this is one of the tasks for which the US Navy uses the F-18 with its developed F404 "leaky" turbojets.

Engine type

There are fundamentally two types of engine for modern combat aircraft, the turbojet and turbofan. Both are usually equipped with reheat (or afterburner), and one fundamental factor governing the choice of engine cycle for aircraft roles is the proportion of augmentation achieved using reheat. The turbojet produces a high proportion of its thrust without reheat but displays poor fuel economy. The turbofan gives a lower proportion of its thrust cold but has much better fuel consumption. Turbofans can achieve as much as 100% boost with reheat — as in the case of the RB.199, which powers the Tornado — but at the cost of very high fuel consumption. The specific fuel consumption (SFC) of the F-14 Tomcat's TF30s is 0·07kg/hr/N thrust cold but 0·29kg/hr/N with afterburner. Because the thrust is also then increased from 54,700N to 93,400N, fuel flow is increased almost sevenfold!

The key to the turbofan's superior cold SFC is the bypass ratio (BPR), the highest for any combat aircraft being 1:1, as demonstrated by the RB.199. Though high BPR yields unrivalled cruise endurance at low altitude, turbofans gasp more readily for air than turbojets when taken to altitude. The very high pressure ratios and high BPRs of turbofans are not easily reconciled with medium-altitude dogfighting. The F100 turbofan (more properly a "leaky" turbojet when compared with civil turbofans) has a BPR of 0·7. In choosing the F100 for the F-16 rather than the less leaky YJ101 (BPR = 0·2), General Dynamics found that for the Light Weight Fighter mission (which entailed a 930km high-subsonic cruise, a maximum-afterburner acceleration with subsonic and supersonic sustained turns, plus a 20min sea-level reserve) use of the F100 saved 590kg of fuel and produced a better supersonic thrust-to-weight ratio. The 70% greater mission radius demonstrated in the LWF fly-off was attributed by General Dynamics to the F100's lower installation weight and fuel flow, in equal proportions. However, the F100 was not entirely troublefree on either the F-15 or F-16. On the former, problems were occasionally encountered with reheat lighting when pressure surges from the afterburner passed upstream in the bypass duct and stalled the fan. This was eventually overcome by extending the fan inflow divider.

The YJ101's much lower bypass ratio and the nature of its design overcame such problems, the bypass air being used only to cool the afterburner and nozzle. Derived from the YJ101 was the F404, which retains this feature but has a higher BPR of 0·34 to give better cruise fuel consumption. In this sense it is very similar to the engines being designed for the USAF's Advanced Tactical Fighter. This aircraft was originally intended to cruise supersonically on the power of an engine of around 125kN thrust without reheat, giving high fuel economy and reduced infra-red signature.

Engine evolution has always been a major driving force in aircraft development. Until recently it was the soaring growth in thrust levels that gave designers their biggest opportunities. Now, however, the emphasis has switched to maintaining output while reducing the bulk of the powerplant. This is exemplified by Fig 136, which compares the J79 turbojet, powerplant of the Phantom, with the F404.

Fig 136 Two generations of jet engine. The newer and smokeless F404 produces as much thrust as the smoky J79 for half the weight and volume and is used on the F-18, F-20 and Gripen.[50]

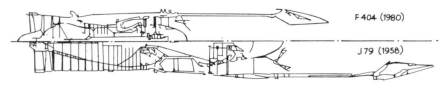

F 404 (1980)

J 79 (1958)

CHAPTER 3

FUSELAGE DESIGN

INTRODUCTION

This chapter deals with the design of the fuselage, the main function of which is to accommodate the crew and house the communications and navigation equipment, the flight control system, and search and fire-control systems. A typical combat aircraft also carries within the fuselage a large proportion of its fuel load and its engines, though these may be podded to lie alongside the body. In addition, at least some components of the undercarriage will be housed within the fuselage, as will a gun and its ammunition. Fuselage-mounted missiles are likely to have their ejection units within it, the more so if for drag reasons the weapons are semi-submerged in the aircraft belly.

The number of engines has a profound influence on mid-fuselage shaping, dictating the layout of the air-intake ducting and fuel tanks and the cross-sectional shape. Not all combat aircraft have body-submerged engines, however, so this book's brief discussion of powerplants will be found in Chapter 2, dealing with air intakes.

This chapter begins by examining nose and forebody shaping. Attention is drawn to the influence that forebody camber, dictated by cockpit visibility considerations, can have on tailplane trim drag. The flow around the nose of an aircraft at high AOA is addressed, since it was found in the 1960s that such flows were having a markedly adverse influence on the handling qualities of certain aircraft. Two other aspects of forebody shaping are also discussed, namely nose-radar requirements and cockpit and canopy design.

The centre fuselage and its volume requirements are examined in conjunction with wing/body blending and the various area rules, which are combined to give minimum drag. Finally, the rear fuselage and fuselage length are briefly discussed, along with the compromise imposed by the shipboard use of supersonic aircraft.

NOSE AND FORWARD FUSELAGE

This section is regarded as including the cockpit and everything forward of it, and is often referred to as the forebody. The nose is the area forward of the cockpit.

Forebody shaping

Several considerations underly the shape of the forebody:

1 Cockpit visibility requirements usually govern forebody camber.

2 High-AOA handling influences forebody length, cross-sectional shape and the application of nose strakes.

3 The requirements of radar and laser-ranging installations influence nose size and shape.

4 Crew accommodation, including cockpit canopy design, governs the cross-sectional area.

Forward camber

One of the commonest reasons for forward fuselage cambering is the requirement for over-the-nose visibility, as illustrated by the following case histories.

Jaguar   One of the earliest questions in the Jaguar programme related to the rear-seat view over the nose of the trainer version. Experience with the Gnat advanced trainer lay behind the RAF's request for much improved rear-seat view. Performance calculations were made for a range of cambered noses in which the two crew members were staggered vertically. One of the limits on camber was imposed by the risk of the drooped nose being hit during the firing of fuselage — mounted missiles.

In the event the British had to accept some loss of visibility while the French got a better view than they had asked for, albeit in a slightly larger and more expensive aircraft. It is interesting to compare the concern with nose droop on the Jaguar with the remarkable vertical stagger achieved on the Hawk, with its flat fuselage undersurface.

Northrop T-38   A similar need for rear-cockpit view was met in the T-38, which not only features downward camber but has a dash of upward camber too (Fig 137). This was done in order to reduce the download on the nose caused by the cambered cockpit section and to increase overall fuselage lift slightly. This forebody lift decreases

Fig 137 Downward camber on the Northrop T-38 tramer was needed to meet rear-seat vision requirements. The resulting nose-down pitching moment is countered by upward camber forward of the cockpit, which also reduces tail download and trim drag.[6]

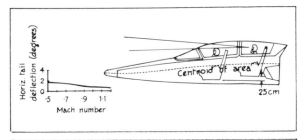

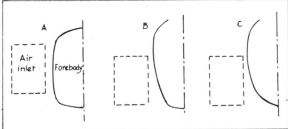

Fig 138 F-15 forebody evolution.

the required tail download by shifting C_{m_o} (pitching moment coefficient) positively, but does not produce any measurable body drag-due-to-lift penalty, which would cancel out the overall drag-due-to-lift benefit of the smaller tail download. Furthermore, the lifting forebody helps to reduce supersonic trim drag, as the aerodynamic centre moves aft.

Grumman F-14   The use of nose camber on the Model 303E was considered by Grumman for its submission to the US Navy in the VFX programme. The VFX, which was to become the F-14, was required to use direct lift control (DLC) on the landing approach prior to interception of the glide-slope. To comply with this requirement the Model 303E needed 2° more over the-nose visibility. Grumman argued that the Navy should relax this demand in its own interests, though the company was mindful of the criticism levelled at the F-111B (Navy version) on the score of cockpit visibility.

The additional 2° of visibility could have been obtained by drooping the nose of the aircraft, so avoiding an increase in maximum cross-sectional area. However, as seen with the T-38, increasing nose camber produces an undesirable nose-down pitching moment, especially at supersonic speeds. As an alternative Grumman offered to raise the pilot an amount equivalent to the extra 2°, thereby avoiding nose droop. However, the alteration to the

canopy lines increased cross-sectional area by 0·16m² and produced a drag increase of 13 drag counts (ΔC_D = 0·0013) at Mach 1·2 and a weight increase of 14kg, which combined to increase acceleration time from Mach 0·8 to Mach 1·8 by six seconds[52].

Grumman regarded neither nose drooping nor pilot elevation as acceptable, and eventually succeeded in persuading the Navy that modified procedures and a revised DLC switch on the control column was the best way of ensuring a safe approach.

McDonnell Douglas F-15   Flow field tests were carried out on the F-15 to establish the best means of integrating air inlet and forebody. Three basic fuselage cross sections and their corresponding inlet locations were examined (Fig 138). Configuration A, with its flat bottom, sharp lower corners and flat sides, produced flow separations, the low-energy air of which entered the air intakes, degrading their performance. It was reasoned that any cross-flow off the fuselage at combinations of high AOA and sideslip would tend to separate at the maximum fuselage width. Accordingly, configuration B had increased lower corner radii, with maximum fuselage width raised above the inlet. It was successful in increasing intake entry flow uniformity. Configuration C took the reasoning further by enlarging the lower corner radius to the extent that the flatness of the fuselage bottom still evident in B was entirely eliminated. Not only was the range of attitudes for good intake entry flow extended but the flow quality itself was improved.

Another F-15 forward fuselage design change removed much of the nose droop. At low AOA with sideslip this was causing downwash at the air inlet which threatened to impair the effectiveness of the inlet's first compression ramp. The final forebody design was Configuration C with raised nose.

Forebody length and shape with reference to high-AOA flight

The legacy of inadequate handling at high AOA of aircraft of the Vietnam War era spawned a new breed of fighters in the 1970s. One of the characteristics of these aircraft is their ability to manoeuvre at much higher angles of attack.

The aerodynamics of aircraft forebodies can have a dominating effect on stability at post-stall angles of attack. The vortical fin's effectiveness is often severely degraded by immersion in the low-energy wake leaving the wing, and furthermore is subject to the vortices shed by the forebody.

Forebody vortex flows

The vortices which emanate from the forebody can be very intense and, depending on their orienta-

Fig 139 Variation in yawing moment at high angles of attack and zero sideslip.[51]

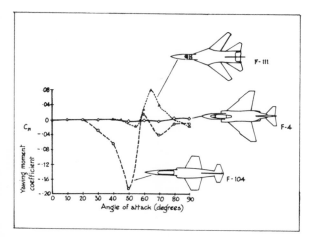

teristics of the vortices, an aircraft may be departure-prone or departure-resistant.

The pioneer in the understanding and exploitation of such nose vortex flows is the Northrop Corporation. The high spin-resistance of both the T-38 and F-5 bears testimony to this.[52, 53]

Asymmetric vortices   The phenomenon of asymmetric vortex-shedding was originally the preserve of missile aerodynamics. But the trend towards very high forebody fineness ratios in fighter aircraft has meant that they too are now affected. Forebody fineness ratio is defined as forebody length ÷ max diameter. In Fig 140 forebody length is expressed as a proportion of the mean aerodynamic chord (MAC) of the wing.

The vortex system, which is symmetric at low angles, can, for sufficiently slender forebodies, become asymmetric at high AOAs as shown in Fig 141. The two cases of low AOA and high AOA for a circular-section fuselage are represented in Fig 142, which shows the vortex arrangement for zero sideslip. At high AOA the asymmetric pattern generates a forebody force with a large sideways component. Acting a long way ahead of the air-

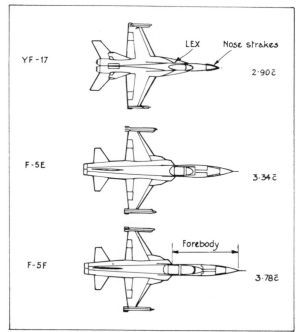

Fig 140 Typical fighter forebody lengths, expressed as a proportion of the mean aerodynamic chord of the wing.[52]

Fig 141 Forebody vortex patterns.

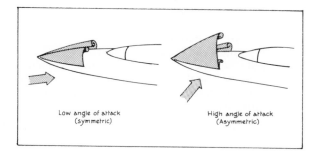

tion, can produce large yawing moments at zero sideslip, as shown for several well-known aircraft in Fig 139. These vortices can also determine the degree of directional stability of a configuration. In particular these vortical flows can largely determine the high-AOA handling qualities and departure and spin-resistance of a fighter. Depending on the strength, orientation and breakdown charac-

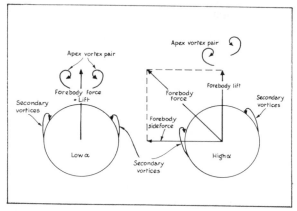

Fig 142 How forebody vortices generate a sideforce at high angles of attack.

craft's CG, the sideforce can produce very large yawing moments at zero sideslip and is the reason behind the striking curves already shown in Fig 139.

The designers responsible for the crop of highly manoeuvrable fighter aircraft which appeared in the 1970s had to take account of these flow asymmetries. Parameters influencing the formation of forebody vortices include nose fineness ratio, bluntness, and cross-sectional shape. All of these are featured to a greater or lesser extent on the most recent aircraft and have been supplemented by the use of nose strakes.

Forebody fineness ratio

Increasing fineness ratio tends to produce large asymmetric yawing moments and lowers the angle of attack at which the asymmetries occur. Ideally, any forebody shape of given fineness ratio should have zero yawing moment at zero sideslip throughout the operating range of AOA. However, forebodies of large enough fineness ratio will probably always suffer from some asymmetric aerodynamic characteristics.

Nose effect on stability

In addition to the effects of forebody vortices on aerodynamic asymmetries, properly shaped forebodies can provide a favourable contribution to stability at high AOA. For example, the Northrop F-5A nose shape was found to be the major contributor to the directional stability of the aircraft at post-stall AOA (Fig 143). On the downwind side the vortices shed by the near-elliptical nose separate, while on the upwind side they provide a strong suction force on the nose to produce a stabilising yawing moment.

Effect of nose cross-sectional shape

The cross-sectional shape of the nose from the apex to two or three diameters aft has a dominant effect on directional stability at high AOA. This is con-

Fig 143 Nose effect on directional stability.[52]

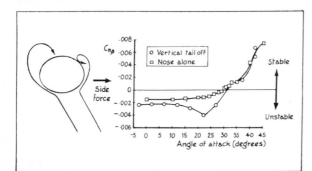

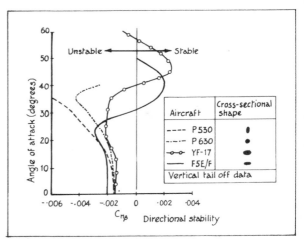

Fig 144 Effect of nose shape on directional stability.[52]

firmed by Fig 144, which shows the variation of directional stability with AOA for several notional finless configurations. The Northrop F-5E/F, P530, YF-17 and P630 configuration shown represent a wide range of nose shapes. As would be expected of configurations lacking vertical stabilisers, all the configurations are unstable up to 30° AOA at least, though at around 20° the cross-sectional shapes begin to assert their individuality. The horizontal elliptic shape of the F-5E/F becomes stable, whereas the vertical ellipse of the F530 becomes more unstable.

The data shown in Fig 144 are only a token example of the large body of evidence supporting the view that flattened nose shapes are very conducive to positive directional stability at high AOA. Such shapes are however longitudinally destabilising, particularly when the lift generated by the nose is far ahead of the aircraft's CG. Northrop compared the variation in pitching moment due to sideslip of the contrasting nose shapes shown in Fig 144. It was found that a horizontally aligned elliptic nose produced significant nose-up pitch above 25° AOA, whereas a vertically aligned elliptic nose showed the opposite tendency. Such side effects can however be put to good use, as in the case of the Northrop F-5. The nose-up pitching moment due to sideslip exhibited by this aircraft at high AOA was appreciated by its pilots. They used the technique of "walking" the rudder pedals in low-speed, full-aft-stick, extreme-attitude manoeuvres to generate enough yaw and thus positive pitching moment to hold the aircraft's nose up for longer.

Nose strakes

A clear distinction has to be drawn between

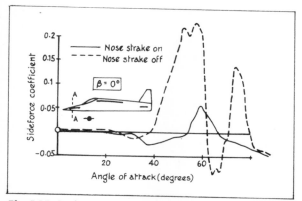

Fig 145 Reduction in sideforce due to nose strakes.[54]

strakes mounted on the nose and those which are integral with the wing-root junction (i.e. leading-edge extensions). Nose strakes are designed to ensure that the forebody vortices will be shed symmetrically at zero sideslip and take the form of thin strips at the maximum breadth of the body (Fig 140). Their very significant effect is shown in Fig 145. Without strakes the excursions in yawing moment for zero sideslips as AOA increases are extremely large and abruptly change sign at around $\alpha = 60°$. The directional stability of the YF-17 was improved by nose strakes, though they were deleted on the F-18 to improve radar performance (see later).

Nose strakes were tested early in the YF-16 programme and, though not eventually used, were found to benefit lateral/directional stability. It was found that strake width and length were the most significant design parameters. Nose strakes were used on the early dual-role versions of the Alpha Jet to improve spinning, whereas other versions have pointed noses for minimum drag or a cropped pointed nose to take a laser ranger.

The great value of nose strakes lies in the fact that without them the vortices shed by the forebody come off at varying positions along the nose, depending on the AOA and sideslip. Nose strakes fix the origins of the vortices so that they are directed along the fuselage in a symmetrical manner.

Nose strakes have a more profound influence on directional stability than forebody strakes/leading-edge extensions since the latter are usually located aft of the actual origin of the forebody vortices. Unfortunately, while in many cases they effectively reduce the asymmetries at zero sideslip, nose strakes can also adversely affect the forebody's contribution to directional stability. Thus the effect of the nose strakes cannot be regarded as consistent, depending as it does on other aspects of the configuration.

Effect of nose bluntness

Nose radius plays a significant role not only in delaying the onset of directional asymmetries to higher angles of attack but also in reducing their intensity. The magnitude of the sideforce on a circular-cross-section nose has been found to decrease with increasing bluntness. In the late 1970s Northrop developed a new nose with a broad, flat, elliptical shape reminiscent of a shark's snout. The geometry of the Shark nose, as it is called, is compared in Fig 146 with that of a production F-5 nose. The Shark nose was developed to attenuate further asymmetric vortex formation while enhancing the favourable directional stability effects at zero sideslip. Evidence indicating Northrop's success in this effort is given in Fig 147.

Fig 146 Geometry of Northrop's Shark nose.

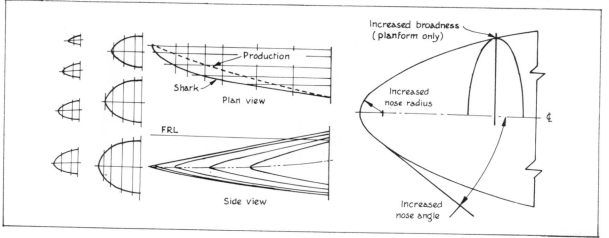

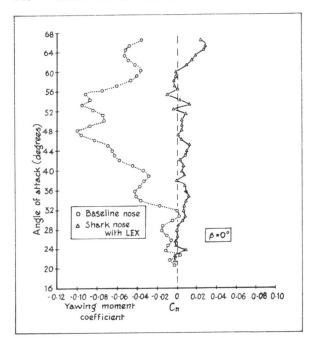

Fig 147 Effect of Shark nose on aerodynamic asymmetries.[52]

Forebody shape and its influence on spinning

One notable instance in which forebody shape was reckoned to have played a major role in spin behaviour took place at the US Navy's flight test centre at Patuxent River, Maryland. An early F-14 engaged in spin testing became locked into a very fast, flat spin. The crew, unable to recover the aircraft, ejected. Almost immediately, with cockpit canopy and both crew members despatched, the aircraft stopped spinning and entered a dive, finally crashing into the sea. This illustrates the influence that forebody shape can have on spin characteristics, At the large AOAs encountered in spinning, the flat/oval/elliptical forebody (or nose strakes on a more conventional section) can be directionally stabilising. While being desirable if it reduces departure tendencies, such behaviour may become dangerous if a spin actually occurs. The into-wind sideforces which the forebody generates can integrate into a propelling moment when rotated in yaw, leading to fast, flat spinning tendencies.

Nose shape as influenced by radar and laser-ranging installations

When a forebody is designed for a highly manoeuvrable fighter an interaction between several sometimes conflicting requirements is inevitable. Typically, good stability and low drag

are required, along with acceptable electromagnetic properties for good radar performance and provision for all the associated black boxes.

The primary geometric factors affecting radar performance are:

1 Location of a pitot-static boom, nose strakes (and sometimes AOA and angle-of-sideslip vanes) adjacent to the radome.

2 High fineness ratio, resulting from aerodynamic shaping of the nose for low drag.

3 Aerodynamic shaping of the nose cross-section for good high-AOA directional stability.

Pitot-static booms are rarely mounted on the extreme nose nowadays, and then only on prototype or test aircraft, though Dassault types are an exception. The angle-of-attack and yaw-angle sensors, in the form of small truncated cones, are located aft of the radome on operational aircraft. The nose strakes on the YF-17 were deleted to improve radar performance on the operationally equipped and fully navalised F-18 Hornet.

The F-4 Phantom is a good example of how radar requirements influence a nose shape otherwise designed for low drag. The original F-4A (F4H-1) had the Westinghouse APQ-50 radar with a 0·6m dish. The F-4B nose was markedly bulged to accommodate the 0·8m dish of the APQ-79 and had a double curvature on the lower profile because the radar was slightly downward-pointing to give better over-the-nose visibility. The advent of the smaller, solid-state APQ-120 with an elliptical dish allowed a Vulcan Gatling gun to be incorporated in an extended nose on the F-4E.

Nose shapes have tended to be at the mercy of anyone claiming a legitimate right to graft on another bit of operational equipment such as cameras, infra-red sensors and laser rangers. Such operational needs can sometimes have remarkable effects on airframe design. The Lockheed YF-12 is a case in point. The large circular nose cross-section required by the radar scanner was located far ahead of the aircraft's CG, leading to a severe loss of directional stability, particularly at very high Mach numbers. Since radar performance could not be compromised, three ventral fins had to be added to restore stability to an acceptable level.

The radome shape giving optimum radar performance is an axisymmetric profile resembling a hemisphere. Such radomes were used on 1950s-vintage "all-weather" interceptors such as the Northrop F-89 and Avro Canada CF-100. But to keep aerodynamic drag low, especially at supersonic speeds, a compromise on radar performance has to be accepted. Radomes of the low-calibre tangent-ogive type, as used on the McDonnell Douglas F-15 and MiG-29, have become the norm. Deviation from such axisymmetric shapes results in a further, significant loss in radar performance. The intended use of Northrop's Shark nose on its F-5G (now F-20 Tigershark) led the company to investigate a dozen different radome profiles. An ogive profile gave the best radar performance in terms of detection range but reduced high-AOA directional stability. An aerodynamically superior, extremely flat nose called Shark I produced less drag and contributed to directional stability at post-stall AOA. But the scattering effect of its very flat profile near the top of the radome resulted in a loss of radar range. The Shark II nose shown in Fig 146 lacks much of its Shark I precursor's flatness, though the elliptical shape is retained. By careful tailoring it was possible to achieve a good compromise with low drag, excellent high-AOA characteristics and acceptable radar performance.

Crew accommodation influences

The forebody cross-section is largely determined by whether the aircraft has one or two seats, arranged side-by-side or in tandem. Nowadays tandem seating is the norm for high-performance types, particularly for supersonic aircraft, which must have a high fineness ratio. The Grumman A-6 and General Dynamics/Grumman F-111 both feature side-by-side seating, however. Both aircraft have naval roots, and though the Navy version of the F-111 was cancelled, the deck lift-dictated limit on aircraft length lives on in the Air Force F-111. The seating arrangement was not popular with F-111 aircrew because of its inferior visibility, and the F-14 Tomcat, successor to the Navy F-111B, has tandem seating and is longer.

Great efforts are made to keep down cross-sectional area to minimise supersonic wave drag due to volume. The need to do so was appreciated early in the days of supersonic flight, as shown in Fig 148. The process has continued, so that the frontal area of the F-14 is 4m² compared with the F-111's 5·2m². The Soviet near-equivalent of the F-111 is the Sukhoi Su-24 Fencer, which also features side-by-side seating. Another feature of the F-111 is its escape module, which, completely enveloping the crew, can be ejected in an emergency. The inboard leading edge of the wing is integral with the module and helps stabilise it in rocket-borne flight. Such a system was to have been used on the Rockwell B-1A strategic bomber, and the prototype aircraft featured not only the escape module but provision for standby crew rest bunks. Severe cost and weight restraints pre-

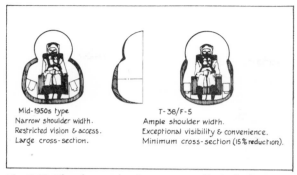

Mid-1950s type
Narrow shoulder width.
Restricted vision & access.
Large cross-section.

T-38/F-5
Ample shoulder width.
Exceptional visibility & convenience.
Minimum cross-section (15% reduction).

Fig 148 The demands of supersonic flight led to a reduction in cockpit cross-sectional area.[6]

vailed, however, and the B-1B has ejection seats, resulting in a weight reduction of 570kg.

In the quest for high performance many aircraft designed in the 1950s and early 1960s were given low-drag cockpit canopies. Because high speed was regarded as paramount, another aspect of combat effectiveness was sacrificed. Good cockpit visibility, one of the prerequisites of a fighter, was lost sight of in spite of the excellent example given by the F-86 Sabre and MiG-15.

Two types illustrate the trend among the earlier supersonic aircraft. The English Electric P.1A, designed originally as a supersonic research/demonstrator aircraft, had a low-drag flush-type hood permitting no rearwards visibility. The P.1B, which entered service as the Lightning, had a domed, more extensive canopy, but visibility remained the Achilles heel of an otherwise successful design. The first 18 examples of the McDonnell F4H-1 Phantom II featured a flush canopy. This contributed to the high fineness ratio required for supersonic flight but provoked much criticism of the view from the cockpit. Following carrier trials, crew visibility was improved by raising the seats and rounding the canopy to give a better forward view.

Lack of excess thrust meant that the first generation of Mach 2 aircraft could not be given good rearward visibility, and it wasn't thought to be strictly necessary for the second generation. Tail-warning radar would show up rear-hemisphere threats, and anyway wasn't dogfighting a thing of the past? Pilots came to accept rear blind spots and manoeuvred to compensate. But then US experience in Vietnam and that of the Israeli Air Force in the Middle East conflicts shattered many illusions about air combat tactics, showing forcibly that dogfighting had not passed into history. Good manoeuvrability and a good view from the cockpit are still paramount.

The American aircraft which appeared in the

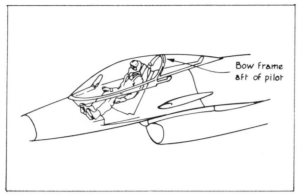

Fig 149 Pilot vision from the F-16 cockpit is 360° in the upper hemisphere, 260° side to side, 195° fore and aft, 40° over the side, and 15° over the nose.[29]

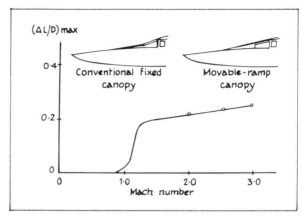

Fig 150 Effect of the XB-70's movable-ramp canopy on lift/drag ratio at increasing Mach numbers.[55]

1970s embodied the bitter lessons of actual conflict. The F-14 and F-15 restored pilot visibility to a standard not seen since the F-86 of the Korean War era. In each the pilot is seated on the highest part of the aircraft to give 360° visibility. He is able to look back over his right shoulder to see the left vertical stabiliser and look for contrails, there often being a tactical advantage in knowing whether a trail is being produced. There is at least 15° of downward visibility over the nose and 5–8cm of vertical seat travel.

The Fairchild A-10 has the excellent visibility needed for battlefield surveillance, with 20° over the nose and 40° over the side. The F-16's high-visibility canopy is unusual in having its structural bow frame behind the pilot, giving an unobstructed view in the upper hemisphere. An average 30° slope of the windshield provides excellent optical quality with minimum distortion. The canopy is held on by eight latches, six of which are reassuringly visible to the pilot. Serious consideration was given to this unconventional design, since in the event of a detached canopy the pilot has no protecting fixed windshield (Fig 149). Accordingly a rocket sled programme was conducted to prove the canopy and the Aces II ejection seat. The F-16 cockpit itself was widely regarded as a trend-setter in ergonomic design, featuring a seat reclined at 30° and raised rudder pedals, which increase g tolerance by $1\frac{1}{2}$ to 2g and a force-sensing sidestick controller.

The demand for improved visibility is also evident in Northrop's F-20 derivative of the F-5, which is claimed to offer 50% more than its predecessor.

Bubble or teardrop canopies do generate a significant supersonic drag increase. Nevertheless, the belief amongst pilots that "If you can't see out of it, it isn't a fighter" was obviously taken seriously by the design teams of the late 1960s and 1970s.

Efforts to improve cockpit visibility for large aircraft reached their zenith in the North American XB-70 of the early 1960s. The aircraft, designed for high cruise efficiency at Mach 3 for $2\frac{1}{2}$hr duration, required a high lift/drag ratio, making a smoothly faired canopy essential. This conflicted with the requirement for good visibility for landing, particularly as the XB-70, with its highly swept, low aspect-ratio delta wing, adopted a very nose-high attitude at low speed. A movable ramp was incorporated (Fig 150), resulting in an insignificant subsonic drag penalty and a supersonic drag reduction equivalent to an increase in $(L/D)_{max}$ of 0·25.

The wheel may be on the turn again, however, since the concern with low radar reflectivity is focussed on those parts of the aircraft which, like the cockpit, make large contributions to radar signature. As a result, submerged cockpits for strike aircraft may reappear.

CENTRE FUSELAGE

The centre fuselage is by definition the area adjacent to the CG. As such it usually contains a large proportion of the internal fuel, which must be balanced about the CG. The centre section also accommodates the main intake ducts for the engine(s) and possibly the main undercarriage, which is attached close to the CG. Hydraulic jacks, accumulators and reservoirs use up more volume. If an armament bay is not provided, ejection units for stores are required. Volume is also required for pipes and cables, and if insufficient space is available within the fuselage a dorsal spine is often necessary. The underbelly spines on the Lightning and Tornado perform a similar role. The hunch-back appearance of the Jaguar resulted from the need to contain larger-than-expected heat-exchangers.

The growth in size of the ventral tank on the Lightning illustrates the difficulties frequently encountered in providing sufficient internal fuel. The large FAST Pack conformal tanks on the F-15 perform a similar function, boosting the internal fuel load of 6,400kg by a further 5,000kg. These area-ruled tanks have been flown at Mach 2.

Space in the centre section is certainly at a premium, resulting in great demands on the ingenuity of the designers concerned with vulnerability to enemy fire and maintain ability. The need for access is very great. Engines require most provision for access, associated as they are with their own pumps and various off-takes for secondary air systems, air conditioning, gearboxes, starters, constant-speed drives, and alternators. In addition, volume must be allowed around the engine to cater for engine development.

One of the advantages claimed for the podded design of the F-14 was that it had superior growth potential, there being less change and lower risk associated with the possible installation of a next-generation engine.

The Grumman Model 303E (which with twin vertical stabilisers became the F-14) exploited the podded engine concept in two ways. It offered the best chance of achieving a satisfactory engine installation, free of the troubles associated with the F-111. It also avoided the need for boundary-layer diverter systems and provided a cleaner installation. These advantages were paid for in the much greater wetted area of the pods and the heavier body structure, though these in turn were offset by lower wing, tail and inlet weights. At the same time, Grumman, and later NASA, were concerned at the possibility of adverse flow in the channel between the engine nacelles. A pressure survey of the channel showed no unusual flow phenomena, however. Indeed, the surface pressures behave much like those of a typical aerofoil section as AOA is varied. Very extensive testing of the podded configuration revealed no sign of any flow problem, with or without stores in the channel.

Compared with the submerged-engined layouts tested by Grumman the podded design showed better longitudinal and directional stability. The former effect was attributed to the "pancake" area aft. The improvement in directional stability is shown in Fig 151, illustrating wing/body com-

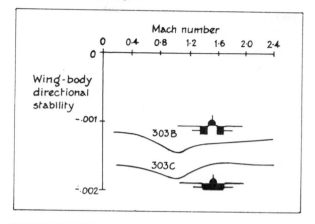

Fig 151 Effect of podded and submerged-engine layouts on wing-body directional stability of early Grumman VFX designs.

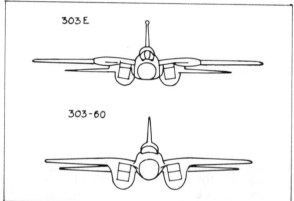

Fig 152 Width of the channel between the Grumman Model 303 engine nacelles was reduced to ease engine-out control problems.[18]

Fig 153 Wing/body blending.

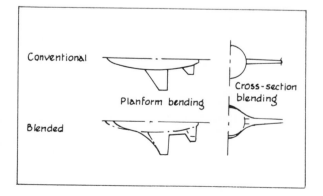

binations with vertical tail off. Though the original channel acted as a flow straightener, the engine-out case was more critical and, as shown in Fig 152, the engine nacelles were moved closer together to improve single-engine control.

Wing/body blending

The slab-sided fuselage which is typical of many modern combat aircraft implies a wing/body junction angle of 90° and generally proves to be the least troublesome of junctions. There are however some notable examples of fuselages which are neither circular nor slab-sided. The reasons for the use of such wing/body blending are various and depend on the application. The nature of the concept is shown in Fig 153.

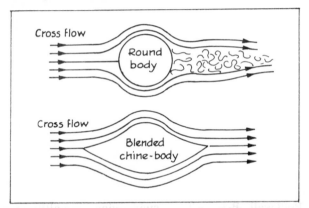

Fig 154 Reduction of sideforce on forebody due to chine.[56]

Lockheed F-12/SR-71   Wing/body blending on this aircraft consists of the use of a fuselage chine (Fig 154) which extends from the extreme nose. Operating as a very-low-aspect-ratio wing, it produces lift as a function of the square of the angle of attack which acts well ahead of the CG (i.e. as a destabiliser). This helps to offset the large rearward movement of aerodynamic centre with Mach number, which is particularly large for a delta wing. It thereby reduces what would otherwise be a very large static margin at Mach 3, together with the trim drag that this would generate. The influence of the chine on the neutral point is shown in Fig 155. To further reduce trim drag the nose of the aircraft just forward of the canopy is cranked up 2° so that it operates at a higher AOA than the wings. This produces a further positive increment in C_{m_o} which collectively halves the bending moment on the very long forebody.

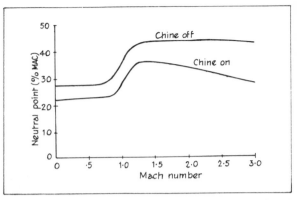

Fig 155 Effect of chines on neutral point of Lockheed YF-12.[56]

The chine also has a strong influence on directional stability, and Fig 154 shows how the sideforce was reduced by the addition of the chine. In elongating the forebody's cross-section, the chine allows an ordered crossflow instead of the separated region that exists behind a circular cross-section. Without the chine, the long, slender forebody displays a marked decrease in directional stability with increasing AOA. With forebody sideforce reduced, however, directional stability increases with AOA. The chine's impact on directional stability is discussed further in Chapter 5.

General Dynamics F-16   General Dynamics considered the use of wing/body blending early in the FX (F-15) programme and then found that this work read across to the Light Weight Fighter (LWF) programme. Wing/body blending was adopted in an effort to minimize weight and achieve a high volumetric efficiency, thereby reducing size and cost since these were primary aims of the LWF.

Superficially, wing/body blending may be thought of only as cross-sectional thickening in the wing root region. In fact it is difficult to achieve this without planform blending, since wing-root thickening requires a longer chord to restrain the growth of the thickness/chord ratio. The concept thus contains the seeds of a tendency towards high volume and low fineness ratio, both of which can cause excessive drag. Constant cross-sectional area can be obtained by reducing the maximum fuselage depth (Fig 156), but this is not easy to achieve when the original cross-section is just big enough to contain the engine. Despite this, a blended wing/body is more amenable to area ruling (see page 153) since the planform can be exploited to permit correct distribution of the volume longitudinally without excessive body waisting. This was done on the F-16 by adjusting the thickness of

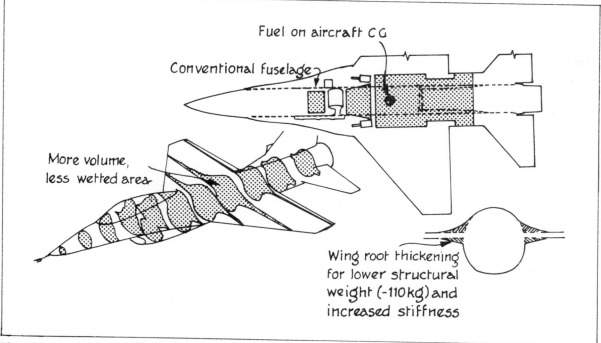

Fuel on aircraft C G

Conventional fuselage

More volume, less wetted area

Wing root thickening for lower structural weight (~110kg) and increased stiffness

Fig 156 Benefits of wing/body blending on the General Dynamics F-16 include increased body lift; improved area distribution, resulting in reduced transonic drag; better wetted area-to-volume ratio; better volume/fuel distribution; and a shorter, 140kg lighter fuselage.[29]

the shelf formed between the wing and tail (Fig 156).

Wing/body blending integrates well with the forebody lift idea, used on the F-16 in the form of strakes, since a wide forebody is a natural consequence of blending. With the forebody strake planform optimised for high AOA, its thickness at the fuselage junction is tailored according to the supersonic area rule. The YF-16 eventually emerged with excessive volume despite efforts to keep the fineness ratio up and the volume down. This allowed nearly 50% more internal fuel than was required by the LWF mission rules, resulting in a 60% increase in air superiority range. The YF-16 did however have a lower fineness ratio (8·5) than was desirable for supersonic flight. Partially offsetting the resulting wave drag penalty were lower wetted area/volume ratio (from a 2% reduction in wetted area and a 9% increase in volume), and higher wing-root structural stiffness, just where the wing bending moments are greatest. This gave a weight reduction of 250kg (Fig 156).

It was estimated that a comparable conventional wing/body design would have required a 1·67m-longer fuselage for the same volume, and a large

vertical tail to compensate. The fineness ratio would admittedly have been higher, but area ruling would have dictated local surface slopes steep enough to negate much of the supersonic drag benefit and add to subsonic minimum drag.

Rockwell B-1   This swing-wing low-altitude penetration bomber incorporates substantial wing/body blending (Fig 157).

Detection avoidance calls for high speed and minimum radar reflectivity. This implies low drag and the avoidance of angular surfaces, both of these aims being served by the minimum wetted

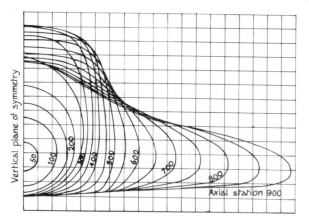

Fig 157 Rockwell B-1 wing/body cross-sections.[57]

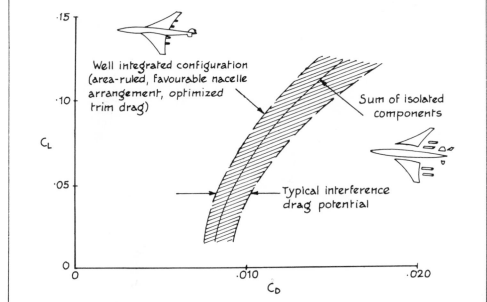

Fig 158 Influence of aerodynamic interference.[58]

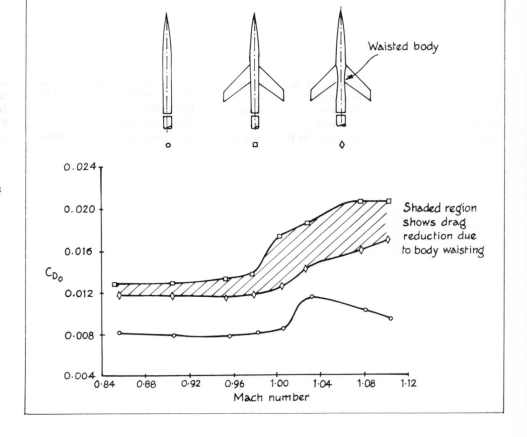

Fig 159 Effect of body waisting on transonic drag.[59]

area and gentle curves yielded by wing/body blending. It also gives an increase in volume and strength at little cost in wave drag. The volume so generated is used by Rockwell for fuel. Indeed, the fuselage of the B-1 has been likened to a huge fuel tank, such is the extent of the tankage within the body.

The Area Rule

When a fuselage and a wing are joined together the airflows around the two surfaces mutually interfere. This interference is especially important at high speeds because of the occurrence of shock waves, which give rise to wave drag. The influence of configuration on drag levels is shown in Fig 158. The interference effects, indicated by the shaded region, total as much as a quarter the sum of the individual drags of the configuration's components.

Whitcomb of NACA conducted a series of tests in the early 1950s which showed (Fig 159) how the drag of a body in isolation, and that of the same body with a simple wing, varies with Mach number and how the drag of the combination might be significantly reduced by careful shaping at the wing/body junction. This work led to the formulation of the Sonic Area Rule, which states that if a wing/body combination including external stores is so designed that the axial distribution of the cross-sectional area normal to the airflow is the same as that of a minimum-drag body, then the wing/body will also have minimum drag. A minimum-drag body is one designed to give minimum wave drag due to volume for a given slenderness ratio, or for an optimum volume and length, or for a given volume and diameter; such a shape is known as a Sears-Haack body.

A normal cross-sectional area (CSA) distribution is shown in Fig 160, along with a body of revolution with the same area distribution. Keeping aircraft frontal area to a minimum is of prime importance, as is a smooth buildup of CSA over the forebody, canopy and fuselage, followed by a gradual reduction over the aft body and tail surfaces. This smooth variation of cross-sectional area with length can be loosely regarded as the essence of the Area Rule.

Though the Sonic Area Rule is a classic of simplicity, it was preceded by a great deal of work aimed at improving the flow at the wing/body junction. Examination of the flow at the root of a plane swept wing and the use of simple sweepback concepts reveals that only the velocity component normal to the leading edge is increased by wing thickness, with the spanwise component remaining unchanged. This inevitably results in the flow

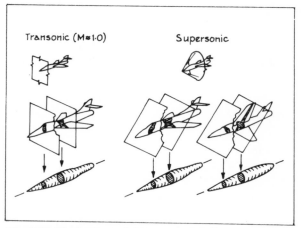

Fig 160 Illustration of the area rules.[60]

being inclined towards the root (Fig 161). However, the root flow is constrained to follow the body. The compression-wave system required to achieve this propagates across the wing span and may ultimately coalesce near the tip to form a shock wave of finite strength. It was argued in the 1950s that the shock wave was mainly influenced by root conditions, and so it was expected that its position and strength could be altered by changing the root contour. Pre-Whitcomb work on waisting the body was essentially aimed at producing root shapes yielding a straight, fully swept subcritical isobar pattern right up to the root and, later, delayed coalescence of the root compression into a rear shock, with a consequent reduction in wing drag at transonic speeds. Modifying the fuselage shape in this way significantly reduced the drag of the combination above the critical Mach number, both at zero lift and at low lift coefficients.

Fig 161 Surface flow on swept wing.

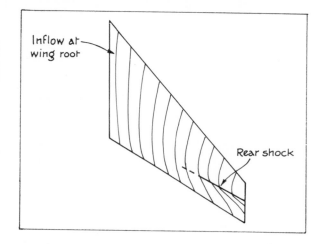

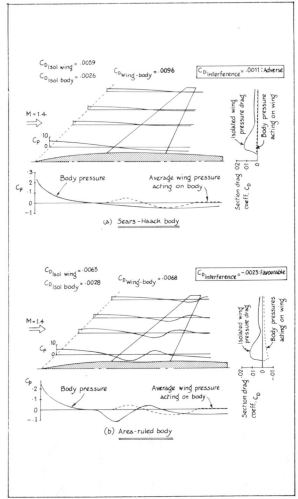

Fig 162 Comparison of wing/body interference pressure fields, showing that the favourable interference produced by careful design integration can reduce combined wing/body drag to little more than that of the wing alone.[58]

The above "near field" approach, as it is known, and the "far field" approach of the Sonic Area Rule are highly complementary. Fig 162 gives an insight into the working of the Area Rule. The sources of the wing/body interaction are the body-on-wing and wing-on body interference pressures, which are plotted in their respective locations. Integration of these pressures over the wing and body surfaces results in a small positive drag for the Sears-Haack body and a substantial negative drag (i.e. thrust) for the area-ruled body. Negative pressures on forward-facing surfaces combine with positive pressures on aft-facing surfaces to give

favourable interference. By regarding the pressure field around the configuration in this manner, it is possible to interpret physically the interaction resulting from area ruling.

Area ruling of a body can be overdone, since its application involves the imposition of adverse pressure gradients on the wing flow. Indeed, it is possible to contour a body too severely, which will lead to rapid compressions and shock waves in the plane of the wing.

The Supersonic Area Rule

Application of the Area Rule for supersonic speeds becomes more complex, as shown in Fig 160. The theories developed by Hayes[61] and Jones[62] require that the parallel cutting planes be tangent to the Mach cone, as shown, with the intercepted areas projected onto a plane normal to the aircraft axis. There is now no single equivalent body, as was the case for the Sonic Area Rule.

At each Mach number there exists a series of equivalent bodies, one for each of the many roll angles, only two of which are shown in Fig 160. The wave drag of a complete configuration for a given Mach number is the integrated average of the equivalent body wave drags through the full roll range of 360°.

The optimisation of a body cross-section in the presence of a wing at Mach 1·4 is shown in Fig 163. A Sears-Haack body, which has minimum isolated wave drag for a given length and volume, is shown recontoured to give substantially improved wing/body interference. The reshaping of the body results in a smoother combined area distribution. The benefit of area ruling in making possible the addition of substantial volume to an unsophisticated body for reduced wing/body wave drag (see insert Fig 163) still exists, although the improvement to interference declines at off-design Mach numbers.

Differential area-ruling

Both the Sonic and Supersonic area rules have been described in terms of minimising zero-lift wave drag. A later design method, by Lock and Rogers,[19] takes a wing/body combination designed for minimum zero-lift drag and modifies it for minimum drag at the design (i.e. non-zero) lift coefficient. The load distribution over the wings to give the specified pressure distribution on the wing's upper surface is derived, and the wing warp (i.e. twist) and additional (anti-symmetrical) fuselage waisting are calculated to give the required load distribution.

The implications of the method are shown in Fig 164. Three examples are cited. Case A has no body waisting but employs large upward wing-root

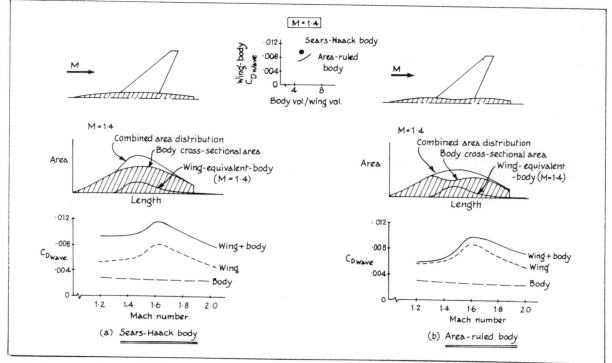

Fig 163 Wave-drag reduction by area-ruling.[58]

twist. Case B shows the other extreme, with little wing-root twist but severe body waisting, which produces distinct shelves on the body. Case C is an intermediate possibility. This differential waisting allows the fuselage side to be streamwise to the downwash produced by the lifting wing at the root. Generally speaking, more waisting is required above the wing and less below it, the total cross-sectional area remaining the same. The most widely quoted example of differential area ruling is the Northrop YF-17/F-18 (see later). Its effect in this application has been explained in an AIAA paper: "The negative pressures which occur above the wing as a result of the area reduction incorporated are transmitted along Mach lines over a sizeable portion of the wing, contributing to the wing's lift. Similarly, the increase in fuselage cross-sectional area below the wing increases the pressure to further enhance the lift."[27]

Applications of the area rule

Numerous experimental applications of the Sonic Area Rule were carried out after it was made public by NACA. However, by far the most famous application was on a production aircraft, the Convair F-102 Delta Dagger. Originally a smooth-sided 60° delta-winged interceptor, the XF-102 prototype was powered by the most powerful after-

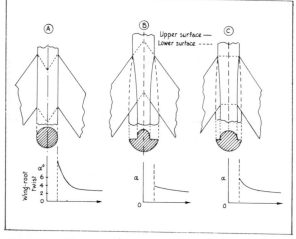

Fig 164 Differential area-ruling.[63]

burning turbojet of its day. Designed to fly super-sonically, it proved capable of only Mach 0·95 in flight tests in 1952. Convair, faced with the possible cancellation of a very large USAF contract, and with aircraft already moving along the production line, anxiously consulted NACA. Area-ruling the XF-102, which then became the F-102A, was achieved by lengthening the nose, sharpening the air inlets, pinching in the fuselage to form a waist

The most well-known application of the Area Rule came when flight tests showed that Convair's F-102 interceptor could not exceed Mach 1. Turning it into the supersonic F-102A called for nose, windshield and intake modifications together with development of a highly waisted fuselage with bulged fairings alongside the tailpipe.

and, most noticeably, adding two large bulged fairings aft of the wing, as shown in Fig 165. With these modifications the F-102A went supersonic in a climb, eventually reaching Mach 1·2.

Later the same year Grumman visited NACA Langley to seek a solution for the excess drag being demonstrated by its Design 98. This, as the F11F fighter, became the first aircraft to be designed using the Area Rule from the outset and also the first combat aircraft to exceed Mach 1 without using an afterburner. The transforming effect that area ruling had on those early supersonic aircraft is evident in Fig 166.

Buccaneer with its weapon-bay rotary door open. The aircraft was the first British production type to be area-ruled, the main visible sign being the fuselage bulge aft of the wing. The rear-fuselage fairing splits in half along its length, opening to form the powerful airbrakes required for high-power carrier approaches. (Flight International)

The use of the various area rules made a distinct impression on a whole generation of aircraft, though sometimes the concept was applied over-zealously.

BAe Buccaneer   The Blackburn B.103, as the Buccaneer was originally known, was modified in 1954 in accordance with the area rule even though it was only a Mach 0·85 aircraft. It emerged with a slight waist and substantial bulges added to the rear fuselage lines. Adjustments were also made to the wing trailing-edge sweep and taper. The need to retain a parallel section on the lower centre fuse-lage for a weapons bay created some difficulty in maintaining good conventional aerodynamic lines, but the transformation in the area distribution was remarkable. The thrust required for high-speed cruise was reduced significantly and a substantial volume suitable for the installation of equipment was made available.

Northrop T-38/F-5   The application of the area rule is clearly evident in these designs. Although they were originally shaped by the Sonic Rule, subsequent wind-tunnel testing showed that shaping for Mach 1·15 was more effective. The body shows distinct waisting and the benefit due to area ruling, taking a straight-sided fuselage as the datum, is a large reduction in transonic drag (Fig 167) and a matching gain in transonic acceleration. This is most important in the primary combat zone for which the F-5 was designed, and because of it the F-5 can accelerate through the transonic region abreast of aircraft having much higher top speeds.

The wingtip tanks on the F-5 were also area-ruled. Early prototype and wind-tunnel testing had indicated that the original tanks would provoke transonic buffet and longitudinal instabilities. Use of area-ruled tanks and the resulting airflow improvement at the tip eliminated the pitch problem and gave a cruise drag reduction of 23 drag counts.

Avro Canada CF-105   The Area Rule was applied in a fairly subtle way to this very large, two-seat all-weather interceptor, since with its highly swept and very thin delta wing it already possessed a good area distribution. The aircraft was area-ruled for Mach 1·5 by means of additions at nose and tail and reductions in cross-section elsewhere.

BAe Lightning   The importance attached to minimum frontal area is exemplified by this air-craft, designed in 1948, long before the area rules had been conceived. The supersonic wave drag theories of the time all suggested that the fuselage should be slab-sided over the length of the slender

Fig 165 Area-ruling for transonic wave drag reduction on the XF-102.[64]

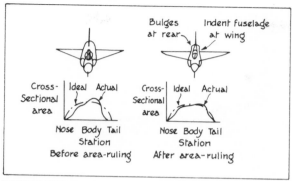

Fig 166 Area Rule's impact on performance.

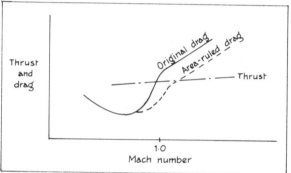

Fig 167 Area-ruling on the Northrop F-5.[6]

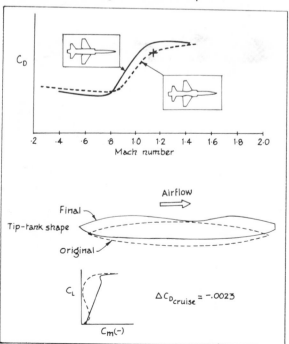

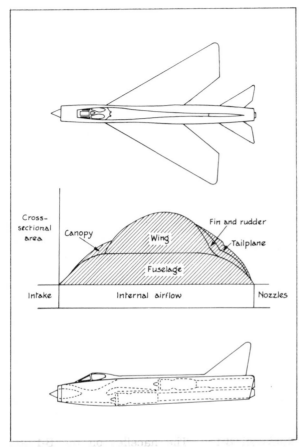

Fig 168 In trying to minimise frontal area, the designers of the English Electric Lightning also unknowingly conformed with the sonic Area Rule without resorting to the extreme "Coke bottle" fuselages which later became common.

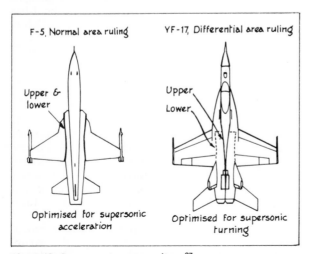

Fig 169 Supersonic area-ruling.[27]

wing. With the wing just thick enough to house fuel and undercarriage, the absolute minimum fuselage cross-section became of vital importance. The only way to achieve this in a slab-sided shape was to stagger the engines one behind the other in a still unique fashion (Fig 168).

The 60°-swept wing spreads its volume thinly over the long fuselage centre section. The canopy and tail surfaces help to fill the dip on the area plot fore and aft of the wing. Thus the Lightning has an area distribution compatible with the Sonic Area Rule, though its design predated Whitcomb's formulation by four years. The Lightning's predecessor, the English Electric P.1A, was intended as a supersonic research aircraft with little need for a large fuel volume, so the production interceptor suffered throughout its career from a lack of internal fuel volume. There was little room within the fuselage, and the ever-growing demand for extended-range interception and endurance during the type's service life led to a marked increase in the size of its belly tank, providing a significant amount of extra fuel while maintaining a shape conducive to low drag.

Saab Viggen   In a prime example of attention to area-ruling detail, this Swedish Mach 2 fighter's weapons pylons were placed in line with other protruding parts such as the fairings on the wing which cover the control surface actuators. Furthermore, many of the protruding antennae were incorporated into the ventral fin to reduce antenna drag.

Although it is not in fact part of the Viggen's area-ruling provisions, the large bulge forward of the fin (on the dorsal spine) is there to improve transonic flow. It was found early in the development programme that the aircraft developed an abrupt pitch-up tendency as it accelerated to transonic speed. This was caused by the shock wave on the upper wing surface moving aft faster than the lower shock, the opposite of what used to characterise the flow pattern on early high-speed fighters. In the Viggen's case the area of suction on the upper surface grew faster than that on the lower surface, leading to the nose-up tendency. Saab studied the effect of various cross-sectional distribution changes on the shockwave pattern before setting on the bulge, which made transonic passage very smooth.

Northrop YF-17/McDonnell Douglas F-18   To optimise its turning capability at supersonic speeds the YF-17 was area-ruled specifically to minimise drag-due-to-lift. With the emphasis on Mach 1·2, extensive wind-tunnel testing was carried out to establish the fuselage cross-sectional area both above and below the wing in the manner proposed by Lock and Rogers.[19] The area distribution was carefully tailored to create favourable lift interference (i.e. increased lift at a given AOA). This was done, as shown in Fig 169, by:

1 Significantly reducing the upper-fuselage cross-sectional area forward of the wing to the mid-chord position. This waisting was additional to that applied for zero-lift drag area-ruling.

2 Increasing slightly the lower-fuselage cross-sectional area from the wing leading edge to the trailing edge (see Fig 164).

This differential area-ruling is compared in Fig 169 with that employed on the F-5 to reduce zero-lift drag and to improve transonic acceleration. The favourable lift interference created by differential area-ruling reduces the AOA required to achieve a given lift coefficient, thereby reducing the drag-due-to-lift at the cost of a small penalty in zero-lift drag.

A 5% increase in sustained turn rate at Mach 1·2 resulted from the drag reduction. The differential area-ruling also generates favourable pitching moments which reduce trim drag. The combined benefits of differential area-ruling helped to expand the sustained turn rate envelope above Mach 0·8.

Another aspect of area-ruling shown clearly in Fig 169 is the positioning of the canted twin vertical stabilisers well forward of the horizontal tails, which helps to fill a dip in the area-distribution curve.

General Dynamics F-16   The philosophy behind the use of area-ruling on the F-16 had three aims:

1 To minimise the drag of each component by keeping thickness/chord ratios low and fineness ratios high.

2 To minimise adverse interference and maximise favourable interference through judicious placement of major components.

3 To shape components locally, only where absolutely necessary, to alleviate any adverse interference which would otherwise exist.

Principles **1** and **2** are illustrated in the YF-16 normal area curve (Fig 170). The teardrop canopy is placed forward on the fuselage, minimising its large protuberance effect, with the air inlet placed so as to offset the aft-facing slope of the canopy. The strake/shelf is shaped to relieve the forward and aft slopes of the wing respectively. The horizontal and vertical stabilisers are staggered, thus avoiding the simultaneous buildup of their leading-edge area gradients.

Some small changes in the area distribution

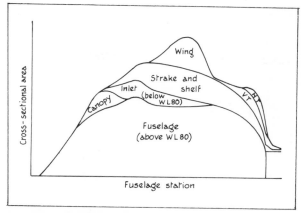

Fig 170 YF-16 normal cross-sectional area distribution. **VT** = vertical tail **HT** = horizontal tail **WL** = water line (structural reference point).[1]

were made late in the YF-16 design process, creating a small but significant fuel volume increase. The aft fuselage just ahead of the nozzle and shelf, housing the horizontal tail actuator, were trimmed to reduce the drag of the aft-end components and the interference between them. The increases ahead of and behind the wing were adjusted to improve the Mach 1·2 oblique area distribution, though not at the expense of the Mach 1·6 distribution.

Rockwell B-1   The nacelles on the B-1 are situated where the cross-sectional area is at a maximum. There was therefore constant demand during design to reduce nacelle cross-section and minimise volume. Furthermore, no compromise was permitted with subsonic drag factors: surface area, inlet cowl curvature and nacelle boat-tail angle. As a result, the propulsion system is slightly less than 40% of the aircraft's maximum cross-sectional area when the wings are in the fully swept position. Moreover, 40% of the propulsion system cross-sectional area consists of inlet capture area.

Northrop F-20 (F-5G)   In developing a third-generation F-5, Northrop was aiming at a quantum jump in performance. A single General Electric F404 turbofan (power plant of the F-18) developing 72kN replaced two J85s rated at 22kN each, resulting in a rear fuselage that was narrower but longer, being lengthened with a 13cm structural plug.

Not surprisingly, Northrop was intent on retaining the excellent high-AOA handling of the earlier T-38/F-5. To this end the Shark nose was developed.

The rear fuselage presented a problem, however, since the F-5 is, along with other twin-engined aircraft, characterised by a wide, very flat belly. This also contributes favourably to high-AOA performance. The question of how to reconcile this with a single engine basically circular in section was solved by adding shelves, not unlike those on the F-16, aft of the wing trailing edge to flatten the aft underbody. The increased skin friction drag was a small price to pay to lessen the risks of the radical change represented by the switch from a twin to a single-engined layout. The shelves house the horizontal tail control runs.

REAR FUSELAGE

Rear-fuselage lines and tailplane spigot geometry have to be compatible with a wide range of tailplane angles, while avoiding the loss of effectiveness caused by leakage through gaps. The pivot axis/aerodynamic centre relationship must be consistent with the load capability of the tailplane actuator and aeroelastic requirements, both static and dynamic. These objectives have been achieved

on the F-16 and F-20 by means of fuselage shelves and on the F-15 through the use of a twin-boom structure.

Engines are commonly located as close to the rear of the aircraft as possible, so reducing structural heating and acoustic effects. This can however pose balance problems if a long nose is not acceptable. The F-4 and Jaguar, with their engines exhausting beneath the empennage, are exceptions to this formula. Though their layout is claimed to result in weight savings and improved ground clearance, it was however necessary to protect the aft fuselage and tailplane of each against the high temperature of the jet exhausts.

Fuselage length

Although wave-drag considerations dictate a long, slim fuselage with a needle-like nose for supersonic aircraft, compromises have to be made. This is particularly true of aircraft based on carriers, with their deck lifts, limited deck space and "spotting factor" (the area taken up by a particular type in the deck park). A case in point is the F-4, a Mach 2 + aircraft. Originally designed for *Midway*-class aircraft carrier air patrol work, the F-4 was 1m shorter than its predecessor, the single-engined

F3H Demon. Two large engines, extensive electronics and large quantities of fuel were somehow accomodated within a fuselage that appears relatively short for a Mach 2 fighter. The length restriction of 17m was eventually relaxed following changes in aircraft carrier design. But the Royal Navy version, the F-4K, had to be no longer than 16.5m when parked, with the result that the radar was modified to permit the complete radome plus aerial to swing through 180°.

A further example of the limitations imposed by carrier operations is the case of the F-111A for the USAF and the F-111B for the USN. The conspicuous difference in nose length between the two was dictated by the Navy's need to restrict overall length to 21·3m. The F-111B had a length of 21·0m and a spotting factor of 1·98 compared with 18·9m and 1·5 for the current F-14.

Engine size plays a major part in sizing the fuselage. By using the triple-spool RB.199 of high thrust/volume ratio Panavia was able to keep the Tornado relatively short. One of the main Tornado design aims was to minimise wetted area for low drag at subsonic/transonic speeds without compromising internal volume for fuel and comprehensive electronics. The result is one of the densest aircraft yet built, Tornado being about 1·5 times as dense as the F-15 at take-off with wings swept at 45°. The F-14, with a roughly similar configuration, is bigger overall by a factor of 1·4. In fact the Tornado's fuselage is no longer than that of the F-104 Starfighter. On the Tornado Air Defence Variant the nose was lengthened by 1·2m to house the larger radar and a plug was inserted aft of the rear cockpit to increase fuel capacity. Both of these measures serve to increase the body fineness ratio and thereby reduce wave drag.

Clearly visible on the private-venture Northrop F-20 Tigershark are the enlarged leading edge extension (LEX), Shark nose and aft-fuselage shelves developed to ensure that this single-engined (F404) development of the F-5 shared its predecessors' excellent handling qualities. (Northrop)

The extremely compact RB.199 turbofan combines with a very short afterburner and thrust reverser to make the Panavia Tornado a dense aeroplane capable of carrying a formidable range of stores. Shown here are 1,500lit fuel tanks, Sky Shadow ECM pods and eight 1,000lb (454kg) low-drag bombs. (BAC)

CHAPTER 4

TAILPLANES (HORIZONTAL STABILISERS)

INTRODUCTION

This chapter considers longitudinal stability and control about the lateral (or pitch) axis and starts by discussing the primary functions of the tailplane. The use of the term "horizontal stabiliser" as an alternative to tailplane is very common but can be misleading, since a tailplane, or indeed a foreplane, does rather more than provide stability. The existence of numerous perfectly effective tailless aircraft testifies to this. Nevertheless, the inclusion of an aft-mounted horizontal surface certainly contributes to stability, and aircraft thus configured are generally regarded as having a "conventional" layout.

The overriding constraint on aircraft design — at least up to the early 1970s — was the need to keep the centre of gravity forward of a specific point to ensure positive stability. Longitudinal stability is defined primarily in terms of CG position, the importance of which is at the centre of any discussion of aircraft stability. But it is wrong to treat longitudinal stability as merely a measure of the CG margin, since this ignores several important influences, particularly air compressibility and aeroelastic distortion of the aircraft's structure. That being the case, this chapter contains a more realistic definition of longitudinal stability, though even this ignores the effects arising from aircraft manoeuvring. But it is the intention here to introduce only the basics needed for an insight into combat aircraft design, and so for the purposes of this book longitudinal stability is expressed in terms of the rate of change of pitching moment with lift, known as the static margin. For a deeper understanding the reader should consult some of the excellent texts given in *Further reading*.

The chapter continues by establishing the criteria for sizing the tailplane of a conventional (i.e. inherently stable and controllable) combat aircraft. The effects of wing downwash, compressibility, aeroelastic distortion and the carriage of wing-mounted stores on tailplane function are examined, and remedies described. The most important of these are tailplane positioning, in both

the vertical and fore-and-aft senses, and the use of the all-moving tailplane. Practical examples show that low-mounted, all-moving tailplanes are now almost universal on high-performance aircraft.

Until the early 1970s all aircraft had to show inherent positive stability in even the most adversely loaded condition in the appropriate regions of the flight envelope. The advent of active control technology in the form of artificial stability has since permitted this constraint to be relaxed somewhat, and certain aircraft now fly operationally with negative inherent airframe stability. This development is the main subject of the section on control-configured vehicles.

The chapter concludes with a look at canard aircraft, in which the tailplane's functions are performed by a foreplane. This answer to many of the demands placed on recent and future combat aircraft has been turned into a realistic proposition by the availability of artificial stability.

THE FUNCTION OF TAILPLANES

On a conventional modern combat aircraft the tailplane has three primary functions:

1 To stabilise the aircraft in pitch

2 To control it in pitch

3 To help, in conjunction with wing control surfaces, to control it in roll (discussed in detail in Chapter 1).

Longitudinal stability

Fig 171 illustrates how the various components of an aircraft contribute to the stability of the whole vehicle. The wing alone shows a nose-up tendency when its angle of attack is increased; this is accentuated when a fuselage is added. The tailplane, on the other hand, provides a stabilising nose-down moment, so that when wing, body and tailplane are brought together in a complete unit the result is a stable configuration.

Two points must be made. First, only static forces and moments have been considered. Dynamic stability lies beyond the scope of this book

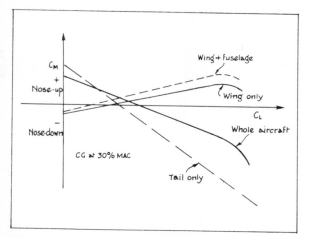

Fig 171 Contribution of the main airframe components to longitudinal stability.

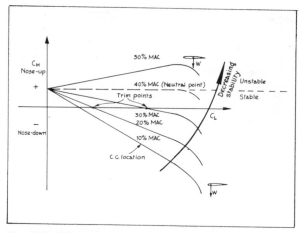

Fig 172 Effect of centre-of-gravity position on longitudinal stability.

(see *Further reading*). Second, a tailplane is not essential to stability. This point is fundamentally important and relates to the effect of centre of gravity (CG) position, which is basic to any discussion of longitudinal stability.

The effect of CG position

The effect of CG position on static longitudinal stability is readily analysed by looking at the wing in isolation. Fig 172 shows the variation of pitching moment with AOA for a range of pivot positions which for our purposes can be regarded as CG positions. As the CG is moved aft, so the slope of the line C_m/C_L becomes less and less steep (negatively) and approaches the neutral position, where there is no change of pitching moment with C_L (i.e. $dC_m/dC_L = 0$), giving neutral stability.

Beyond this CG position (called the aerodynamic centre), the slope is positive (i.e. upwards to the right), showing that as the AOA is increased so the pitching moment acts so as to further increase the angle. This is a divergent (i.e. unstable) condition. For the example above, 40% wing chord is the aftmost position for the CG. If the CG is moved beyond this into the unstable region, some way must be found to counteract the resulting out-of-balance moment, which threatens to turn the wing leading edge over trailing edge. On a conventional aircraft this is achieved by means of a tailplane. If however the CG is kept ahead of the 40% point (in this hypothetical case) then the wing itself is inherently stable: once disturbed it will tend to return to its original position unaided. This aspect of stability thus depends on the relationship of the CG and the point at which the wing lift acts. Flying wings and all but the most recent deltas have relied on careful positioning of the CG in order to avoid

the need for a tailplane.

The main benefit of a tailplane lies however in the fact that it allows a further aft CG limit, the principal constraint being need to keep the CG forward of where the centre of lift of the whole aircraft (i.e. the neutral point) is located.

Stability margins

So far the emphasis has been on the aircraft's actual CG position in relation to the neutral point. This is where the CG would have to be to give neutral stability, with the slope dC_m/dC_L equal to zero. If the effects of air compressibility and structural distortion were neglected the neutral point would remain fixed. The aircraft's static stability would then be indicated by the CG's distance ahead of the neutral point. Under these conditions the distance of the aft-most position of the CG ahead of the neutral point, measured as a fraction of the wing chord length, is known as the CG margin.

For this simple case a change in CG position has the same effect on stability at all speeds. However, because of the significant changes in aerodynamic loading which occur at high speed, with the force and moment coefficients themselves varying with Mach number, the neutral point cannot be regarded as being fixed; it moves with changes in speed. An aspect of this has already been discussed in previous chapters, in which the aerodynamic centre of a wing section was noted to move backwards from its typical quarter-chord position to around the half-chord point across the transonic regime. Although at speeds below about Mach 0·8 the changes are nowhere near as profound, the effects of compressibility cannot be neglected.

The inflexible structure implicit in the use of the CG margin cannot be assumed when considering real aeroplanes. All of the major components of the aircraft are subject to twisting and flexing, which can alter their contributions to the sum of static stability. Because the distortion is largely a function of dynamic pressure, its effect on stability varies with speed. This, together with compressibility effects, requires that the simple CG margin approach be replaced by the concept of the static margin.

The static margin is proportional to the CG margin:

$$\text{static margin} = \text{CG margin} \times \Psi_1$$

where Ψ_1 is a factor of proportionality whose value depends upon the aircraft speed in such a way that the static margin and hence stability (i.e. slope of curve of pitching moment versus lift) is not necessarily increased by a forward movement of the CG.

Even the static margin definition of stability has its limitations, since it does not account for changes in the neutral point position which arise when an aircraft is manoeuvring. A pull-out from a dive, for example, introduces additional lift forces, notably at the tail, which contribute to stability. This calls for a new stability margin, the manoeuvre margin. Nevertheless, throughout this chapter static stability will be treated as though it were adequately measured in terms of the static margin. An aircraft will thus be regarded as stable if its CG is forward enough to keep the static margin positive, as indicated by a negative slope on the C_m/C_L curve.

TAILPLANE SIZING

Limiting CG positions

Variations in fuel, crew, weapon and other loads result in a range of possible locations for the CG, even during a single flight. On a combat aircraft — the F-4 Phantom, for example — the CG might move, due to fuel usage and weapon firing, from around the 31% mean aerodynamic chord (MAC) position at take-off, forward to 28% MAC in mid-mission and back to 34% MAC by the end of the flight. This 6% MAC shift in CG position might be exceeded on another flight starting with an alternative store configuration. But whatever the CG range encountered, it must have been catered for in the design of the aircraft and expressed in the form of forward and aft limits on CG shift.

The aft CG limit

This is the restriction placed on CG position to ensure that the static margin and hence stability are always positive and of an acceptable level. Too

low a level of stability can give rise to a range of difficulties centred on the control system and the provision of the variation of stick forces expected by the pilot. For example, if the minimum level of stability is too low, then the variation in control forces at forward CG become intolerably high.[32] The aircraft may also be oversensitive to changes of trim, while at the other extreme the minor adjustment to the flightpath required in low-level, high-speed penetration calls for extremely high-resolution control actuators.

The way in which the aft CG position effects tailplane size for stability is evident in Fig 173, which

Fig 173 Tailplane sizing diagrams, with natural and artificial stability.

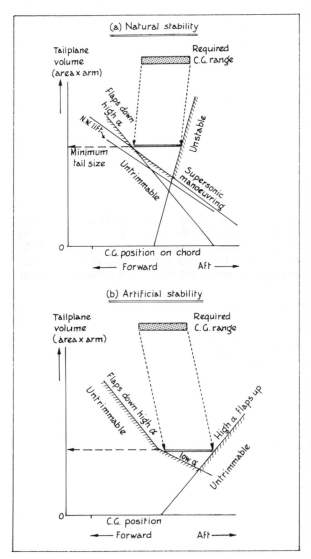

shows that for a naturally stable aircraft the required size of tailplane grows rapidly as the CG is moved aft. The region indicated as unstable shows CG positions at which the static margin is intolerably low or even negative. Generally speaking, the critical aft-CG case (i.e. where stability is lowest) is in high-subsonic flight at low altitude, when gusts and other disturbances to the flightpath are most intense. Another consideration affecting the aft-CG case is inertia coupling. Rapid rolling induces simultaneous rates of roll and yaw which generate a gyroscopic pitching moment, causing excursions in AOA and normal acceleration which increase as the margin of stability is reduced. Without adequate pitch stiffness, defined as rate of change of pitching moment with AOA, these deviations can lead to structural overloading and/or a risk of stalling.

The forward CG limit

The forward CG position is governed by the controllability of the aircraft as provided by the downward lifting power of the tailplane. Three distinct phases of flight have to be catered for:

The landing case

In this phase leading and trailing-edge high-lift devices contribute to the already large nose-down pitching moment generated by the basic airframe at its relatively high AOA on the approach. This moment has to be balanced so that the resulting pitching moment about the CG is zero; the aircraft is then in a "trimmed" condition. It is under these circumstances that the tailplane is operating at its maximum, albeit negative, lift. Indeed, one of the ground rules for sizing the tailplane is that it should be possible, using not more than 90% of full negative tailplane travel, to apply a normal acceleration of 1·1g to the aircraft during landing at 1·15 times the stalling speed. The impact that the forward CG position can have on required tailplane size for trimming is shown in Fig 173, which indicates a fairly rapidly growth in size with forward movement of the CG.

The take-off case

With a forward CG the tailplane has to overcome the moment due to the aircraft weight minus lift times the distance X shown in Fig 174 in order to rotate the aircraft nose-up about the main wheels. Clearly the position of the main undercarriage is important, and in extreme cases may create the critical forward-CG design case for the tailplane. On the McDonnell Douglas F-18, for example, the main undercarriage is so far back that with a forward CG the twin rudders must be used differentially to assist the tailplane in lifting the nose-

Fig 174 Tailplane sizing for nosewheel raising. Tailplane lift needed to raise the nosewheel is a function of air density, rotation speed, and tailplane area and lift coefficient. Tailplane area varies directly with wing lift coefficient and inversely with tailplane lift coefficient.

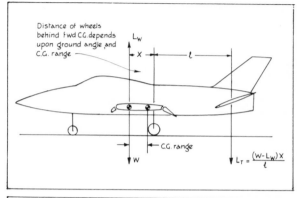

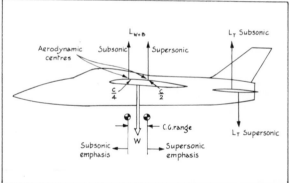

Fig 175 Tailplane sizing for supersonic manoeuvrability.

wheel within a reasonable take-off run. The common convention is that nosewheel lifting should be possible at a speed allowing rotation to take-off attitude to be accomplished at a mean rate of 5°/sec without delaying lift-off beyond the nominal 1·2 V_{stall}. The variation in tailplane size with CG position for a naturally stable combat aircraft is shown in Fig 173.

Manoeuvring at supersonic speed

At Mach 1 + the large rearward shift in the aircraft's aerodynamic centre causes the static margin to increase markedly (Fig 175). This — being a measure of stability, which is itself a token of the aircraft's reluctance to change attitude — means that manoeuvrability is severely curtailed. Whereas a lifting tail may have been required in the subsonic case, at supersonic speeds a significant download is called for.

The intended role of the aircraft dicates the forward-CG case that will predominate. When good airfield performance has been achieved by means of high-lift devices (e.g. the Panavia Tornado), it is likely that the take-off and landing cases will dominate. When heavier emphasis is laid on supersonic manoeuvrability, an aircraft with limited high-lift devices (e.g. the McDonnell Douglas F-15) will have this as its forward CG tailplane sizing case.

In summary, the forward-CG cases require a download while at aft CG an upload is needed. However, the upload requirement is always less severe than the download, and the tailplane never operates at its maximum upload condition. The combined constraints upon the tailplane are summarised in the typical tail sizing diagram (Fig 173). The shaded area represents the CG range needed to cover the anticipated combinations of stores, fuel, crew, etc. To find the minimum tail size, given as a tail volume (i.e. tail area × tail arm length), this CG range is slotted into the diagram. In the example shown it is the ability to trim during a high-lift landing approach that limits the forward CG position.

Trim drag

This important factor must be carefully considered when sizing the tailplane. Trim drag results when the tailplane is deflected to obtain zero pitching moment about the aircraft's CG, i.e. to trim the aircraft. The tailplane has its own zero-lift drag, to which must be added the increment induced when the tail is producing up or down loads. Conventionally, the variation in tailplane angle needed to trim versus speed for a given CG position is such that the trailing edge of the tailplane must be deflected progressively downwards as speed increases. Abrupt changes in this variation may occur across the transonic regime. Then at supersonic speed a variation akin to the pre-transonic variation re-establishes itself.

There is a crucial need to minimise the trim drag of aircraft which, like the North American XB-70 and Lockheed SR-71, are designed to cruise for long periods at supersonic speed. To counteract the nose-down pitching moment resulting from the rearward movement of the aerodynamic centre as the aircraft accelerates transonically, the centre of gravity can be moved aft to match the increase in static margin. On the two aircraft mentioned this was achieved by pumping fuel aft when accelerating through Mach 1 and forward again when decelerating to subsonic speed. In this way the deflections required of the external trimming control surfaces and their trim drag were minimised (Fig 176).

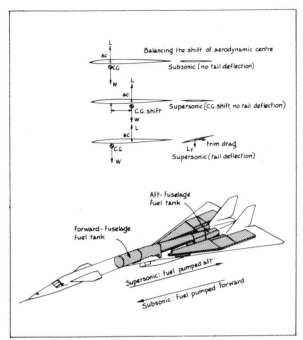

Fig 176 Centre-of-gravity control in supersonic aircraft. Without CG control, the need to counter the rearward shift of the aerodynamic centre can result in unacceptable trim drag.

But this method is inappropriate to fighter aircraft, which do not cruise supersonically for any length of time. Trim drag is nonetheless of great concern to the fighter designer, becoming very significant during manoeuvring. The Northrop YF-17 and its F-18 derivative were given a tailplane larger than was needed to meet stability and control requirements. Having a span 60% that of the wing, the YF-17's tailplane enabled the aft CG limit to be placed further back, thereby reducing the trim drag. Northrop claimed that the Mach 1·2 trim drag coefficient was less than one-third that offered by the conventional approach.

The wing itself also generates trim drag, and it is larger than that of the tailplane. In a pitching manoeuvre the tailplane download is increased to give the required rate of pitch. This requires the wing lift to be increased, for a given net lift, to make up for the tail load. Thus the wing's lift-dependent drag is also higher.

INFLUENCES ON TAIL EFFECTIVENESS

Downwash

In producing lift, wings generate a trailing-vortex system which induces downwash behind the surface. The influence of this flow field on the tailplane can be profound, though it is highly configuration-dependent. Indeed, depending on the wing's planform and geometry and the vertical location of the tail, tailplane effectiveness may be dominated by the wing's flow field.

The two major effects commonly encountered are:

1 A reduction in the angle at which the flow approaches the tail.

2 A reduction in the dynamic pressure of the flow approaching the tail, particularly if the tail is immersed in the wake leaving the wing.

Both of these effects cause reductions in tailplane effectiveness which can create severe problems at high AOA. As the AOA is increased to generate more lift, the downwash behind the wing becomes more intense. As angle of attack is further increased, or with significant shock-wave-induced boundary-layer separation, an inherent characteristic of swept wings manifests itself. This is the phenomenon of tip stall (discussed in detail in Chapter 1), in which flow separation occurs on the wing upper surface at or near the tips, sometimes well before total wing stall. Though the resulting wing lift loss is of no great consequence in itself, the location of the lift reduction in relation to the aircraft's CG is of prime importance. The lift is lost at the tips of the swept wing, behind the CG, so that the aircraft is generating more lift ahead of the CG than behind it (Fig 177). This imbalance can normally be rectified only by an upload from the tailplane. But the effectiveness of the tail, already reduced by the increasing downwash, may now

Fig 177 Wing-panel stall wake impinges on the tailplane, reducing its ability to counter pitch-up.

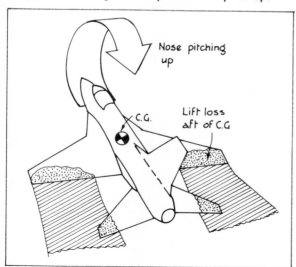

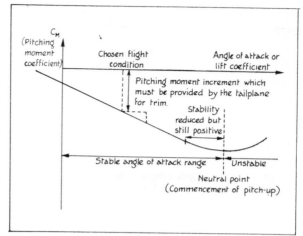

Fig 178 Generalised curve of pitching moment against wing angle of attack (or lift coefficient).

also be affected by a loss of effective dynamic pressure due to the wake being shed by those portions of the wing on which separation has occurred. Though stability is not lost, it is certainly reduced, as shown in Fig 178.

As angle of attack is further increased the wing separated-flow region spreads inboard and eventually the nose-up (i.e. unstable) moment due to the lift loss behind the CG may be too great for the tailplane to handle. The aircraft will then undergo a rapid uncontrolled nose-up rotation call pitch-up, which was a very worrying characteristic of many early swept-wing aircraft. It can have such serious consequences as complete stalling of the wing and air intakes, leading the aircraft into a superstall or spin.

Compressibility effects

In the course of acceleration through the transonic speed regime the aerodynamic centre moves aft from about quarter-chord to half-chord of the wing, with the result that pitch stability is more than adequate at supersonic speeds (Fig 179). This increase in stability across the transonic regime is further illustrated in Fig 180, which also shows a loss of tailplane effectiveness, resulting in the dip in the curve below Mach 1. This is attributable to the fact that while tailplane lift curve slope grows with Mach number, the tailplane's lower aspect ratio prevents it growing as fast as that of the wing.

Aeroelastic effects

Aeroelastic deflections of wings and tailplanes may be significant, especially on the relatively thin surfaces used on high-speed aircraft. For example,

Fig 179 Increased longitudinal stability at supersonic speed.

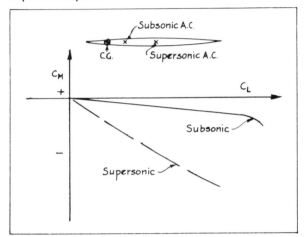

Fig 180 Variation of longitudinal stability with Mach number.

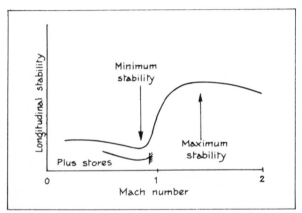

Fig 181 Aeroelastic effects.

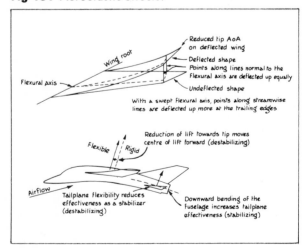

when a swept-back wing or tailplane bends upwards, the leading edge twists downwards, reducing the local AOA. This reduces the lift at the wingtips and moves the centre of lift forwards and inwards. For both surfaces this is a destabilising effect, though the very-low-aspect-ratio tailplanes commonly used tend to suffer less because of their higher relative stiffness. In addition, bending of the fuselage can also occur, though as shown in Fig 181 this can increase the apparent AOA of the tailplane and thereby increase its effectiveness.

Store wake and forebody effects

The wide variety of "un-aerodynamically" shaped stores carried on combat aircraft can very often have adverse effects on the tailplane, resulting in a loss of longitudinal stability. Modern combat aircraft, most of which have tailplanes set at the same level as the underwing stores, are particularly affected (Fig 180). The reduction in stability arises from the stores' self-generated lift forces, their induced effects on wing flow, and the impingement of store wake on the tailplane, influencing downwash and, more likely, lowering dynamic pressure at the tailplane location.

On the Panavia Tornado it was found that, with the air intake running at less than full mass flow, some spillage around the swept outboard sideplate produced a vortex. At low and moderate AOA the vortex passed close to the tailplane root, thereby unloading the leading edge of the tailplane and pushing the aerodynamic centre aft. This shift led to a reduction in effective tailplane stiffness (dC_m/dC_L), making it necessary to change the tailplane leading edge slightly in order to restore an acceptable degree of longitudinal stability.

TAILPLANE LOCATION

Vertical position

Early swept-wing aircraft with tails mounted low on the fin (e.g. Hawker Hunter) had difficulty in countering pitch-up. As a result, since the 1950s the trend has been decisively towards low fuselage-mounted tailplanes. The aim is to keep the tailplane as far away as possible from the region of intense downwash/wake behind the wing, particularly when aspect ratio is low. The two critical flight conditions are high AOA and high subsonic speed when shock-induced flow separation occurs.

During the 1950s both high and low tailplanes had their proponents among designers seeking to avoid loss of effectiveness. High tails were used on the F-101, F-104 and Buccaneer and low tails on nearly every other type, including the F-105, Lightning, A3J and F8U. While the Korean War-vintage North American F-86 Sabre had its tail low on the fin, the company's next fighter, the supersonic F-100, featured a tail at the extreme bottom of the fuselage.

High or T-tails

Defenders of the high-mounted tailplane held that if the tail was high enough it would not enter the wing wake and should therefore retain its effectiveness even at high AOA. (Nevertheless, an increase in AOA generally reduces the stability contribution from the tail, which inevitably moves closer to the wing's downwash.) Furthermore, a high tail operates in a relatively clean airflow, and by "end-plating" the fin can effectively increase the latter's aspect ratio, making it more effective. At very high AOA — say in a spin — the high tail does not mask the fin and rudder, and yields an increased tail moment arm because it is mounted on top of a swept fin.

When designing the F-104 Starfighter Lockheed considered every conceivable position and type of tailplane, including slab T-tail, a rectangular tailplane below the rear fuselage, foreplanes, strakes along the rear fuselage, and even boundary-layer control on large areas of the fuselage, wing and cockpit canopy. In fact the low tail almost always cured pitch-up and associated problems, though at the cost of detriment to directional stability, drag and weight, and overall combat utility. In the case of the F-104 the pitch-up came not from its swept wing — quarter-chord sweepback is only 5° — but from a combination of separated airflow leaving the intake and nose of the very slender body, together with flow separation from the very sharp leading edges of the stubby wings. Though the pitch-up proved to be almost insurmountable by any means, it was eventually decided in late 1953 to use a high T-tail to overcome inertia-coupling problems. (It was around this time that the F-100 was showing stability deficiencies which led to inertia-coupling incidents.) The F-104 was to have a system to reinforce its natural stability and to give stall warning. This had to include not only an AOA sensor but also pitch-rate sensor to activate a stick-shaker and stick-pusher to move the tail if the pilot ignored the warning signals. Though this was by far the most complex stability augmentation system fitted to a fighter up to that point, it still left something to be desired.

The fitting of a high T-tail to the British Buccaneer naval strike aircraft resulted in problems with "locked-in" stalls, the tailplane being unable to function in the turbulent wake from the

The high T-tail of the Lockheed F-104 is evident in this view of an early model (note the absence of the half-cone intake shock ramp). Anhedral was required on the sharp-leading-edge wings to compensate for the large dihedral effect imparted by the tailplane's influence on the vertical fin.

stalled wings. This was cured by using leading-edge boundary-layer control — already built in to reduce the wing size — to keep the outer wings unstalled. The Buccaneer also has BLC on the tailplane leading edge though this is required to increase the download on the tail rather than generate the upload needed in the event of pitch-up.

The Buccaneer's tail-fin junction is of interest. At high subsonic speeds some of the early pre-production aircraft developed random yaw, one in particular suffering severe tail-plane vibrations. The cause was shock-induced flow separation towards the top of the fin. A major change in the tail/fin fairing shape was the cure.

Low tails

The low-set tailplane, located close behind the wing, experiences the maximum downwash gradient from the wing, which diminishes its effect as a stabiliser at low AOA. As AOA increases it

RAF F-4M Phantom shadowing a Soviet Air Force Tu-95 Bear. The outer panels of the anhedral tailplane have stainless steel skins. This and other Phantom variants have a fixed inverted slat on the tailplane to counter the large nose-down pitching moment created by the drooped ailerons, which were themselves introduced for extra lift. (MoD)

moves into a less severe downwash field, allowing it to make a growing contribution to stability and so offset the pitch-up tendency. It also provides a strong pitch-down moment at high AOA, thereby minimising pitch overshoots into region in which a general breakdown of aerodynamic characteristics might be encountered. In addition, the low-mounted tailplane avoids any dead air from stalled portions of the wing at high AOA. For all of these reasons an aircraft with a low tail can be expected to operate at higher angles of attack before becoming longitudinally unstable. It is not sur-

prising therefore that the low tail is almost universally adopted nowadays for combat aircraft.

There are some apparently slight though very significant variations on the theme of low-mounted tailplanes, as shown by the following examples:

McDonnell Douglas F-4   In order to avoid the structural and weight problems of a high horizontal tail, as used on previous McDonnell designs such as the F3H and F-101, extensive wind tunnel testing and analytical work was carried out to arrive at the unique tail configuration of the Phantom. The tailplane is mounted just high enough to stay out of the direct path of the jet exhaust. The inner portion is however subjected to exceptionally high temperatures, and so is made largely from titanium. Anhedral of 23° lowers the outer portion to ensure adequate longitudinal stability through the designed AOA range, to provide adequate directional stability up to the maximum designed

Mach number, and to counter the rolling moment of the outer wing panels in yawed flight. The high degree of anhedral was made possible in part by the ground clearance afforded by the overhanging aft fuselage.

BAe Harrier   Pitch-up at high Mach number due to shock-induced flow separation was one of the primary aerodynamic concerns in the design decisions in the late 1950s. The tailplane was set as low as was consistent with keeping it out of the jet exhaust with the vectoring nozzles turned aft. At low AOA the Hawker P.1127 suffered from low pitch stability because the tailplane's contribution was so small. This was caused by the tail's close proximity to the exhaust, so that the local AOA was more a function of jet velocity than aircraft AOA. The rate of change of downwash with AOA was dominated by jet entrainment resulting in a minimal contribution to stability. Moreover, the stringent weight controls on the V/STOL design kept the tail small, contributing further to the problem.

Severe pitch-up arose in high-AOA and high-speed (i.e. high-g) flight. Despite improvements in wing geometry and local fixes, pitch-up limited manoeuvrability at high Mach number. Anhedral on the tailplane was investigated without success. Then it was discovered that favourable sidewash flows existed just outboard of the tips of the tailplane. Indeed, the only useful flow at high AOA lay beyond the tips of the original tailplane. The tailplane was therefore increased in span and given anhedral to take advantage of this flow, as shown in Fig 182.

The P.1127 itself featured a 0·6m increase in span and 18° anhedral was applied to the outboard portion. On the Kestrel, a service version designed for trials with the Tripartite Evaluation Squadron (with British, US and German personnel), the tailplane was reduced in area and the anhedral reduced to 15°, though now it extended to the root so that the tailplane tips were in the same position as they had been on the modified P.1127. The Kestrel was however still only marginally stable statically at low AOA and moderate Mach numbers despite a major effort to improve the static margin. The stability deteriorated further when underwing fuel tanks were carried.

The Kestrel tailplane was subsequently given another 0.6m increase in span. This put the additional area in the best position to take advantage of the favourable flows outboard of the jet exhaust. The Kestrel (the Harrier has the same tail) thus ended up with a tailplane whose span was 60% of the wing span. This provided an adequate level of

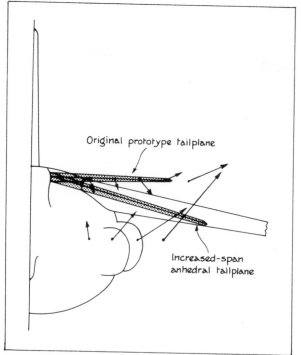

Fig 182 BAe Harrier tailplane down/sidewash patterns.[36]

stability but raised a structural problem encountered only on the ground. When the engine was running at high power with nozzles aft the tailplane began flapping, the motion being excited by the shearing at the edges of the jet exhausts. This was overcome by tying down both tailplane and aircraft during ground running. On Harrier ground runs the nozzles are deflected 10° down, which keeps the vibration and noise impingement on the tail to an acceptable level.

McDonnell Douglas F-18   Set at the mid-fuselage level, the tail could not have been lower because its sweepback would have caused tail scraping on take-off.

BAe Lightning, BAC TSR.2, MiG-25, F-14, F-15, Mirage F.1, Su-24, Tornado   All of these aircraft were designed with high, shoulder-mounted wings and mid-fuselage-mounted tails. This combination keeps the tail outside the wing wake at low AOA and avoids flutter caused by aerodynamic interference between the two surfaces.

BAe Hawk (and other military trainer/strike aircraft)   The low-wing layout typical of these types gives no opportunity to place the tail below the wing. The tail is accordingly mounted high on the fuselage at the base of the fin and, in the case of the Hawk, has 10° anhedral. This angle puts the tailplane tips outside the intense wing downwash at high AOA. The Hawk's wing, with only 26° of leading-edge sweep, is unlikely to suffer the rapid pitch-up typical of more highly swept designs. In addition, mounting the single-piece tail at the rear of the base of the fin makes good use of the volume there to house the tailplane actuators. A location on either side of the tailpipe would, by contrast, complicate the structure and could require external blisters.

Fore-and-aft position

The tailplane is generally placed as far aft as is practicable to maximise the tail moment arm. One restriction on this is engine noise-induced structural fatigue. Northrop has tackled this in the past by placing no structure aft of the exhaust nozzle exit plane. This means in practice that the tailplane trailing edge lies ahead of the steep part of the aft-fuselage boat-tail. This practice, as demonstrated by the F-5, was not as rigidly adhered to on the YF-17, but even this type contrasts markedly with the F-15, in which a good deal of structure overhangs the nozzle exit plane.

TAILPLANE SHAPE

In general a moderately swept, low-aspect-ratio, symmetric-section tailplane is used on high-speed aircraft, partly to give low zero-lift wave drag and partly to avoid the sudden stall associated with low sweep, high aspect ratios and thin symmetric sections. The actual planform and thickness/chord ratio tend to be determined by the need to incorporate a spigot, variations in hinge moment with Mach number, and aeroelastic considerations. Tailplane aspect ratio is invariably less than that of the parent wing.

Probably the most distinctive current tailplane is that of the F-15, which has a dogtooth or snagged leading edge. McDonnell Douglas discovered in wind-tunnel testing before the first aircraft flew that the proposed horizontal tail was more flutter-prone than early analytical studies had indicated. Reduction in aft-fuselage structural cross-sections for area-rule and base-drag reasons had resulted in a tail-support boom structure relatively short of bending and torsional stiffness. When this was combined with a simultaneous increase in size of the twin fins and deletion of the ventral strakes,

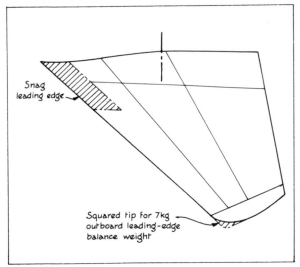

Fig 183 Alternative schemes for flutter avoidance on F-15 tailplane.[66]

both vertical and horizontal surfaces became flutter-critical. Wind-tunnel tests had shown that the flutter to be expected was of the explosive kind, giving little warning of its onset. Many models were destroyed in testing, in which tailplane tip deflections of a tip-chord length were reached within 3–5 oscillations. Applied to the full-scale aircraft, this corresponds to an interval of less than half a second between the first sign of flutter and structural failure. After a good deal of effort McDonnell Douglas found itself faced with the choice, shown in Fig 183, of either extending the tailplane tip and adding 7kg of leading-edge balance weight to increase the flutter speed by 11%, or "snagging" the leading edge of the stabilator to avoid the need for balance weights. Though both approaches offered an adequate flutter speed safety margin, the snag leading edge was lighter and had no negative effect on subsonic drag or stability/handling characteristics. Moreover, had a further increase in flutter speed proved necessary, balance weights could always have been added.

The tailplane's raked tip (Fig 183) was associated with these measures. The rake was applied normal to the tailplane's elastic axis, it having been shown that this would call for less weight to balance out the trailing-edge weight if leading-edge tip weights did prove necessary. The raked tip has no adverse aerodynamic effect and is lightly loaded, especially at supersonic speed, and was thus left on just in case!

The first three F-15s off the production line were too early to have the snag tail and were fitted with balance weights instead. Both tailplane halves are interchangeable, as on the F-111 and F-16, to help reduce production costs and spares requirements.

Tailplane modifications

Two significant tailplane modifications have been applied to aircraft designed for operation from aircraft carriers to improve the downward "lifting" capability of the tail.

BAe Buccaneer Tailplane lift augmentation, needed for the high-lift carrier approach configuration, was achieved by means of a tailplane trailing-edge flap slaved to aileron droop (used to further increase lift), plus a BLC slit along the tailplane leading edge.

McDonnell Douglas Phantom The F-4J, -K and -M variants are equipped with drooped ailerons to increase lift and reduce approach speeds at increased weights. This was achieved at the cost of a large nose-down pitching moment. The original tailplane stalled before it could supply enough downwards lift to trim the aircraft. A fixed, inverted slat was therefore fitted to the lower leading edge to delay the stall and so enable the tailplane to carry on lifting to a very much higher AOA.

THE ALL-MOVING TAILPLANE

First-generation jet fighters

Aircraft such as the Gloster Meteor, de Havilland Vampire and Lockheed F-80 had fixed tailplanes with manually operated elevators. These types, with their relatively thick unswept wings, experienced local regions of supersonic flow while diving at approximately Mach 0·8. The strong shock waves which terminated the supersonic flows inevitably caused flow separation (Fig 184), leading to abrupt changes of trim. This was a repeat of the experience of the high-speed piston-engined fighters of the Second World War. The characteristics of the manual elevators with which they were equipped varied rapidly with small changes of speed, making precise control difficult. It also proved increasingly difficult to ensure freedom from flutter as aircraft speeds moved further into the transonic region.

The shock waves which developed on the tail surfaces limited the region over which the elevator movement could have any effect to that area aft of the shock wave. This was because the elevator's effect propagated, like all small pressure changes, with the local speed of sound, and could not there-

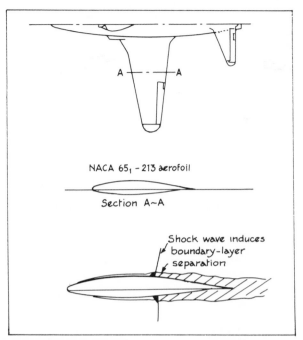

NACA 65₁ – 213 aerofoil

Section A~A

Fig 184 Compressibility effects on Lockheed F-80.

Fig 185 How shock waves limit elevator effect.

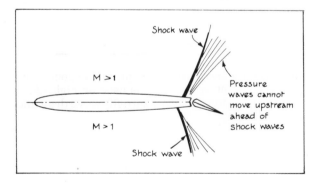

fore penetrate into the supersonic region upstream of the shock wave (Fig 185). Elevator effectiveness was therefore reduced, and might indeed have disappeared altogether at high-subsonic speeds over a small range of Mach number, as shown previously in Fig 93. Ways of delaying this loss of effectiveness included making the trailing-edge angle very small, either by using a very thin control (with the risk of aeroelastic distortion) or by giving the elevator a blunt trailing edge. However, further increases in maximum flight Mach number following the use of sweptback surfaces (which usually had swept control-surface hinge lines) further reduced elevator effectiveness.

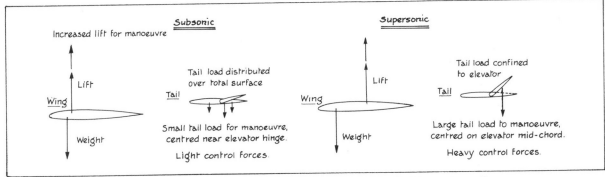

Fig 186 Elevators are unsuitable for longitudinal control at supersonic speeds, requiring high control forces and being less effective than at subsonic speeds.

Early transonic jet fighters

These included the F-86, Hunter, Javelin and Mystère, all of which had movable trimming tailplanes with manual or powered elevators. In fact one of the first operational jet aircraft, the Me262, had featured a trimming tailplane. By the early 1950s it had become increasingly difficult with manual controls to handle the rapid variations in stick force and to ensure freedom from control-surface flutter, and so powered controls were becoming common.

Supersonic fighter aircraft

The advent of the truly supersonic aircraft, represented by the F-100 Super Sabre, was accompanied by the almost universal adoption of the fully powered all-moving tailplane, also known as the slab tailplane. Early applications were the F-101 Voodoo, F-104 Starfighter, F-105 Thunderchief and the English Electric Lightning.

There were four pressing reasons for the adoption of the all-moving tailplane:

1 The rearward shift of the centre of lift on the aircraft produces excessive longitudinal stability (see *Compressibility effects*, page 167). This demands large control deflections for manoeuvre if a flap-

Fig 187 Control-surface effect in subsonic and supersonic flows.

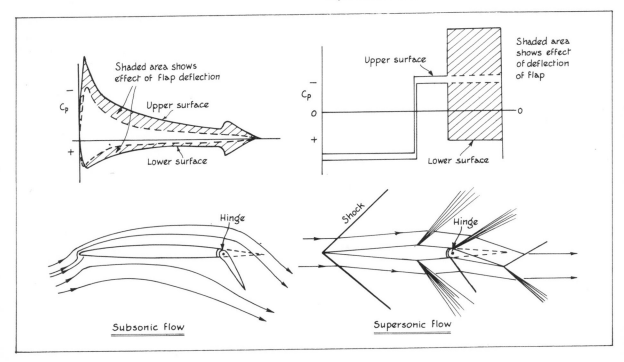

type surface (i.e. an elevator) is used, as shown in Fig 186.

2 The effect of a flap-type surface in supersonic flow is limited to the area downstream of the hinge, compared with the whole-surface effect obtained in subsonic flow (Fig 187).

3 With the centre of lift on the surface itself lying at approximately mid-chord, the size of the force needed to move the surface renders manual control impractical.

4 The aeroelastic distortion of a relatively high-aspect-ratio elevator further reduced effectiveness and lowered flutter speed.

Currently most all-moving tailplanes not only perform the functions of stabiliser and pitch control but also operate differentially to provide roll control (see *Chapter 1, Lateral control,* page 102).

CONTROL-CONFIGURED VEHICLES

Control-configured vehicle (CCV) is the name given to an aircraft resulting from a design process in which the control system plays an early and very influential part in shaping the airframe, rather than the other way round. Before the late 1960s the design started with the performance requirements: take-off and landing distances, payload/range, speed versus altitude, and so on. Studies were then performed to determine the combination of wing area, weight, thrust and other parameters needed to meet the requirement. More detailed work was then conducted by the aerodynamics, propulsion and structural design groups to produce a basic configuration. This would then be repeatedly refined in order to minimise, say, weight or cost while maintaining the required performance. Finally, with every major aspect of the design settled, work would begin on the control system.

Delaying consideration of the control system to this stage often resulted in handling qualities which, though acceptable, were rarely if ever the optimum. Under the CCV philosophy the control system is a major driving force in shaping the aircraft. However, simply bringing forward the introduction of control system design into the aircraft's evolution would not of itself achieve the significant advance that CCV represents. On the contrary, it is only because of the remarkable developments which have taken place in the fields of electronics and control engineering that the concept can be anything more than just that. The ways in which such active control technology (ACT) is used, and the rewards it offers, are considered next.

Active control technology

ACT is not in fact a new idea, having formed the basis of autopilots for several decades. Strictly, an ACT control system is one which, like an autopilot, constantly monitors and reacts to disturbances (i.e. it is *active*). Currently, however, ACT implies the use of feedback control for functions which go far beyond previous applications to improve aircraft performance in the broadest sense, including size and cost reductions. These improvements result from the use of the control surfaces to redistribute, alleviate or enhance the aerodynamic forces acting on the aircraft.

Such an approach had previously not been feasible, since with ACT the very safety of the aircraft depends upon the complete reliability of the system. In the past, for example, if the system designed to augment the inherent stability of the airframe failed, enough "natural" stability would remain to permit the aircraft to return safely, though careful handling might be required. ACT systems can offer such high reliability at acceptable weight and cost that an aircraft can be designed to be inherently unstable, relying totally on ACT for its stability. In the event of a total failure the loss of the aircraft is however inevitable. The system must therefore be very reliable indeed, and this is generally accomplished by at least triplicating the primary system; duplication is insufficient because a majority vote is needed to identify the faulty channel.

If the penalties for failure are so severe, then the many design teams now exploiting ACT must have been attracted by some very significant benefits. ACT in fact offers a remarkable range of facilities hitherto largely unattainable:

• Load alleviation through gust-load control and manoeuvre-load control
• Ride-quality control
• Fatigue-damage control
• Flutter control
• Centre-of-gravity control
• Flight envelope-limiting
• Artificial stability, permitting relaxed static stability

This chapter deals with longitudinal stability, and so confines itself to the opportunity offered by ACT to relax inherent static stability. Early papers on the subject of ACT[67, 68] are recommended to readers seeking a deeper insight into the other applicatios of ACT.

Stability augmentation and relaxed static stability

Until the 1970s flight control systems were used primarily to relieve the pilot's workload and to improve handling beyond the standard achievable by aerodynamic means alone. Stability augmentation in this form played a big role in the aircraft of the time. Nonetheless it was often regarded as little more than an adjunct, however vital, even in aircraft with a degree of inherent airframe stability which was at times minimal. Modern developments in active control systems have made them so versatile and reliable that the aircraft designer has had available ever-increasing levels of stability augmentation should he need or wish to use them. It was this advance that made relaxed static stability (RSS) possible. This aspect of the control-configured vehicle (CCV) concept, which emerged in the 1970s, is based on the use of active controls for more than mere stability augmentation or a cure for some localised design deficiency. The idea was much more revolutionary: if the principles of RSS were allowed to help shape the aircraft, improvements in performance, efficiency and cost would follow.

RSS calls for a relaxation of the demand for inherent airframe stability, while keeping the aircraft controllable by electronic means. Up to the late 1960s the requirement for natural longitudinal static stability was treated as an inviolate design constraint. It was considered difficult if not impossible to fly a modern combat aircraft which was inherently unstable in pitch. Interestingly enough, all of the Wright Brothers' aircraft were unstable in this sense, it being considered that the pilot should be in full command at all times.

RSS and static margin

Fig 171 showed that the tailplane on a conventional aircraft provides a measure of pitch stability, though this is ultimately governed by the CG position (Fig 172). A conventional aircraft is one in which the CG is forward of the neutral point, i.e. there is a positive static margin. Moving the CG aft of the neutral point (NP) would produce an unstable configuration, giving a positive slope to the C_m/C_L curve, i.e. a negative static margin (SM).

In the unstable case a nose-up disturbance will aggravate the nose-up tendency, though this could be countered if the increased wing lift ahead of the CG could be balanced by an upload on the tail to restore equilibrium about the CG. This is the essence of relaxed static stability, with the active control system driving rapid-response actuators with no input from the pilot to transform an inherently unstable aircraft into a stable one, albeit artificially. Superficially there appears to be no great virtue in replacing the tail download needed to balance the aircraft with an upload. But this is precisely where the great benefit of RSS resides, as will be explained in the next section.

Is a tailplane really necessary?

An aircraft with RSS will possess a tailplane no bigger than is absolutely necessary to meet its requirements. Such a tailplane does not necessarily provide static stability, since a tailplane's only *essential* function is the provision of pitch control and trim. Static longitudinal stability depends entirely on the relative location of the aircraft's CG and its aerodynamic centre (AC) or neutral point (NP), and the presence of a tailplane does not alter this fact. Of course, once installed the tailplane makes a contribution to overall stability, but nothing that an equivalent forward shift of the CG could not match. Having thus relieved the tailplane of any responsibility for stability, it is possible to concentrate on designing it purely for the pitch control and trimming functions.

Stability versus manoeuvrability

It has been seen that on a conventional aircraft in subsonic manoeuvring flight, and more especially at supersonic speeds, large downloads are needed for longitudinal trim. The lift loss due to trimming typically amounts to 10–15% of maximum lift. Use of a high-authority feedback control system on an aircraft whose inherent longitudinal static stability has been relaxed (by shifting the CG aft) so much that it is now negative can give a significant reduction in tail downloads or even a lifting tail. Wing loads are reduced significantly by a lifting tail, since the tail loads are aiding rather than opposing the wing's lift. This gives a reduction in drag and improves manoeuvrability.

Artificial stability also allows the full upward lift capability of the tail to be used for trimming purposes. The rear CG limit is in fact determined by the balance of upload on the tail at its maximum lift (with some safety margin) opposing the unstable moment from the wing lift. In this way the tail's maximum positive lift and maximum negative lift (forward-CG case, nosewheel lifting or landing trim) are exploited at both ends of the CG range. Instead of wasting the positive lift capability, as is the case with natural stability, artificial stability makes possible smaller tail surfaces, leading to further drag and weight savings.

Tail size

The tail sizing diagram (Fig 173a) alters its shape significantly when stability is artificially provided (Fig 173b). In both cases the tailplane size is reduced for the same required CG range and the aft CG limit can be moved further back. It is necessary to move the main wheels aft with the CG in order to maintain an adequate static load on the nosewheel (the minimum being 8% of the aircraft weight) for steering and to prevent the aircraft

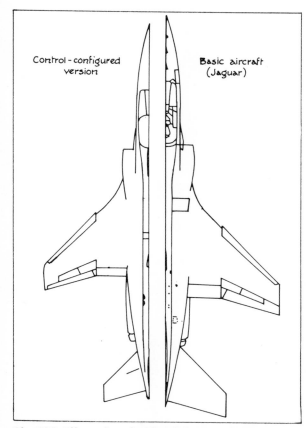

Fig 188 Effect of artificial stability on aircraft size.[69]

from tipping on its tail. The F-111E carries lead ballast in its nosewheel bay to avoid tipping when parked with its wings in the aft position. Fig 173b also shows that the forward-CG limiting condition in flight has changed from the download needed to trim in the flaps-down, high-AOA case to that for the low-AOA case.

Benefits of artificial stability

Artificial stability can be exploited either by enhancing the performance of an aircraft or reducing its size and weight for a given performance. Application of the latter approach to a typical strike fighter could yield a weight reduction of as much as 8–10%.

A higher wing loading — for the same airfield and combat performance — is permitted by the greater usable lift created with RSS. The lower drag from the smaller wing and tail surfaces means that less fuel is burned. The weight savings resulting from the reduction in aircraft size and fuel load allow a smaller engine. Thrust/weight ratio remains the same, and the result should be a smaller, lighter and more efficient aircraft for a

given task (Fig 188). Even larger rewards may be obtained with delta-plus-foreplane layouts.

RSS and aircraft growth factor

The benefit of RSS to weight saving is even more apparent when account is taken of aircraft growth factor (or weight "snowball effect"). This is the amount by which the all-up weight changes as a result of a given increase in systems or component weight. Typical figures for growth factor are between 5 and 7, i.e. a 1kg increase in avionics weight could result in a 5–7kg increase in take-off weight. RSS allows the structure, fuel and power-plant weights to be reduced for a given mission. Since the weights of crew and payload remain fixed, the ratio of fixed weight/AUW increases and the growth factor decreases. General Dynamics claimed a growth factor of only 2·5 for the YF-16.

If increased radius of action or heavier payload is required, the RSS aircraft has a head start in its ability to avoid the steep escalation in growth factor suffered by the conventional one. There is however a limit on this welcome deflationary spiral. In one retrospective application of RSS to a combat aircraft[70] the process shrank the airframe (wing area and weight) by 9%. Going beyond this would have left insufficient volume for fuel, although without this restriction a reduction of 15% was possible.

Mission-dependent benefits

The benefits of RSS are closely related to the nature of the aircraft's mission. One authority[22] argues that the more exacting the requirements the greater the gain from artificial stability. Comparing the low-altitude strike and air superiority roles, most of the fuel expended in the former is used to overcome profile drag, trim drag being relatively unimportant. In the air superiority mission, loitering and sustained high-g combat account for a large proportion of the fuel used, so that the prime need is to reduce lift-dependent and trim drags. Every drag count avoided on the YF-16 offered a 2kg reduction in aircraft weight. Indeed, assumption of RSS in design studies for the air superiority role produced the following figures: 10% improvement in sustained turn rate (thrust-limited); 15% improvement in attained turn rate (lift-limited); and 25% increase in radius of action (10% claimed for the F-16).

The F-16: A bold step

General Dynamics boldly put its money on the CCV concept for its Model 401 contender in the USAF Light Weight Fighter programme, which as the YF-16 first flew in February 1974. The aircraft featured relaxed static stability, envelope-limiting,

and a full-time fly-by-wire (FBW) flight control system, along with other advanced features. As the F-16A it became in 1978 the first production aircraft to feature full-time (i.e. with no mechanical back-up) FBW. An earlier G-D aircraft, the F-111, has FBW with mechanical back-up.

Trim drag at high g is crucial to the performance of a highly manoeuvrable fighter. In the YF-16 trim drag was minimised by balancing the aircraft to give superior supersonic manoeuvring. This strategy resulted in longitudinal instability at low lift coefficients in subsonic flight. The negative static margin was 6% MAC for the air combat configuration, extending to 10% MAC for configurations with the larger external stores. The aircraft balance is shown in Fig 189, where it is compared with the conventional. The value of operating at a

Tornado ADV and ACT Jaguar (with visible trailing vortex cores) deploy their high-lift devices in order to formate on the slow-flying photographic aircraft. A conventionally stable aircraft, the Tornado requires a tail download to trim. But the highly unstable ACT Jaguar copes nicely with a slightly lifting tail. (BAe)

negative static margin subsonically lies in the fact that a tail upload is demanded; this changes to a smaller-than-conventional tail download at supersonic speed, when the aerodynamic centre and CG are again related in the conventional manner. A conventional design generally requires a minimum positive static margin of 3% MAC. If the conventional approach had been used on the YF-16 this minimum, occurring at low speed, would have risen to 6% at Mach 0·9 and 15% supersonically. The

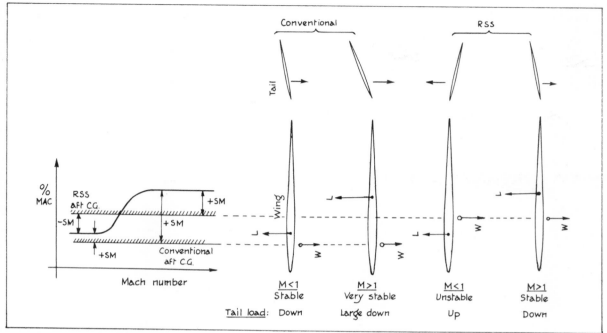

Fig 189 F-16 longitudinal balance : conventional versus RSS. **SM** = static margin.

use of RSS means that the static margin is negative at Mach 0·9 and is reduced by 8% at Mach 1·2.

The tailplane deflections required for the above cases, together with the resulting trim drag, are shown in Fig 190. Noteworthy are the much reduced trim drags at the high C_L characteristic of air-superiority combat manoeuvring. On the YF-16 the trim drag was reduced by up to 50%, which increased the supersonic turn rate by 15% and the subsonic turn rate by 8%. The reduction in supersonic static margin permits the aircraft to manoeuvre supersonically to its design load factor without being limited by longitudinal control power. RSS also increased radius of action by 10% for a 10% negative static margin, with a corresponding 0·5% reduction in take-off weight.

The maximum negative static margin at which the YF-16 operated routinely basis was 13%. The aircraft was not originally designed for ground strike, and the subsequent use of the F-16 with two additional store stations for large and inevitably destabilising external loads meant that without modification the negative static margins would have gone beyond the previous limit. The tailplane area of production F-16s was therefore increased by 15%.

A predecessor of the F-16, the B-58 Hustler, required artificial stability because it was unstable in pitch at its aftmost CG position. The Boeing Model 818 contender for the TFX contract,

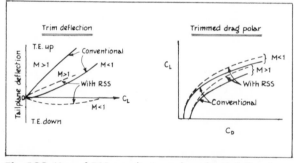

Fig 190 Use of RSS results in reduced tail deflection and drag.

eventually awarded to General Dynamics with the F-111, was designed in the early 1960s to fly with a negative static margin of up to 7%. Since the advent of the F-16 it has become clear that RSS and many of the other aspects of CCVs are well established. Indeed, the adoption of RSS led to the resurgence of canard layouts in the early 1980s (see *Foreplanes*, page 180).

The risks of RSS

Clearly, if basic flight safety depends at all times on the control system, a complete failure is intolerable. In high-speed flight at low altitudes loss of control would result in structural failure through the imposition of inertial or aerodynamic loads in 1–2sec. The higher the level of instability, the quicker the aircraft will depart from controlled flight. Sufficient redundancy is therefore built into all parts of the control system and power supplies to ensure survival of local failures and to reduce the risk of total failure to a very low level. The customary design target is no more than one catastrophic failure in 10 million flying hours. This is equivalent to a failure rate of less than one per millenium of continuous flight per aircraft. To put these rates in context, during 1964–1973 USAF fighters suffered one accident due to flight control system failures[67] every 200,000 flying hours.

FOREPLANES

It might seem that a stabilising surface in front of the wing is somehow different from one behind. However, putting the difference between stabilisers and wings aside for a moment, the surfaces can be regarded simply as lifting planes. The distinction between leading and trailing surface depends on relative size only: if the foreplane is relatively large then the aircraft's layout is conventional; if the foreplane is relatively small then the layout is regarded as a canard configuration (e.g. Saab Viggen).

A wing located as the leading surface is destabilising as a result of its nose-up moment about the aircraft's CG, while the tailplane in the trailing position provides stability. At first sight the foreplane of the canard arrangement may appear to be another destabilising surface. This is not in itself significant, because a judiciously placed CG takes care of overall stability.

One early application of the foreplane to high-performance jet aircraft was the Nord 1500 Griffon. The purpose of the fixed foreplane in this case was to counteract the increasingly nose-down trim change occurring as the aircraft passed through the transonic region. Without the upload generated by the foreplane the Griffon would have required a significant amount of up-elevon at the rear of its delta wing, causing a large trim drag penalty.

Attractions of the canard layout

One of the attractions of the foreplane is its location clear of the wing wake and its downwash, which diminishes the effectiveness of aft-mounted surfaces. In fact, because the foreplane is ahead of the wing, in the latter's upwash, its influence is magnified. This has meant that past canard configurations have required a very forward CG position (Fig 191) to maintain longitudinal stability, since the destabilising effect of the foreplane moves the neutral point forward (Fig 192). The net

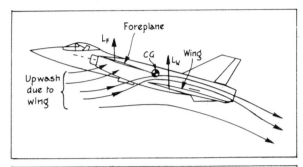

Fig 191 Destabilising effect of foreplanes.

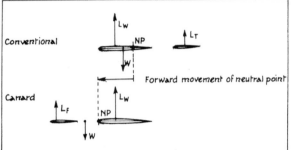

Fig 192 The use of foreplanes moves the neutral point ahead of the wing, requiring a forward CG position in order to maintain inherent stability.

result is that it is very difficult to obtain an adequate CG range when a foreplane is combined with a high-lift wing. The need for such a wing is however obviated somewhat by the most widely quoted advantage of the canard layout, namely the fact that both wing *and* foreplane are lifting. This is contrary to the case of the conventional layout, in which the horizontal stabiliser may carry a download for much of the time, and particularly in the high-lift approach and take-off phases. Cases in point are the configurations which were thrown up in the mid-1950s in response to the Royal Air Force requirement for a supersonic strategic bomber. Three designs in particular, from Avro, Handley Page and Vickers, used the canard arrangement not so much for high lift as to allow rotation to take-off AOA with a very long, slender fuselage.

Adverse effects of the foreplane

Just as wing downwash diminishes the load produced by the tailplane, so can a foreplane adversely affect the lifting capability of the parent wing. Until the late 1970s the major proponent of the canard configuration was Sweden's Saab, which clearly appreciated the importance of mounting the foreplane high in relation to the wing.

Fig 193 Effect of relative position of lifting surfaces on wing vortices.[37]

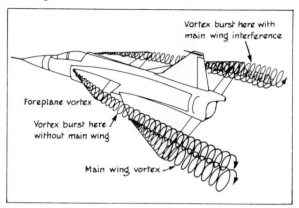

Fig 195 Effect of foreplane downwash on main-wing lift.[37]

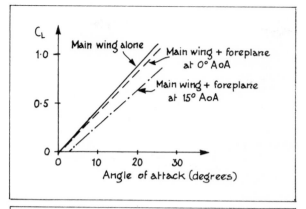

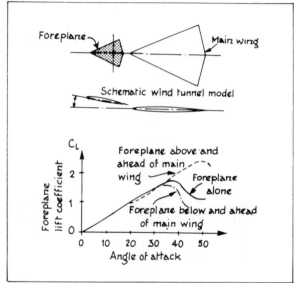

Fig 194 Effect of position on foreplane lift.[37]

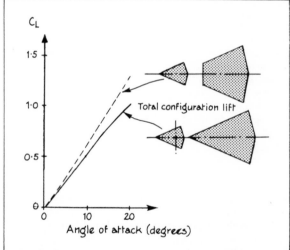

Fig 196 Effect of main-wing apex cut-off on total configuration lift.[37]

The design of the Saab Viggen further demonstrated the influence of the close-coupled parent wing in delaying bursting of the foreplane's vortex system to high AOA (Fig 193). This vortex system flows into the wing's low-pressure flow field (i.e. down a favourable pressure gradient), where it is stabilised so that bursting does not occur before it reaches the wing's trailing edge. This has a large effect on the foreplane's lifting ability, as shown in Fig 194, which also indicates the lift advantage resulting from the high foreplane position and the value of having a parent wing downstream to maintain vortex stability.

Unfortunately, when the foreplane/wing arrangement is correct for good high-AOA characteristics,

the foreplane's downwash inevitably impedes the lift generation of the parent wing at low AOA. The extent of the damage done by the foreplane's downwash is shown in Fig 195. Serious consideration was given to removing the vertex region of the Viggen's main wing completely, so low was its aerodynamic loading. Redistribution of the area to regions of high lift production (i.e. outboard of the foreplane's vortices, where there is a strong upwash) was investigated. It was found that a straight cut-off would give the best result in this respect (Fig 196), but then high-subsonic wind-tunnel testing revealed the formation of strong shock waves just aft of the truncated wing's leading edge, adverse vortex interactions and severe pitch-up tendencies. The proposed solution was thus unacceptable, and not until the inboard leading-edge sweep was increased to 45° did adequate transonic qualities manifest themselves.

The forward CG position dictated by past canard designs meant that it was more important to achieve high lift from the foreplane than from the wing. The high span loading of a highly loaded foreplane induces high vortex drag, though this is not crucial for a low-altitude, high-speed attack aircraft because vortex drag is relatively unimportant, being typically only 5% of the total. For the air superiority role, however, vortex drag can approach 90% of the total and is a severe handicap to sustained manoeuvrability, in which excess power (i.e. T-D/V) is the controlling factor. Nevertheless, a closely coupled canard layout with highly swept surfaces can produce favourable interactions between foreplane and wing at high lift. In these circumstances the foreplane acts rather like a strake, inducing a vortex field which improves the pressure distribution on the parent wing. This lift enhancement can be as much as 20–30% by comparison with the maximum lift obtained by the surfaces in isolation. A 50% improvement is expected on the European Fighter Aircraft. The benefit is limited to high AOA, so that manoeuvrability is improved while take-off performance benefits little if anything. The favourable interaction can allow a smaller wing to be used for an air combat type. This has the additional pay-off for a low-altitude aircraft of reducing its gust sensitivity and drag.

Apart from the foreplane's influences on wing flow, there are other factors which govern its position. Chief among these are its effect on air intake efficiency, pilot visibility, convenient location of its spigot and actuators, and vortex interaction with the vertical stabiliser.

Recent applications

Tests were carried out in the early 1970s with an F-4 Phantom equipped with a foreplane mounted on the upper forward portion of the air inlets (Fig 197). It was found that the aircraft was more manoeuvrable, being able to pull a full g more at 470km/h and 9,000m, and had a 14km/h lower approach speed.

Another comparatively recent application of foreplanes was the Mirage 5 variant known as the Milan. Dassault equipped the aircraft with small retractable foreplanes known as "moustaches". These were flapped aerofoils which could produce constant lift over a range of aircraft AOAs. This was achieved by ensuring that the foreplanes operated only beyond their stalling angle (Fig 198). This application was intended to improve the Mirage 5's poor airfield performance, a characteristic of all basic deltas. Deployed at low speed, the foreplanes produced nose lift, requiring down-elevon to trim. Lift was thereby added both fore and aft, and with the foreplanes giving constant lift, stability was unaltered.

The Milan package was a relatively inexpensive way of improving airfield performance, low-altitude handling and manoeuvrability. It has been adapted, in the form of fixed foreplanes, for the Israel Aircraft Industries Mirage variant, the Kfir-C2, and the Dassault Mirage 4000. The long-coupled canard configuration typified by the XB-70 of the 1960s and the earlier proposed British strategic bombers has not subsequently re-emerged. The small vanes on the nose of the Rockwell B-1 are not used as foreplanes as defined in the present context but as active ride-control

Fig 197 How the application of CCV technology to an existing design resulted in improved turning performance. Speed was Mach 1·6, altitude 14,000m and gross weight 18,000kg.[71]

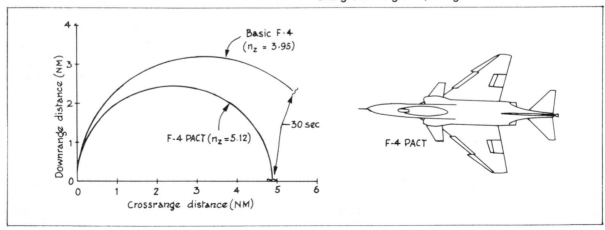

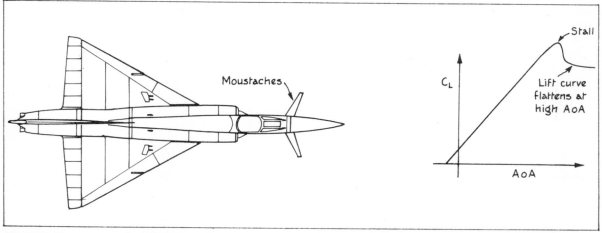

Fig 198 The "moustache" foreplanes of the Dassault Milan helped to maintain lift at high angles of attack, improving airfield performance in particular.

The IAI Kfir-C2 is a mixture of technology from the 1950s and 1970s. The plane delta wing was developed from that of the Mirage III, principal new features being conical camber and a leading-edge dogtooth. The foreplanes and nose strakes help to make the Kfir much more manoeuvrable than its French predecessor, although airfield performance was not greatly improved. (IAI)

devices, required for the low-altitude high-speed penetration role.

Designers have tended to avoid canards for several reasons:

1 Lack of background experience. The foreplanes must stall before the main wing, otherwise pitch-up occurs; accurate absolute pitching-moment data from wind-tunnel testing are hard to obtain.
2 If the vortices shed by the canards (or strakes for that matter) impinge on the fin, it will suffer signifi-

cant buffet, particularly at high AOA if the vortices burst not far downstream. The F-18 has suffered from this problem.

3 The destabilising effect of wing stores aft of the CG.

4 The belief that the canard layout imposes severe restrictions on wing planform.

5 The enforced forward CG position required to achieve inherent airframe stability demands a highly loaded foreplane carrying perhaps 10% of the total lift. Because of its small span, say 40% that of the wing, its span loading $\left(\dfrac{W}{b}\right)$ and hence lift-induced drag will be over six times that of a of wing carrying the same lift. Thus with a foreplane carrying 10% of the total lift, the total induced drag is 50% higher than that of an ideally balanced tailed aircraft.

Artificial stability and the foreplane

The experience gained with artificial stability on aircraft like the F-16 and F-18 has settled many of the misgivings which confined the application of foreplanes to all but a handful of aircraft. With many nations currently working on relatively light-weight agile aircraft, canard layouts are in abundance. Leading examples include the Saab JAS39 Gripen, Israeli Lavi, BAe EAP and Dassault-Breguet Rafale.

Artificial stability relieves the need for inherent airframe stability (with CG being the driving force). The deficiency in stability is corrected by the computers at the heart of the automatic flight control system (AFCS), which send signals via a fly-by-wire network to the control surface actuators. The absence of the restriction on forward CG position allows a near-ideal CG location (i.e. close to the wing/body aerodynamic centre) to be used. This results in a less highly loaded foreplane and thereby cuts the vortex drag penalty, yielding lift drag ratios comparable to those of conventional aircraft. With the aft movement of the neutral point in supersonic flight, positive foreplane lift to trim the aircraft gives an L/D in manoeuvre superior to that of a conventional aircraft with a down-loaded tail and similar to that of aircraft with artificial stability and tail uploads.

Other points in favour of the canard layout with all-moving foreplanes are:

1 Favourable trimmed-lift interference at high AOA subsonically.

2 Lower supersonic drag due to the better aftbody lines resulting from the absence of tailplane and spigot supporting structure.

3 If rear-end thrust-vectoring is used, a canard layout helps to eliminate the possibility of longitudinal stability and trim changes by moving the horizontal tail as far forward as possible.

4 Higher potential for gust alleviation, since the foreplane lift required to cancel the pitching moment arising from active-controlled flaps is additive to flap lift in opposing gust effects. A tailplane counteracts this effect.

5 The possibility of direct-force manoeuvring by means of the following combinations: flaps plus foreplane, giving direct lift control; flaps plus foreplane with AOA change, giving drag modulation; and differential foreplane plus rudders, giving direct sideforce control.

6 Canards go well with the forward-swept wing (e.g. Grumman X-29). There is little room aft for a rear tail, and almost all contemporary FSW aircraft feature a foreplane. This is of particular benefit to the wing root region, where forward-swept wings have their highest loading and consequent root stalling characteristics. The downwash from a foreplane can be used to spread the loading more evenly across the whole wing. In addition, the X-29 was designed to be neutrally stable in pitch in supersonic flight. This results in the massively negative stability margin of 35% MAC in the landing approach. The large supersonic aft movement of the neutral point which this demonstrates is apparently a characteristic of foreplane-equipped FSW aircraft.

CHAPTER 5

FINS (VERTICAL STABILISERS)

INTRODUCTION

In dealing with fin design, this chapter has to consider certain aspects of lateral/directional stability. The discussion begins with an explanation of the need for a vertical stabiliser and demonstrates its contribution to the overall stability of the aircraft. Brief reference is made to the dynamic response of an aircraft to show how fin size governs the motion subsequent to a disturbance in yaw and in roll.

Flight at high speed causes compressibility and aeroelastic distortion to diminish fin effectiveness. In addition, flight at high AOA can give rise to a plethora of lateral/directional control problems, the result of adverse flows. The ways in which these problems affect the fin and how they can be overcome, are discussed and many examples are given.

The convention is to install the fin, as the main directionally stabilising surface, on top of the aft fuselage. This provides the longest moment arm, minimises interference with other airframe components, and eliminates ground clearance problems. Examples show this practice in action and explain some of the variations on the basic theme. The use of ventral fins, a common feature of combat aircraft since the 1950s, is also discussed. Finally, the factors underlying rudder design, and the increasing use of the aileron/rudder interconnect, are examined.

THE FUNCTION AND SIZING OF FINS

The need

Some form of vertical stabiliser is needed to give directional stability (also called weathercock stability). If a stable aircraft is disturbed in yaw — by a gust, say, as shown in Fig 199 — it will tend to return to its original equilibrium state. The forward fuselage ahead of the aircraft's centre of gravity produces a side force which tends to make the nose swing away from the relative wind and thereby increases the angle β. This is an unstable tendency, and if it is unchecked the nose will diverge further away from the direction in which it was originally pointing. Thus a force to counteract this diverging tendency is required: the wings contribute little, and though the rear fuselage does counter the motion to a degree, a vertical stabiliser or fin is needed for acceptable directional stability. The effects of the component parts of the aircraft on directional stability are shown in Fig 200.

No mention has yet been made of the pilot's reaction to the disturbance in yaw; indeed, in this analysis the pilot is assumed not to be touching the controls. What is of relevance here is inherent airframe stability, which is the tendency of the aircraft to return automatically to its undisturbed condition with no input whatsoever from either pilot or autopilot/flight control system. Such inputs and their influence on design are discussed later.

Fin size and shape, position and number all contribute to directional stability. The minimum permissible fin area can be fixed by the requirement for inherent static weathercock stability. If this requirement was the sole criterion, aircraft would have smaller vertical stabilisers than they do. In practice fin size is however influenced by a host of other constraints, such as how quickly the disturbance is to be eliminated, spin prevention/recovery, asymmetric flight, and the intended speed/manoeuvre envelope of the aircraft.

Fin area requirements

The destabilising effect of the fuselage is roughly proportional to the product of maximum depth of the fuselage (usually at the canopy crest) squared and the moment arm forward of the CG, as shown in Fig 201. The fin must be sized to offset this destabilising effect and to provide sufficient stability to suppress sideslip rapidly. Because the resulting stability is the difference of two large quantities — i.e. the moments generated by the destabilising forebody and stabilising fin — directional stability in practice can vary widely from design estimates, based as they are on a ±10%

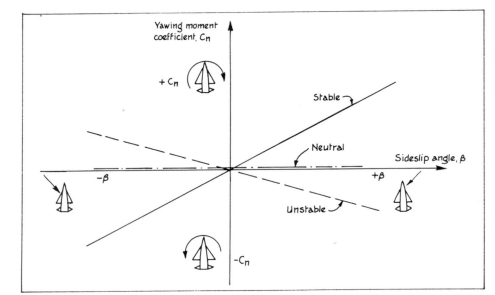

Fig 199 Directional stability.

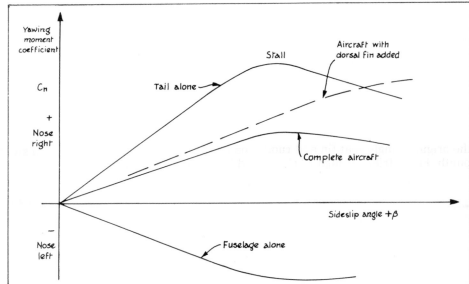

Fig 200 Contribution of the various airframe components to directional stability.

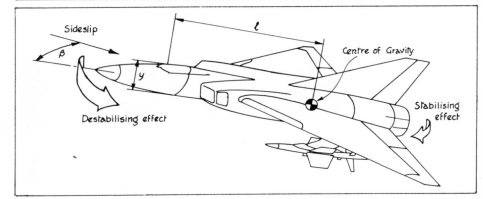

Fig 201 The destabilising effect of the fuselage is the product of maximum fuselage depth (y) squared and the moment arm ahead of the centre of gravity (l).

tolerance. Moreover, there are few rules to define the required levels of directional stability. Because directional (yawing) stability and lateral (rolling) stability are so interlinked, so that a change in the one inevitably affects the other, it is impossible to design a fin in isolation.

Examples of fin sizing to maintain static directional stability in 1g flight which highlight the destabilising effect of the forebody are given below.

Both the Lockheed F-104B Starfighter and MiG-23U two-seaters were given vertical tails enlarged in comparison with those of the single-seat versions to counteract the increased fuselage side area. On the F-104G the leading edge of the fin was moved forward to account for the adverse effect of the enlarged range of underwing stores to be carried by this ground attack version.

The directional stability of the General Dynamics B-58 suffered severely when the large ventral mission pod was being carried. Increased fin area was considered, but aeroelastic effects meant that the results were disappointing. In any case, additional vertical tail area would have complicated an already difficult balance problem, with the CG in the aftmost position on take-off. In fact the bomb pod was deliberately placed well forward to ensure that the aircraft balanced in the fully fuelled condition, and the fin was placed in the extreme rearmost position.

The case of the F-104B is paralleled by that of the two-seat Harrier T2, which when first flown had the original single-seat fin and rudder on a 0·28m plinth. Flight trials at high AOA showed however that a fintip extension of 0·46m was needed to keep the handling up to the single-seat standard.

The most extreme case of the effect of forebody shape on fin size is probably the Lockheed SR-71/F-12 (Fig 202). The SR-71 has forebody chines which extend right to the extreme nose, and a vertical tail comprising twin fins mounted on the engine nacelles. The YF-12 interceptor version required a large-diameter radar dish in the nose. To give good electromagnetic visibility the chines were cut back to behind the radome, which was increased in size. This increase in forebody side area so far in front of the aircraft CG resulted in so severe a loss of directional stability at high speed that a large folding centre line ventral fin and twin ventrals on the nacelles had to be added. A similar folding fin is used on the MiG-23 Flogger.

In addition to offsetting the destabilising effect of the forebody, the fin must be able to restore sideslip to zero within a reasonable time following a disturbance. It also has to react the asymmetric moments resulting from lateral control deflection, inertia coupling and wing-mounted weapon release without generating excessive sideslip. These requirements are considered below.

Lateral response characteristics

Analysis of aircraft response in yaw following a twitch of rudder shows that the notion is made up of three modes, roll, spiral and Dutch roll. The most important of these is the oscillatory one, the Dutch roll. This combination of yaw and roll can be visualised as follows. Take a swept-wing aircraft with a strong dihedral effect. Imagine the aircraft yawing

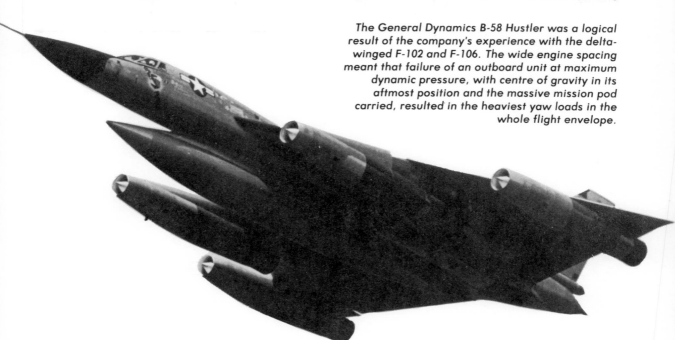

The General Dynamics B-58 Hustler was a logical result of the company's experience with the delta-winged F-102 and F-106. The wide engine spacing meant that failure of an outboard unit at maximum dynamic pressure, with centre of gravity in its aftmost position and the massive mission pod carried, resulted in the heaviest yaw loads in the whole flight envelope.

The large extended dorsal fin of the MiG-23B Flogger is augmented at high speed by a ventral fin (shown here folded for landing).
(MoD)

to the right as a result of, say, a side gust. As it does so it effectively sideslips to the left, though its flightpath remains a nearly straight line. Sideslipping to the left causes the aircraft to roll right-wing-down due to the dihedral effect. This induces a sideslip to the right. While all this is happening, the inherent directional stability is tending to yaw the nose back to the left to counter the original disturbance. The large dihedral effect now raises the right wing so much that the aircraft begins to sideslip to the left, with the directional stability yawing the nose back through the equilibrium position as it damps out the original yaw. This is an oscillatory motion, and the wingtips, viewed from the cockpit, describe a locus resembling an ellipse. The motion

is critically dependent on the roll-to-yaw ratio, and when yawing is dominant the motion is called "snaking".

Dutch roll is the most difficult mode to control and needs to be well damped, especially in rough air, in which the aircraft may never settle down from one gust before being upset by another. Airworthiness authorities require the motion to be damped out to half amplitude in one cycle. For combat aircraft the period of motion is typically 2–4sec.

Insufficient directional stability can result in two basic problems:

1 Too long a time for the sideslip to subside. The time to halve the amplitude of the sideslip increases quite rapidly with reduction in fin area. This is an important parameter in weapon-aiming, being proportional to the period of time during which the target is out of sight following a distur-

Fig 202 The Lockheed YF-12A was fitted with three ventral fins to counter the destabilising effect of its nose radome.

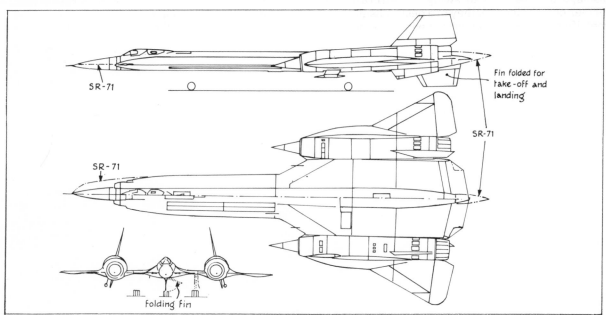

SR-71

SR-71

SR-71

Fin folded for take-off and landing

folding fin

bance. Early Tornado flight testing revealed an excessively long Dutch roll period and lower-than-expected directional stability at Mach numbers between 0·9 and 0·95. As related in Chapter 6, the culprit was flow separation on the afterbody at the base of the fin.

2 Excessive roll in response to lateral gusts. The roll is induced by the sideslip generated by the gust. A reduction in fin area causes peak sideslip angles to increase rapidly, leading to unacceptable induced roll angles.

The unwanted yawing motions produced by roll control deflection, discussed more fully in Chapter 1, are eliminated in most modern combat aircraft by aileron/rudder interconnect (ARI). Part of the automatic flight control system (AFCS), ARI introduces "opposite rudder" to eliminate the yawing moment. This is particularly important when the aircraft has a large dihedral effect, which produces strong rolling moments in response to sideslip.

Rapid rolling/inertia coupling

When an aircraft rolls, the distributed masses representing the wings, fuselage and tail unit are all put into motion about some axis and then brought to rest again at the end of the roll. Fig 203 shows an aircraft which is yawed slightly out of wind rolling steadily about an axis parallel to the relative wind. For simplicity's sake the aircraft is idealised into masses representing the fuselage and wings. The centrifugal forces acting on the fuselage masses tend to swing the aircraft still further out of wind, i.e. they are destabilising. The centrifugal forces acting on the wing masses tend to oppose the fuselage forces and are therefore stabilising. However, on almost all aircraft the destabilising forces are the more powerful.

Both the fuselage and wing centrifugal forces are proportional to the square of the rate of roll. Thus if the aircraft rolls sufficiently quickly the destabilising moment from the fuselage forces will overcome even the stabilising aerodynamic moment of the fin. The aircraft will thus be directionally unstable, with the yaw angle diverging with possibly catastrophic results.

On the type of aircraft shown in Fig 203 the spanwise inertia is high compared with its longitudinally distributed inertia, and the critical rate of roll (i.e. that at which divergence occurs) is likely to be much higher than the roll rate which the aircraft could actually achieve. Thus the problem of inertia coupling does not arise. If however the aircraft is of a slender configuration — like those designed in the 1950s and subsequently for Mach 2 + , such as the F-104, F-105 and TSR.2 — then the

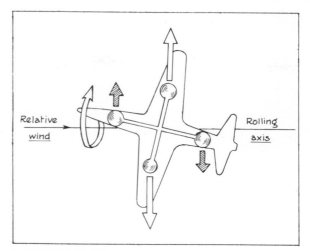

Fig 203 Inertial cross-coupling in roll.

problem may limit the allowable roll rate and also the number of consecutive rolls. A slender aircraft with small span has most of its mass concentrated in the fuselage and is capable of high roll rates, resulting in a tendency to inertia-coupling problems. On rolling, the aircraft will rotate about its own principal axis, the line of least resistance, rather than the flightpath. The problem is particularly severe when the aircraft starts to roll with its principal axis inclined downwards, as would happen in the case of an aircraft with wings at a very low angle of incidence and flying at high speed. In this case the sideslip which developed might help to increase the already high rate of roll. Beyond the critical roll rate, the aircraft would diverge in yaw, with roll rate increasing further. If the yaw angle divergence remained unopposed the yaw angle would exceed the aircraft's structural limit, leading to breakup. Fin size and thus the level of inherent directional stability can thus have a crucial bearing on flight safety.

Rapid rolling is not the only source of inertia coupling. The case of the F-100 in the 1950s dramatically drew industry's attention to the phenomenon. The F-100A's inherent directional stability was insufficient to keep the aircraft pointing the way it was going when pulling out of a high-speed dive. One particular accident, discussed at length by Gunston,[72] prompted a very expensive programme of modifications, including increased wing span and 27% more fin area. These changes in fact restored the design to its original standard, which had been changed to save weight and drag.

External store asymmetry

Imbalances which occur when external stores are released singly can be significant:

1 Mass asymmetry (lateral CG offset), the result of the presence of stores under one wing only, causes an increasing rolling moment as g is increased in a pull-out. Allowing the aircraft to sideslip towards the heavy wing (i.e. heavy wing down) can alleviate the amount of lateral control input needed to hold the wings level. But if directional stability is insufficient, the aileron deflection required may make control difficult under varying g loads.

2 The flow field caused by a winged missile mounted on the fuselage can induce a significant yawing moment and therefore sideslip on launch. When combined with the rolling breakaway manoeuvre, this compounds the rapid rolling problem if directional stability is inadequate.

INFLUENCES ON FIN EFFECTIVENESS

Compressibility effects

The destabilising effect of the fuselage in front of the CG does not vary much with Mach number, as shown in Fig 204. The figure also indicates how a fuselage-mounted external store acts to further reduce the directional stability, though large stores are rarely carried beyond Mach 1. Fin effectiveness, which increases slightly transonically, diminishes beyond about Mach 1·4 to below its subsonic value. To compound the difficulty further, the aeroelastic distortion and consequent forward movement of the fin's centre of pressure reduces surface effectiveness to about 75% that of a comparable rigid fin at design limits.

Fins usually have very low thickness/chord ratios (e.g. Avro Canada CF-105, t/c = 0·04) and are prone to severe distortion at high indicated air-

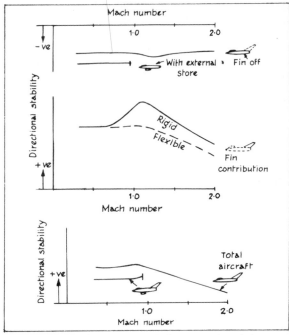

Fig 204 Typical variations in directional stability.

speeds (i.e. high dynamic pressure). A larger fin is one way of improving directional stability, though this will increase the drag by virtue of the larger wetted area. Reducing thickness ratio could help, but this further exacerbates the distortion problem. Even more important though, use of a larger fin could result in a reduction in fin moment arm. It would also increases fin weight, moving the CG aft and so further reducing the directional stability — the very opposite of what was sought in increasing fin size in the first place. The most common solution to the dilemma is to install yaw

The Avro Canada CF-105 Arrow was highly ambitious project based on very advanced and powerful Canadian-developed afterburning turbojets. A 1950s design, the CF-105 featured a huge internal missile bay and extremely thin aerodynamic surfaces

dampers in the control system. Driven via a sensor used to measure the aircraft's rate of yaw response, yaw dampers move the rudder as necessary to damp out unwanted motion.

A good example of the reduction of fin effectiveness at supersonic speed was the BAe Lightning, the fin of which had to be steadily increased in size as both Mach number capability and weapon/fuel load increased. Test work related to the provision of ever-larger belly fuel tanks required the addition of very large dorsal fin extensions.

A more extreme example still was the North American XB-70, which could actually increase its effective fin area by means of folding wingtips. As shown in Fig 205, the tips folded down to 65° at Mach 3, thereby restoring some lost fin effectiveness and allowing the twin verticals to be proportionately reduced in size. This had the effect of improving the supersonic lift/drag ratio by 5%.

Another example is the SR-71, which rapidly loses directional stability as it approaches high Mach numbers. Coupled with the potentially violent yawing moments induced by intake unstarts, this problem required the provision of directional stability augmentation.

A more recent illustration of the reduction of directional stability at supersonic speed, which is in fact characteristic of all aircraft, is the F-16. The table below shows this type's variation of static directional stability with Mach number, as expressed by the rate of change of yawing moment with sideslip (C_{n_β}).

Mach number	Basic airframe	With AFCS augmentation
0.8	0.004	0.0055
1.2	0.006	0.009
2.0	0.002	0.008

As can be seen, the basic airframe's stability reaches a peak at Mach 1.2, whereupon it drops to a low level at Mach 2.0. With the automatic flight control system programmed to input rudder deflection so as to oppose the yawing motion picked up by the AFCS sensors, a high degree of stability augmentation is achieved, especially at the highest Mach number.

Flight at high AOA

In the past, fins were usually sized to meet stability requirements at low and moderate angles of attack (up to $\alpha = 10°$ typically). In fact most of the previous generation of combat aircraft — e.g. F-4, A-7, Jaguar and F-111 — cannot be flown safely up to the wing stall boundary because of lateral/directional control deficiencies. On many of these aircraft, vortices shed from the near-circular-section forebody and/or the wing root junction (see Chapter 3) increase the destabilising effect of the forward fuselage and reduce the stabilising effect of the fin. The consequences of the latter are more important, but the overall effect is shown in Fig 206. In addition, as angle of attack is increased the fin is borne deeper and deeper into the wake

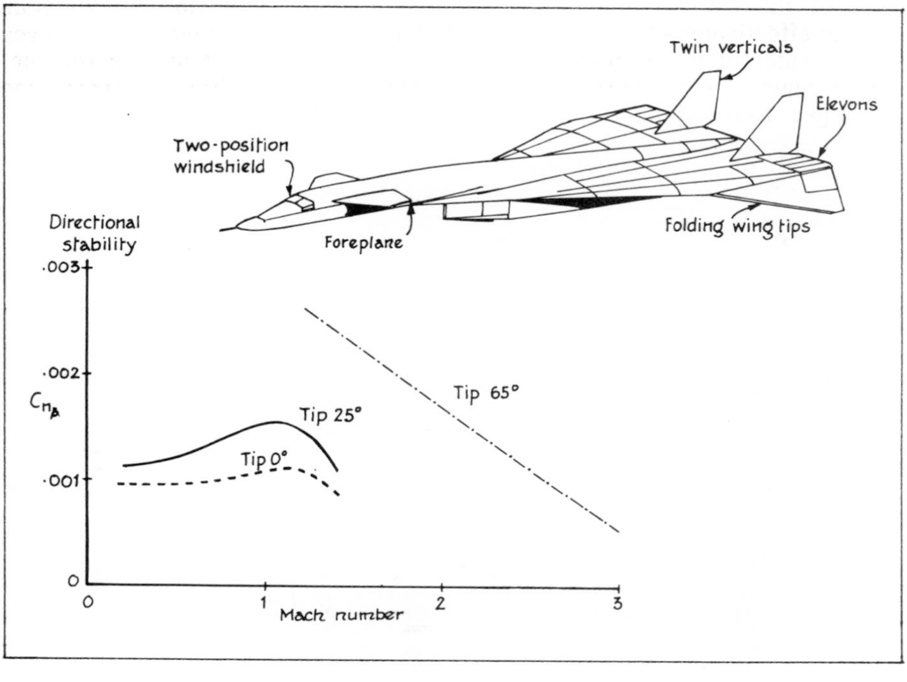

Fig 205 Variation of XB-70 directional stability with Mach number.

Fig 206 Relationship between directional stability and lift coefficient as a function of angle of attack.

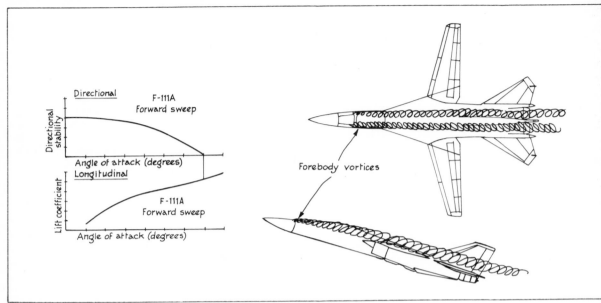

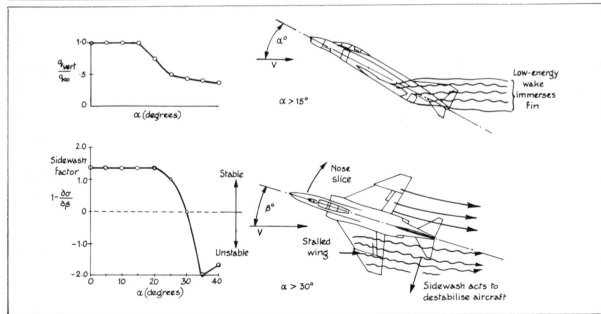

Fig 207 Conditions leading to nose slice on McDonnell Douglas F-4.

$$\frac{q_v}{q_\infty} = \frac{\text{dynamic pressure at vertical tail}}{\text{dynamic pressure of freestream}} . 1 - \frac{d\sigma}{d\beta} = \text{sidewash factor.}^{73}$$

shed by the fuselage, so that again fin effectiveness is reduced.

These effects make themselves felt in a number of ways:

1 Straight yaw-off (nose slice) due to directional instability. As AOA increases, dihedral effect pro-

vides an ever greater contribution to flightpath stability. But if fin effectiveness is diminishing rapidly and dihedral effect is insufficient to compensate, divergence occurs. This is attributed to wing-induced sidewash on the fuselage afterbody and vertical tail, and the reduction of dynamic pressure at the vertical tail location. These effects are shown in Fig 207. The adverse sidewash is related to stalling of the leading wing panel during sideslip at high AOA. The dynamic pressure at the fin is reduced because of shielding by the aft fuselage and/or the stalled wake of the wing. No weapon aiming is possible after the onset of nose slice; indeed, in the F-4 generation of aircraft, by the time the pilot has recognised the symptoms it is usually too late to prevent a spin. Nose slice and wing drop are typical of the motions resulting when a pilot pulls back on the stick to get that last bit of turning performance out of the aircraft.

2 Yaw-off due to adverse aileron yaw combined with low directional stability. A pilot is more conscious of roll due to sideslip than he is of the change of heading, particularly in manoeuvring flight at high g, when lateral g is not easily sensed. If the pilot applies lateral control to keep the wings level and this lateral control gives adverse yaw (as do uncompensated ailerons at high α), then the adverse yaw can override the low directional stability and lead to divergence. The following two examples illustrate more graphically the nature of these types of behaviour.

LTV A-7 Corsair   As shown in Fig 70 (page 83), the roll augmentation system of the A-7 is automatically turned off at $\alpha = 18 \cdot 5°$ to preclude pro-spin aileron inputs in the stall/departure region; roll control thereafter is by use of the rudder only. The stall occurs at 20°, at which point the aircraft also becomes directionally unstable. Very heavy buffet is accompanied by weak lateral/directional stability, which results in nose wander in yaw. Departure from controlled flight will occur at around $\alpha = 22°$ in the form of rapid nose slice accompanied by snap rolls. At $\alpha \geqslant 40°$ the aircraft regains directional stability (see Chapter 3).

McDonnell Douglas F-4   In contrast to the A-7, the basic Phantom has a maximum local lift point at $\alpha = 18°$ (Fig 70) and a later $C_{L_{max}}$ at $\alpha = 26°$. Above 11° angle of attack (buffet onset) lateral control is pro-spin and could induce early departure from controlled flight. The rudder is used beyond this angle for roll control, its pedal shaker being activated at 17° to supply artificial stall warning. Departure will occur at above 25°, characterised primarily by nose slice, with roll in the direction of yaw.

There are three main areas in which the reduction of directional stability due to compressibility and high-AOA flight can be attacked: roll control/wing design, forebody shaping and fin design. Only the last is considered here.

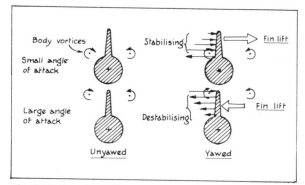

Fig 208 Fuselage/fin vortex interference.

Increased fin height

The forebody vortices which stream past the fin destabilise the lower part of the fin and act favourably on the upper part. A tall fin therefore minimises the decay of stability with AOA, as shown in Fig 208. On the other hand, the likelihood of adverse sidewash due to leading-wing stall during sideslip at high AOA, together with reduced dynamic pressure because of shielding by the aft fuselage and/or wake from a partially stalled wing, makes an increase in fin height an unattractive approach for improved C_{n_β} at high AOA. Should the vertical tail become destabilising at high AOA (as it does on the F-4 at $\alpha > 30°$), the enlarged surface would further aggravate the situation, as is shown for the F-4 in Fig 209.

In addition, a tall swept fin loses a large proportion of its effectiveness at high speed as a result of twisting off at the tip. Typically, 20–25% of fin effectiveness can be lost from rudder distortion and spanwise twist resulting from bending.

Twin fins

The use of twin fins can overcome the problem of tall flexible single fins provided they are far enough apart laterally to overcome mutual biplane interference. They are more compatible with twin-engine aircraft (e.g. F-14, F-15, F-18) than with single-engined types (e.g. F-16). It is however worth noting that the twin-engine Tornado has a large single fin; this may be because this aircraft was originally designed for the strike role and only later considered for long-range interception, which does not demand the α and β envelope required of the US twins.

Twin fins come into their own at high supersonic speed, when mutual interference disappears as the Mach lines from each fin pass behind its neighbour. However, for low Mach numbers at least, twin fins are not necessarily the most efficient way of improving directional stability. Low-speed wind tunnel tests on models at 15° AOA have shown that

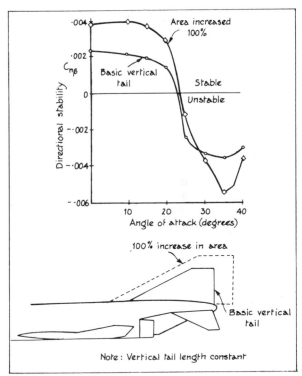

Fig 209 Effect of increased fin area on directional stability of McDonnell Douglas F-4.[73]

increasing the area of a single fin by 30% could increase directional stability by 55%, giving a relative efficiency of 120%. Doubling the fin area by the use of twin fins increased directional stability by only 20%, however, giving a relative efficiency of just 70%. Evidence to suggest the value of a larger single fin for the F-4 at lower AOA was shown in Fig 209, though at high angles the loss of stability was aggravated. The moral then is that fin effectiveness is highly dependent on AOA. The main argument in favour of twin fins is that there is always one vertical surface in relatively clean flow to provide directional stability regardless of the AOA/sideslip combination.

In the case of the McDonnell Douglas F-15 the choice between a single large fin and smaller twin fins fell initially to twin fins of 3·7m² and ventral strakes of 1·96m² mounted at the extreme rear of the tail support booms. However, in a subsequent drag-reduction effort the ventrals were deleted and the fins increased in area progressively from 3·7m² to 5·85m² to give a 5·5% reduction in Mach 0·9 cruise drag while maintaining satisfactory directional stability at high AOA at transonic and supersonic speeds. Several factors contributed to the choice of twin fins for the F-15:

1 The "end-plating" effect of the twin verticals

results in far more effective horizontal tail control.

2 The twin verticals provide a more constant value of C_{n_β}; high C_{n_β} for improved Dutch roll characteristics; and rudder control redundancy for combat survivability (an argument very forcefully put in the case of the Fairchild A-10, with its widely spaced engines and twin fins).

3 Located on engine booms, vertical fins offer more infra-red shielding of engine exhaust, yielding greater stealth.

4 Only two boom structures were required, compared with the third "spine boom" needed for a single vertical (eg, F-16); a weight saving was thereby claimed. However, the Tornado, with its single fin, does not require the twin booms anyway, so that the saving claimed for the F-15 is perhaps more apparent than real.

5 The reduced height of the twin fins means less torque on the fuselage and makes them less susceptible to flutter than a tall single fin.

6 The greater distance of the twin verticals from the engine centreline results in a less intense noise and temperature environment and permitted lighter structures compared with the single fin and its supporting structure.

Grumman F-14   All of the F-15 arguments apply, plus the value of twin fins in limiting fin height to match hangar space on aircraft carriers.

McDonnell Douglas F/A-18   The vertical tails on the YF-17 and F/A-18 were sized and located to provide positive directional stability beyond the maximum trimmed angles of attack across the speed range. They are canted outboard to place them correctly within the vortex flow-field generated by the wing leading-edge extension (LEX). Fig 210 shows directional stability as a function of angle of attack for single and twin vertical tail configurations of the same total fin volume ($S_F \times l_F$)/($S_W \times \bar{c}$) operating in the flow field of the F-18's hybrid wing. The twin fins maintained positive stability across the complete α range, enhancing spin resistance, while the single vertical tail results in strong instability at high AOA.

The excellent manoeuvrability of the chosen configuration may be gauged from the figures recorded on early YF-17 test flights: maximum (trimmed) AOA of +63°; maximum sideslip angle of 36°; minimum airspeed of 20kt (37km/hr). No departures nor spins were encountered and the aircraft responded fully to pilot commands.

General Dynamics F-16   The wind-tunnel work on the YF-16 started with two basic designs: one with a single fin, the other with a blended body with

Fig 210 Directional stability of Northrop YF-17 at Mach 0·2 with single and twin vertical tails.[27]

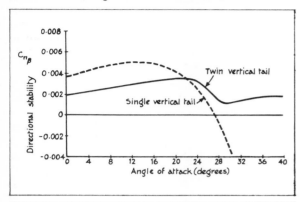

Fig 211 A single vertical tail proved better for General Dynamics YF-16 directional stability.[1]

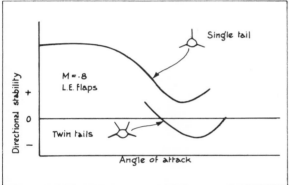

twin fins mounted on booms extending aft on either side of the single engine (Fig 211). The results showed that flow separations from both forebody and wing at high AOA interacted adversely with twin verticals. Despite many attempts to improve the flow behaviour around the twin fins it became clear that satisfactory vertical tail effectiveness would be more easily achieved with a single fin. So severe were the interactions between the twin fins that under certain combinations of α and β visible buffeting of the tails occurred; this has led to cracked fin skins on the F-18. Given the uncertainties attending the use of the novel wing strakes, with some shapes giving questionable levels of directional stability, General Dynamics considered that the additional risks of twin verticals were unacceptable. The wind-tunnel data revealed that the height of the vertical tail above the wing chord plane was the dominant design parameter. The directional stability yielded by the competing fin arrangements (of equal tail volume) is shown in Fig 211. The single fin scored significantly in reducing exposed area required, thereby cutting structure weight and skin friction drag.

FIN POSITION AND SHAPE

Location (fore and aft)

In almost all cases modern combat aircraft have their vertical tails as far aft as possible to maximise the moment arm.

Northrop YF-17 (F-18)   One notable exception to this general rule is the McDonnell Douglas Hornet, with verticals located well forward of the extreme rear of the aircraft (Fig 83, page 90). This reduces interference between the vertical and horizontal tail surfaces, especially at high AOA, and at the same time smoothes out the cross-sectional area distribution to conform to the various area rules for minimum drag. The fin support structure and tailplane actuators are also cleanly integrated into the fuselage.

Lockheed SR-71/YF-12   As with so many aspects of its design, this aircraft has a fin mounting taken almost to the extreme. Both fins and ventral stubs are canted inboard 15° to stay on the correct side of the vortices shed by the nacelles (Fig 212). As a result, the rolling moment due to sideslip and required vertical tail deflection is decreased. Since the side load on the twin tails acts normal to the surface, the resulting moment arm at supersonic speed is reduced by a function of the sine of the cant angle; there is however no loss of fin effectiveness. Again at supersonic speed, the rolling moment due to sideslip is further reduced as angle of attack increases. This is also true at low speeds, when the delta wing characteristically gives a high rolling moment due to sideslip and additional rolling moment from the fins could make life difficult for a pilot trying to keep the wings level on the approach.

Fig 212 Effect of vertical stabiliser cant on Lockheed SR-71 rolling moment.[38]

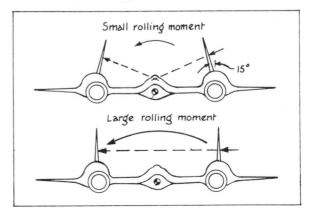

Grumman F-14   At one stage in its development the Tomcat had its fins displaced laterally to the edge of the fuselage and then canted outboard 25°. This fin layout, which is possible on a wide fuselage, was shown to give directional stability up to $\alpha = 32°$. However, since the aircraft was found to be relatively stall/departure-free and use of the available high-lift wing slats improved not only the directional stability but all of the aerodynamic characteristics, this location was not considered for production aircraft, which have fins canted 5° outwards.

McDonnell Douglas F-15 Eagle   It was found that the most significant reduction in vertical tail interference drag resulted from a 2° toe-out angle. Vertical tail cant and axial location (up to 0·6m forward of the present location) had negligible effect.

Fin shape

A fin surmounted by a high tailplane and originating in a fuselage is effectively borne between two endplates. This increases the effective aspect ratio of the fin, making it more powerful as a stabiliser. This type of layout has however not been seen since the F-104 Starfighter of the 1950s. Contemporary aircraft all feature low-mounted tailplanes, and fin effectiveness is improved only by fuselage end-plating. Although the sideforce generated by a low-aspect-ratio fin is smaller for a given sideslip angle than that of a fin of higher aspect ratio, the risk of fin stalling, which is catastrophic, is reduced (Fig 213). It is for this reason that the fin aspect ratio is less than that of the wing and generally less than that of the tailplane. In the past, aircraft have "grown" dorsal fin extensions during their development to combat the risk of fin stalling. The fin extension does not improve effectiveness very much at small sideslip angles but it has powerful anti-stall and stabilising properties at large angles.

It is not possible to comment extensively on the actual shape of fins apart from noting cases which appear to characterise particular groups of aircraft. Examples are the fin shapes typical of aircraft emerging from the former Hawker design office at BAe Kingston. The very graceful fins on the Hunter, Harrier, P.1154 and Hawk all seem to bear testimony to the philosophy that if a shape works and there aren't good reasons to change it, then leave well alone! Soviet designers favour raked tips, notable examples being the MiG-23, Yak-36, MiG-25, Tu-28 and MiG-29. The main reason for this preference appears to be the fact that a reduction in structural mass aft of the fin's

Fig 213 The effect of a dorsal fin fairing.

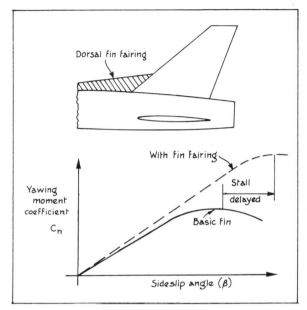

Fig 214 Effect of angle of attack and Mach number on directional stability.

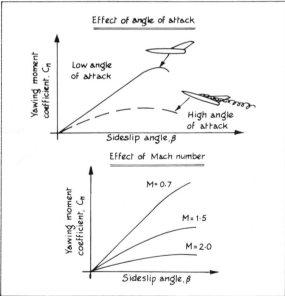

torsional axis results in an increase in fin flutter speed. The reduction of fin effectiveness due to the loss of area at the fin tip is minimal, since for supersonic speeds at least the aerodynamic loading in this region is very low. Moreover, all of the aircraft mentioned, apart from the MiG-25, feature large dorsal extensions.

The Mig-25R reconnaissance version of the Foxbat differs from the basic interceptor in having a straight wing leading edge and provision for cameras. The Mach 3 Foxbat was originally designed to counter the XB-70 and, with its huge overhanging intakes and twin fins with raked tips, set the style for the US F-14 and F-15. The fairings under the intakes house actuators for drooping the lower intake lips during take-off and landing.

Ventral fins or strakes

The deterioration in directional stability with increased angle of attack and/or increased Mach number (Fig 214) means that the modern combat aircraft needs a much larger fin than its older and slower predecessor. There have been many instances of an initial lack of fin effectiveness having to be rectified by the use of ventral fins.

A fin set below the fuselage becomes more effective at high AOA, since it will often be working in clean air and will act against dihedral effect. In fact ventral strakes are sometimes more efficient than additional upper fin area because of the favourable interference effect created with the

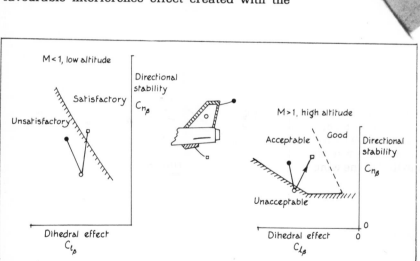

Fig 215 Effects of additional basic fin area compared with ventral fin of same area on stability and handling qualities.[69]

rear fuselage, their comparatively high structural stiffness, and the reduction in dihedral effect which they cause (Fig 215). However, though their full effectiveness may be retained at high AOA, at low AOA interference from fuselage-mounted stores may severely degrade their performance.

Ventral strakes have appeared on 80% of fighter-type aircraft entering service since 1960. The types which have featured such surfaces are listed here, in order starting with the earliest: SO 4050 (1952), SE 5000, Nord Griffon, Yak-25, Grumman F11F, F-104, F-105, F-8, MiG-21, Lighting, YF-12, Harrier, F-111, Jaguar, Viggen, Mirage F.1, Mitsubishi F-1, Su-19, MiG-23, MiG-25, Su-24, F-14, F-16 and MiG-29.

In the case of the F-104 prototype the need arose to accommodate a larger engine and increase fuel capacity. The resulting larger fuselage had an increased destabilising tendency, and so a ventral fin was added.

The YF-12 has three ventral fins, one on the aircraft centreline which folds down when the undercarriage retracts and two stub ventrals on the engine nacelles. The MiG-23 has a large underfin which folds up to give ground clearance when the undercarriage is lowered; this is one of the main constraints on the use of ventral fins. The F-111 has a single fin and two ventrals designed to improve directional stability at high Mach number and high altitude.

Ventral fins were added to the Jaguar to restore the directional stability loss caused by the large underbelly drop tank, which was increased in size after the initial design had been frozen.

Not all design teams believe in ventrals, however. Northrop claims that they complicate engine access/removal. McDonnell Douglas had ventrals on its original F-15 submission but enlarged the fins and dropped the ventrals in a drag clean-up programme. When designing the CF-105 Arrow, Avro Canada considered using ventral fins to increase effective fin area by around 50%. But the performance penalties were unacceptable and the inherent airframe stability was brought up to scratch by means of a stability augmentation system.

RUDDERS

Design factors

Of the factors which contribute to rudder design the most important relate to crosswind landing; high-AOA flight, including spin recovery; asymmetric stores; transonic effectiveness; asymmetric thrust.

Crosswind landing

The crosswind landing case is by far the most critical, though it has been argued that the requirement to trim out a sideslip equivalent to zero drift at touchdown is unnecessarily severe. Nevertheless, it is the ability to handle a 90° crosswind of a given velocity that is the rudder control criterion most often quoted. In the case of the Lockheed YF-12, for example, the figure is 65km/hr.

High-AOA flight

Rudder effectiveness at high AOA can be greatly reduced by a loss of dynamic pressure at the fin, caused by shielding from the wing and/or low-mounted tailplane. The impact of wing planform on rudder effectiveness is significant, especially at high AOA. The differences between planforms in this respect are related to the stall patterns of individual wings and the position of the stalled wing's wake in relation to the fin and rudder. A similar situation, though more typical of the very high angles of attack encountered in a spin (50–60°), arises when a low-mounted tailplane blankets the fin and rudder (Fig 216).

Examples of aircraft with exceptionally good spin recovery are the Lightning, Hawk, F-5 and F-18. On these aircraft the rudder is in clean air even at very high AOA. Some inertially slender aircraft are however designed to use roll control rather than rudder for spin recovery; in such cases the rudder may be immersed in tailplane wake at high AOA with no untoward consequences.

An interesting case is the F-4, which has a particularly nasty spin mode, the flat spin, from which no recovery is possible. Beyond $\alpha = 11°$ the only lateral/directional control available is the rudder. In the flat spin interference between the vertical and horizontal tails actually produces propelling yawing moments rather than yawing moments to oppose the spin. Design studies revealed that moving the tailplane aft one chord length eliminated the flat spin.

Fig 217 shows the variation with AOA of the yawing moment produced by ailerons and rudder for right roll and right yaw control inputs. The yawing moments produced by ailerons at low AOA are favourable (nose right) for right roll control but become adverse (nose left) at high AOA. Right rudder input produces a normal nose-right

Fig 216 How careful empennage design avoids fin/rudder blanking at high angles of attack.

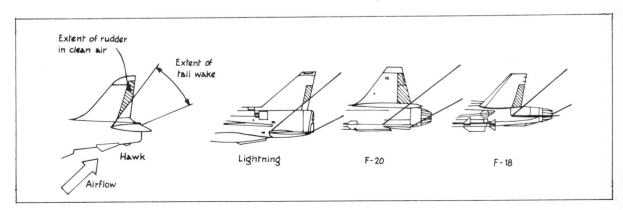

Fig 217 Yawing moments produced by lateral/directional controls.

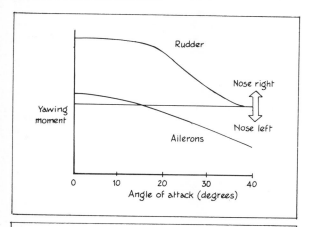

Fig 218 Illustration of roll reversal.

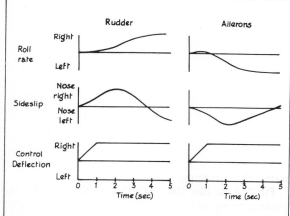

Fig 219 Stick-to-rudder interconnect.

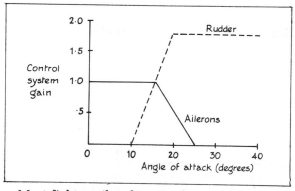

moment, but at high AOA the rudder loses some of its effectiveness because of the immersion of the fin in the low-energy wake from the partially stalled wing. In the example shown the adverse moments due to the ailerons are much larger than the corrective moments available from the rudder. When the resulting adverse moments are coupled with low directional stability at high AOA, a reversal of roll response occurs, with the aircraft rolling in a direction opposite to that commanded by the pilot.

Fig 218 illustrates roll reversal for a typical configuration at $\alpha = 25°$ responding to right roll control inputs of rudder alone and ailerons alone. The aircraft responds to rudder alone by yawing to the right, with dihedral effect inducing a roll to the right, as normal. By contrast, aileron alone causes adverse yaw (nose to the left). The dihedral effect works normally but this time the roll is left-wing-down, thus opposing the rolling moment generated by the aileron input.

Most fighter pilots have in the past adapted to this situation by switching from lateral stick inputs for roll control at low AOA to rudder pedal inputs for roll control at high AOA. But how best to phase in the transition in order to obtain maximum performance, particularly during the stress of combat? The most effective solution devised so far is aileron/rudder interconnect (ARI) (Fig 219), which causes lateral stick movements to produce aileron inputs at low AOA and rudder inputs at high AOA. In Fig 219 the ailerons are phased out by $\alpha = 25°$ whereas the rudder input has been growing from $\alpha = 10°$ to reach a maximum gain at $\alpha = 20°$, so that stick inputs move the rudder only.

The Convair B-58 was an early example of the use of ARI. It was needed to overcome the effects of the adverse pressure field generated on the side of the fin adjacent to the upgoing elevon. The aircraft's highly swept delta wing had an inherently large dihedral effect which produced strong rolling moments in response to the adverse yawing moment at the fin, leading to roll reversal. ARI effectively eliminated the yawing moment by automatically applying opposite rudder in response to lateral stick inputs (i.e. roll commands). (See also Chapter 1, *Lateral controls* for further comment on ARI.)

Asymmetric stores

The rudder must be capable in all flight conditions of balancing the aerodynamic asymmetry created by loads of stores in the wings and the associated roll-control-induced yawing moment. Though not a major design criterion, this requirement must be accounted for.

Transonic effectiveness

A high-aspect-ratio unswept rudder is preferable for the crosswind-landing case, but loses much of its effectiveness in the transonic regime. This is due to the inherent reduced aerodynamic efficiency of a flap-type control surface at supersonic

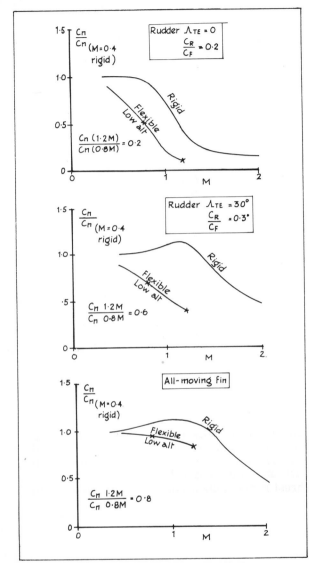

Fig 220 Transonic change in rudder effectiveness: effect of fin and rudder geometry.[32]

speeds. Aeroelastic distortion is another problem which rules out the use of a high-aspect-ratio rudder, with the rudder tending to twist away from the hinge point. Both of these factors, which can cause rapid changes in rudder effectiveness, have led to the use of large swept rudders. The variation of rudder effectiveness with Mach number is shown in Fig 220 for three different designs; losses due to surface flexibility are also indicated. The arguments in favour of the use of stiff, wide-chord, swept rudders to ensure transonic effectiveness are evident.

The aerodynamic value of the all-moving fin has been appreciated for many years and exploited on several aircraft, including the North American A3J (A-5) Vigilante, BAC TSR.2, Boeing 818 (TFX competitor) and Lockheed YF-12/SR-71 Blackbird. BAC backed up the relatively small all-moving fin on the TSR.2 fin with directional stability augmentation to ease the expected problems with yaw trim and loss of rudder effectiveness at transonic speed at low altitude. This also resulted in lower gust sensitivity and reduced aeroelastic distortion. The fin was half the size of a conventional fixed surface, resulting in significant reductions in profile drag, aircraft weight and cost. An all-moving fin is specified for the European Fighter Aircraft.

Asymmetric thrust

The asymmetric-thrust design case is generally critical only for large aircraft with widely spaced wing-mounted engines; examples include the B-52, B-58 and B-1. Indeed, in the case of Convair's B-58 Hustler, with its widely spaced four-engine delta-wing layout, an outboard engine failure at maximum dynamic pressure with the CG in its aftmost position and the mission pod aboard represented the most critical design case for fin and rudder. On the Boeing Model 818, with body-mounted engines fed by dorsal intakes, the all-moving fin was sized to ensure control after an engine failure at maximum afterburning thrust. For this case an area of 28m^2 was required, based on a fin $C_{L_{max}}$ of 1·2. This was only 3m^2 less than the fin area required to give adequate directional stability at $M = 2·5$.

The most spectacular demand made on rudder effectiveness is probably that of the Lockheed YF-12 during an air intake unstart. The aircraft has a low level of inherent directional stability at its very high cruise Mach number. In the event of an unstart, when the highly complex and sensitive shock wave system is expelled from an engine pod, the effects are dramatic. The primary result is a sudden violent yaw in the direction of the failed engine, caused by the decreased thrust and simultaneously increased drag. The problem is accentuated at high altitude by low aerodynamic damping. The problem is an alarming one for the pilot, since his helmet can bang sharply against the side of the cockpit canopy and his pressure suit inflates rapidly if the failed engine is the one responsible for cockpit pressure. The necessary immediate corrective action is supplied by the aircraft's full-time stability augmentation system, which rapidly commands rudder and elevon deflections to counteract the yaw, pitch and roll which ensue. The pilot is left to select the intake restart mode, to reduce the thrust and drag differentials and to maintain engine performance within allowable limits.

CHAPTER 6

EXHAUST NOZZLES AND AFT-BODY SHAPE

INTRODUCTION

The function of the engine nozzle is to expand the hot gases leaving the jetpipe via, perhaps, an after-burner down to the surrounding or ambient air pressure. The nozzle achieves this by transforming some of the available thermal energy into kinetic energy. The two basic nozzle types are considered: convergent and convergent-divergent, with ejector nozzles included amongst the latter. The operation of each type is discussed, and examples of hardware given. The convergent nozzle is shown to have limitations in supersonic flight, and the need for a diverging section is explained. The evolution of the various forms of convergent-divergent nozzles is described, and there is a discussion of the problems which led to demands for variable geometry. Examples of the various ways in which variable geometry has been incorporated are given. The last section on exhaust nozzles examines the ideas behind thrust vectoring for reduction of landing distance and increased manoeuvring agility, and the benefits to current and future combat aircraft of such nozzles are discussed.

The need for careful consideration of the aft-body shaping of combat aircraft is the topic of the final section of this chapter. Practical examples show up aspects of exhaust flow interaction which can cause a loss of potential thrust or an increase in airframe drag.

CONVERGENT NOZZLES

The simplest type of nozzle, the convergent, accelerates the gas flow by means of a duct of decreasing cross-sectional area (Fig 221). When the back pressure p_b (i.e. that external to the nozzle) is slightly lower than the upstream total pressure p_0, the flow is subsonic throughout. It accelerates to the throat, where the velocity is at a maximum, so that the nozzle exit pressure p_e just matches the back pressure p_b. As the ratio p_0/p_e increases — caused, say, by an increase in engine rpm — so the velocity at the nozzle throat increases towards the local speed of sound. The pressure ratio at which the throat velocity V_t equals the local speed of sound is called the critical pressure ratio; the term "critical" refers to the fact that the Mach number at the throat is unity. This is commonly referred to as nozzle "choking". Convergent nozzles are used on all subsonic aircraft and many older low-supersonic aircraft.

If the pressure ratio is higher than the critical value (i.e. $p_0/p_b > 2$) then full expansion to give $p_e = p_b$ cannot occur within the nozzle and thrust losses are inevitable. Many turbojet engines operating under sea-level conditions generate nozzle pressure ratios of around 4. This is low enough to permit retention of a convergent nozzle, particularly if some exit-area variability is incorporated, since the thrust loss due to external expansion may be as low as 1%. In flight at supersonic speed the nozzle pressure ratio may become very large (e.g. around 16 at Mach 2) and a very significant thrust loss arises, typically more than 10%. This happens because the gas leaving the nozzle is at a very much greater pressure than the surrounding air and its full potential for producing thrust is not being used. (The means of exploiting this potential more fully will be explained in *Convergent-divergent nozzles*, page 202.)

Even at subsonic speeds, the nozzle pressure ratio p_0/p_e varies widely, and it may be worthwhile to include an ability to vary the nozzle exit area.

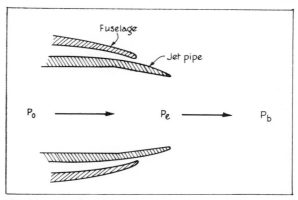

Fig 221 Simple convergent nozzle.

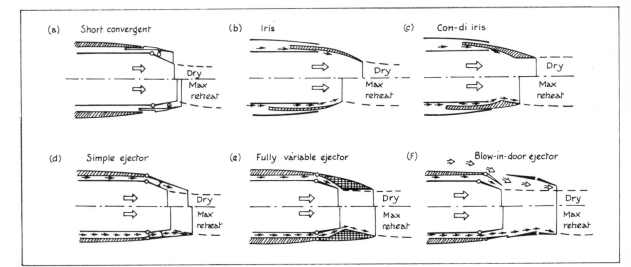

Fig 222 Typical nozzles for afterburning engines. The top half of each nozzle shows its configuration at subsonic (cruise) conditions. The lower half shows the maximum reheat configuration, used for take-off, transonic acceleration/combat, and supersonic flight.[74]

Figs 222a and 222b show convergent nozzles with exit area variation, the top half of each drawing indicating the configuration in subsonic (cruise) condition and the lower half the maximum reheat condition (e.g. take-off, supersonic flight). Intermediate settings are possible between the two extremes (e.g. military, partial reheat). The short convergent nozzle shown in Fig 222a is mechanically simple and light in weight but suffers the major aerodynamic disadvantage of forming a large, drag-producing annular base area in the closed position. The more mechanically complex iris nozzle (Fig 222b) avoids the annular base problem but still suffers a thrust loss because of its inability, inherent in all convergent nozzles, to fully exploit the exhaust flow.

CONVERGENT-DIVERGENT NOZZLES

The need for a diverging section

Long before the first aircraft ever flew, it was known that the use of a simple convergent nozzle to deliver hot gas to a pressure well below the upstream value would result in an uncontrolled expansion, as shown in Fig 223a. Addition of a divergent section to the convergent nozzle (Fig 223b) allows the expanding gases (still at a pressure above the downstream back pressure) to

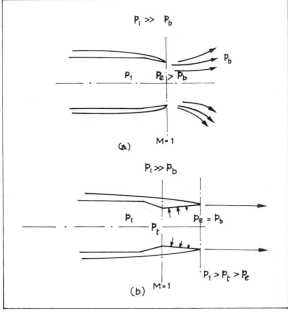

Fig 223 How a diverging section (b) prevents uncontrolled expansion.

exert a reaction on the rearward-facing divergent walls, so giving more thrust. In the ideal case the nozzle exit pressure falls to the ambient back pressure, thereby permitting full internal expansion of the gases to be achieved. Some losses do arise from fluid friction on the divergent walls, though at high pressure ratios the thrust may be only 2% short of the ideal. Fig 224 shows the gain in thrust to be obtained using an ideal supersonic nozzle instead of a convergent one on a typical supersonic engine. The advantage appears even more striking when

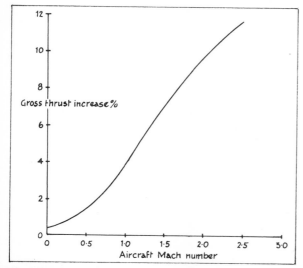

Fig 224 Gross thrust increase due to use of an ideal supersonic nozzle instead of a convergent nozzle on a typical supersonic engine.[75]

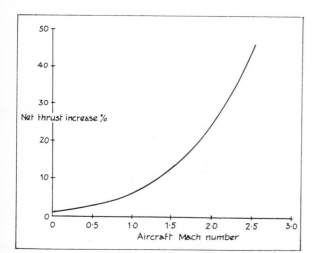

Fig 225 Net thrust increase due to use of an ideal supersonic nozzle instead of a convergent nozzle on a typical supersonic engine.[75]

it is noted that the actual thrust produced by the engine is the difference between the gross thrust and the inlet drag. At high speeds both these quantities become large, and thus the improvement as a percentage of net thrust is much more marked, as shown in Fig 225.

Evolution of the convergent-divergent nozzle

The disadvantages of the simple convergent nozzle for supersonic aircraft led to a great deal of development. However, before examining the various nozzles that resulted, it is important to understand some of the problems inherent in the use of con-di nozzles. There are two main drawbacks, both of which call for some form of variable geometry.

Area ratio for optimum expansion

The ideal area ratio for a nozzle may vary by a factor of three across the flight envelope. In fact, at higher aircraft speeds the nozzle exit area required is so large that it would be much larger than the engine and would cause a great deal of drag. A limit on the area ratio A_e/A_t of 1·7 to 1·8 is usually taken as the norm. Fig 226 shows F-16 nozzles with $A_e/A_t = 1·6$ and 2·7; the latter is the ratio needed for optimum internal expansion at Mach 2, while the former is the one actually used.

Off-design nozzle operation

The second problem, associated with the need to avoid low separation within the nozzle, appears in two forms for a fixed nozzle designed to operate at a high supersonic Mach number.

Off-design operation of fixed nozzle at low-supersonic speed

In this case the nozzle tries to expand the flow down to its design pressure, which is below the actual back pressure. This overpansion will occur at some point within the nozzle, but since the back pressure needs to be reached, a compression must take place. This is achieved by an oblique shock wave, which invariably induces flow separation from the nozzle wall. In fact the wall boundary layer influences the flow to such an extent that the flow follows an approximately axial direction (see Fig 227).

Surprisingly, the separated flow tends to improve the thrust compared with the "ideal" normal-shock case, there being less loss across the oblique shocks than across the normal shock. In addition, the back pressure which now acts on the nozzle walls in the separated zone is higher, than that which exists when the flow is overexpanded in this region. Nonetheless, despite the benefit which shock-induced separation confers on performance in this region, there remains a substantial loss.

Off-design operation of fixed nozzle at subsonic speeds

In this case the nozzle again tries to expand the flow down to a pressure below the back presure. However, the low pressure ratios characteristic of subsonic flow mean that even though the convergent section is behaving as a nozzle, the divergent section behaves as a diffuser. Sonic conditions are not reached at the nozzle throat and the boundary

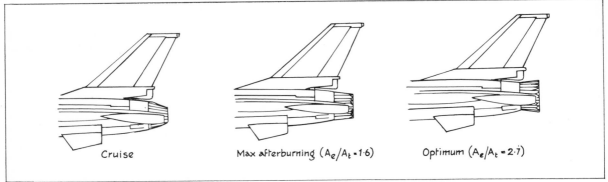

Cruise   Max afterburning (A_e/A_t =1·6)   Optimum (A_e/A_t = 2·7)

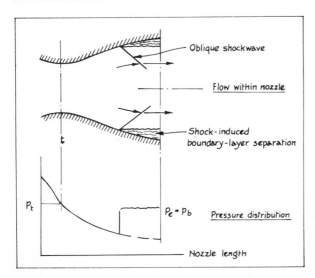

Oblique shockwave

Flow within nozzle

Shock-induced boundary-layer separation

P_t

P_e ≃ P_b Pressure distribution

Nozzle length

Fig 226 (*above*) General Dynamics F-16 nozzle set for cruise, maximum afterburning, and a notional optimum for internal expansion at Mach 2.

Fig 227 (*Left*) Nozzle off-design operation at supersonic speed.

layer, again encountering a large adverse pressure gradient, may separate. The result is again a significant loss of thrust, arising from the pressure distribution illustrated in Fig 228.

An example of thrust loss on a con-di nozzle at low speed affected a Panavia Tornado development aircraft. The aircraft was flying at 520km/hr at 300m when a birdstrike damaged the left engine. The pilot selected full afterburner and then combat power on the good engine but, unbeknown to the crew, the reheat did not light. With the nozzle fully open but no reheat on, the good engine gave significantly less than its maximum dry thrust. A potentially dangerous situation was resolved only when the engine surged: the pilot instinctively throttled back and the nozzle closed, whereupon thrust increased and the aircraft was able to climb away. It had always been intended to provide positive indication in the cockpit that reheat had lit and was burning, and thus was subsequently applied along with several other modifications to production aircraft.

Two other considerations militate against the use of a fixed con-di nozzle, except for very low supersonic speeds. First, at low aircraft speeds there is also a possibility of unstable flow separation in the nozzle, with the jetstream attaching itself repeatedly to one side and then the other, producing violent vibration and possible failure of the jetpipe. Second, if an afterburner is to be used, then some form of area variation is almost essential.

Having established the need for some nozzle area variation, designers found themselves for some time seeking in vain for the true variable con-vergent-divergent nozzle. The mechanical com-

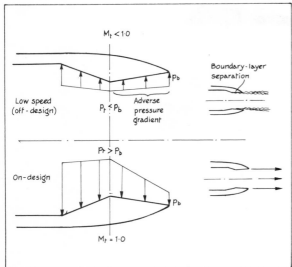

$M_t < 1·0$

Boundary-layer separation

Low speed (off-design) $P_t < P_b$ P_b

Adverse pressure gradient

$P_t > P_b$

On-design P_b

$M_t = 1·0$

Fig 228 Nozzle on and off-design operation at subsonic speed.

plexity of the moving parts, losses due to imperfect shape and sealing at high speed, and high weight and cost appeared to preclude its use. This remained the case, until a requirement for long periods of operation at high-supersonic speeds emerged. In the meantime, by the late 1950s it had become clear that variable nozzles would overcome flow instability at low aircraft speeds and provide a 25% increase in net thrust at Mach 2·5 compared with a convergent nozzle. Thus the position was that though the variable nozzle had something to offer, the benefits didn't outweigh the problems of complexity, weight and cost. A simpler solution was therefore sought, and an American design practice, introduced before the need for the con-di nozzle existed, greatly aided its development.

Ejector nozzles

In the USA it had long been the practice to cool jet-pipes with relatively large amounts of air bled from the intake. In the search for a way of controlling the expanding flow from the nozzle, use of this cooling air to govern the effective area ratio of a convergent-divergent nozzle were explored. And so the ejector nozzle was born. In its simplest form it consists of a conventional convergent primary nozzle (which for afterburning purposes was made variable), around which is hung a shroud of fixed con-di shape which blends the cooling secondary

airflow with the primary jet (similar to Fig 222e but without a hinge on the con-di shroud). The air feeding the gap between primary nozzle and shroud comes from the main inlet ahead of the engine. If the issuing primary jet has a pressure ratio greater than two it will attempt to expand after leaving the nozzle. The amount of expansion is controlled by the pressure of the surrounding secondary airflow, which at high-supersonic speed is made relatively low to allow the expanding supersonic primary jet nearly to fill the shroud. At low speed the secondary air pressure is made relatively high, so preventing any overexpansion of the primary jet and avoiding internal losses and instability. Losses do occur, but such an ejector nozzle is capable of producing almost as much thrust as a mechanically variable con-di nozzle (Fig 222c).

In a fixed ejector nozzle at low speed 10% of main airflow (i.e. to the engine) is required to control nozzle flow efficiently. At high Mach numbers only nozzle cooling air is needed. Under some circumstances the secondary air may come from the engine inlet via bypass ducting; from secondary

This view of the Saab JA37 Viggen shows two of the three secondary air inlets for the ejector nozzle. The passageways also serve as the path for exhaust gases during thrust reversal. The very thin wing and fin require external fairings for the elevon and rudder actuators. (Saab)

air inlets in the fuselage; or from a rear intake in the fuselage just upstream of the nozzle. This last arrangement is suitable for tight-fitting installations (e.g. Saab Viggen).

Intake/nozzle matching

The ejector nozzle is essentially just another way of providing a mechanically variable con-di nozzle while avoiding its weight and complexity. However, when secondary air is drawn from the main air inlet, inlet/nozzle demands must be properly matched.

In a supersonic aircraft with a fixed air intake — e.g. Jaguar, F-16, F-18 — it is invariably found that if the intake size is chosen to suit the engine requirements at, say, Mach 1·0, then at around Mach 2·0 the intake area is much too big, with the result that air is spilled around the intake and spillage drag is high. Conversely, at low speeds the intake isn't really large enough, so that an auxiliary intake open only at low speeds may be needed, as in the case of the Jaguar. Thus at high Mach the fixed inlet has air to spare, while at low speeds it has too little. This is precisely the opposite of what is required by the ejector nozzle.

Variable-geometry ejector nozzles

The need for a variable-geometry ejector nozzle arose for a number of reasons:

1 The afterburner, with its variable-area primary nozzle, complicated ejector design.

2 The large change in primary nozzle area also gave problems with base drag, creating boat-tails with steep angles and large base areas.

3 Higher gas temperatures demanded more cooling air than ever before and made the task of finding a suitable fixed-geometry ejector almost impossible.

Interim solutions centred on short-shroud ejectors sucking in large quantities of air to fill the annular base during non-afterburning periods. But since bringing extra air aboard is expensive in terms of ram drag (i.e. inlet momentum drag), the ejector diameter was minimised to keep the base filled with the mixture of exhaust gas and a reduced amount of high-pressure cooling air for afterburner operation at high speed.

As aircraft pushed into the higher supersonic regime, thrust losses during subsonic cruise, associated with fixed ejectors, became very large and the extra weight of variable ejector geometry became unavoidable. Early designs limited variable geometry to a translating shroud, but variable-diameter ejectors soon emerged and have since been successfully applied to aircraft all over the world.

Examples of variable-geometry ejectors

There are two types of variable-geometry ejector nozzle: the variable-flap ejector and the blow-in-door ejector. The fully variable ejector nozzle is briefly described but has not flown on a production aircraft.

Variable-flap ejector (VFE) The basic version appeared in 1953. As shown in Fig 222d, it has flaps on both the primary and secondary nozzles. Both sets of flaps are mechanically linked. Relatively large secondary airflows were required, resulting in significant internal drag penalties. However, improvements in the form of lengthening the ejector shroud flaps and adding internal contours to guide exhaust gas expansion have improved performance while reducing the secondary air needed. Cooling of the extended ejector flaps requires a minimum of 4% of engine airflow. VFE weight for engines in the 90kN–110kN thrust range accounts for 10–20% of basic engine and afterburner weight, depending on the performance level, and is a function of the length and actuation methods used. VFE has been used on the F-104, B-58, F11F, F-4, A-5, XB-70 and Avro Arrow. In the last the installation comprised 12 individually operated segments.

Blow-in-door ejector The blow-in doors admit external air to prevent the primary flow from over-expanding as the expansion area ratio required to produce maximum thrust decreases with decreasing pressure ratios. The floating doors also open to supply large quantities of air to fill the large annular base around the primary nozzle, thus avoiding low internal pressure and thrust loss when the afterburner is not lit.

In the installation shown in Fig 222f a secondary airflow is used in conjunction with the tertiary airstream through the doors to control the primary jet. The secondary flow can also be used to cool the inside surface of the nozzle shroud when the afterburner is being operated with the blow-in doors closed. The doors open when the external pressure is greater than the internal, which is the case at subsonic and low-transonic speeds. The gap incorporated between the throat of the primary nozzle and the divergent nozzle to admit the secondary air has to be quite large. However, the airflow must be handled carefully to avoid losses in the sharp turnings of the secondary and tertiary flow passages. Losses do inevitably occur but performance remains acceptable. The secondary airflow may be obtained from an inlet bypass of a boundary-layer bleed system. Some 4% of engine air is needed to cool the ejector shroud at maximum afterburner and high speed.

The divergent section of the nozzle shroud may also be hinged so that at higher speeds and altitudes, when a large nozzle exit area is required for maximum thrust, the free-floating shroud section will open more and the doors close. This arrangement was applied to the YF-12/SR-71, on which the short ejector flaps are not actuated but float as the jet changes size. The blow-in doors operate below Mach 1·1 and the floating flaps begin to open between Mach 0·9 and Mach 2·4, depending on flight conditions. The blow-in-door ejectors used on both the YF-12/SR-71 and F-111 are lighter than the variable-flap ejector. However, the performance of this type of nozzle is sensitive to merging of the internal and external flows. External-flow non-uniformities may cause unfavourable interference, particularly with closely spaced nozzles like those of the F-111.

Fully variable ejector This design (Fig 222e) yields optimum aerodynamic performance, since the throat area and divergence are independently variable and the required secondary mass flows can be kept low. High weight and complexity are the drawbacks.

Variable-geometry con-di nozzles
The first practical variable-geometry con-di nozzles appeared in 1967, and with slight variations this arrangement has subsequently appeared on the F-14, F-15, F-16, F-18, B-1, Tornado and other aircraft. The basic principle of operation is shown in Fig 222c. The iris motion, applied to the carefully shaped flaps, produces a convergent shape for the internal contours in the rearward non-afterburning position. This gives a smooth external boat-tail shape. In the forward position the realignment of the movable flaps causes a convergent-divergent nozzle shape to be formed internally, yielding a very small boat-tail angle. The variations in throat size and divergence are mechanically coupled. On the F-14, for example, Grumman developed a design with overlapping flaps, the most efficient contour of which is maintained by causing them to move fore and aft along suitably shaped guide rails in response to signals from the engine's fuel control unit. The fore and aft motion needed to give the desired variation in nozzle exit area is appreciable, while the area itself varies from 0·33m² to 0·7m².

In low-bypass-ratio turbofans or "leaky" turbojets, as the engines on the F-14 and F-15 are called, the same fan air that cools the afterburner (about 8% of engine airflow) is used to cool the nozzle. This air, as shown in Fig 222c, discharges near the nozzle throat to form an internal film over the short

length of flap exposed to the hot exhaust gases. Because turbojets have no fan stage ahead of the low-pressure engine compressor, and because compressor bleed air is so costly, the above form of cooling is impractical for the pure jet. The "self-cooling" ability of turbofans is claimed not only to reduce weight and produce a drag reduction in the internal air passages, but also to offer lower risk than when the designer attempts to match the unknown flow characteristics of a complex ejector nozzle and a secondary air supply system. In the past ejector nozzles have underperformed to such an extent that risk reduction is an important consideration. But this is not to imply that the con-di nozzles currently in use were totally without development risk. For example, the F-15's Pratt & Whitney F100 engine, intake and nozzle were not flight-tested before the aircraft's first flight, very heavy reliance having been placed on the wind-tunnel testing of large-scale powered models. Indeed, 1,540 wind-tunnel hours and extensive computer flow modelling were devoted to an aft-end drag reduction programme alone.

In choosing a con-di nozzle with an area ratio of 1·6 for the F-15, McDonnell Douglas compared a baseline convergent nozzle with two con-di nozzles (area ratios of 1·4 and 1·6) and a design with twin throat plugs. At the supersonic energy manoeuvrability point, the chosen nozzle was the only one to achieve a specific excess power increment while meeting the other performance requirements.

THRUST VECTORING

Thrust reversers

The primary purpose of thrust reversers on combat aircraft has been the reduction of ground roll on landing. Aircraft not equipped with thrust reversers can achieve acceptable landing distances by means of a combination of low wing loading, high-lift/high-drag devices and an optional braking parachute. However, because parabrakes are more efficient at high speed, they are less effective on aircraft with relatively low touchdown speeds (e.g. Panavia Tornado and Saab Viggen). In addition, the effects of climate on runway condition, especially in Europe, have led to an increasing awareness of the benefits of thrust reversers. The table below illustrates some of these benefits. The datum value of 1·0 for relative ground roll distance is based on a landing on a dry concrete runway with only wheelbrakes applied. In the critical case of an icy runway the ground roll is increased by a factor of 3·2. Addition of a thrust reverser reduces ground roll in these conditions to the datum value. Full reverse thrust must however be available immediately after touchdown, since at high rolling speeds the effectiveness of wheel braking alone is reduced by the wing's remaining lift.

	Relative ground-roll distance	
Runway condition	**Brakes alone**	**Brakes plus thrust reverser**
Dry	1·0	0·6
Wet	1·3	0·7
Icy	3·2	1·0

On a dry runway reverse thrust would cut ground roll by 40%. This could be of great value to operations from the typical 3,000m-long runways scattered around Western Europe, many of which would be found lacking in undamaged concrete and arresting gear in times of hostility.

There are a number of arguments against the incorporation of thrust reversers. One of the most important is the extra weight. In designing for the TFX competition which led to the General Dynamics/Grumman F-111, the two companies rejected the use of thrust reversal and thereby saved an estimated 300–400kg on take-off weight. The unsuccessful Boeing contender, the Model 188, had thrust reversal and was expected to be able to land in 800m after clearing a 15m-high obstacle. Thrust reversers have also been considered for application to carrier-based aircraft. Such aircraft require an instant source of excess power in the event of missed approaches, and this is generally achieved by means of large airbrakes. By producing large drag increments an airbrake allows approaches to be made at high power settings. In the event of a wave-off, closing the airbrake produces an instantaneous excess of thrust over drag. A rapid-acting thrust reverser performs the same function while also allowing more positive power control during the approach and landing. Use of this technique by land-based aircraft would reduce the problems, inherent in conventional thrust-reverser usage, of delays in reverser deployment and slow engine acceleration.

The need to operate from bomb-damaged runways and/or unprepared areas has been growing increasingly important. Current efforts are aimed at developing high-performance tactical aircraft with short take-off and landing (STOL) capability, defined as the ability to land within 350m. While some current fighter aircraft can achieve this target if lightly loaded, none, BAe's Harrier apart, can do so at normal loads.

Thrust reversers alone cannot confer such performance, and improvements across the whole field of high-lift aerodynamics, thrust vectoring, thrust reversal and integrated aircraft propulsion controls will be needed to meet the requirement. In addition to the lift enhancement needed to reduce approach speeds, any thrust vectoring which is used will have to act more to spoil thrust and balance moments, so that reaction controls like those on the Harrier may be required. The importance attached to STOL may be judged from the very large number of separate studies being carried out on both sides of the Atlantic. The most visible of these is the joint USAF/McDonnell Douglas Agile Eagle programme, for which an F-15 has been equipped with foreplanes mounted on the intake ducting and two-dimensional thrust-vectoring nozzles. The aircraft is expected to be capable of all-weather, day/night take-off and landing within 400m, and to be more manoeuvrable than the standard F-15.

Thrust-reverser problems

Three major types of problem are associated with thrust reversers.

Structural

On a highly integrated propulsion system (i.e. non-podded engines) the reverser compromises the overall aircraft design to some degree. Primary design points are structure weight, actuation method, ground clearance and maintainability.

Hot-gas reingestion

During reverser operation the reingestion of hot gases into the engine intake causes pressure and temperature distortions at the engine face. Thrust losses or even engine surges may result. During the landing ground roll the initially forward-directed reverser efflux is deflected backwards to some degree, depending on the aircraft's speed. Thrust-reverser operation must be cancelled before the rolling speed has fallen to the point at which the reverser efflux begins to enter the air intake. The lower jet of the efflux, which deflects forwards along the ground, is the main source of trouble. The cut-off speed tends to be about half the touchdown speed, though it can be reduced significantly by continuously throttling the engine down.

Apart from the hazards of hot-gas reingestion, the reverser jets can disturb loose ground material which may then be sucked into the air intake and damage the engine.

Stability

Aerodynamic interference between the reverser efflux and fin, tail and wing can cause serious stability problems. In particular, the degree to which the upper jets are deflected sideways can have important consequences for aircraft lateral stability. Reverse thrust with aft-mounted engines is a naturally unstable mode of operation, and difficulties were encountered by both the Viggen and Tornado during early flight testing. The problem presented itself quite dramatically on the Tornado, with pilots occasionally finding it difficult to keep the aircraft running straight down the runway during reverser operation. In order to avoid efflux interaction with the fin and rudder the reverser cascades had been designed to angle the flow slightly outboard, so ensuring that it would always remain detached from the fin. In practice, however, the flow sometimes unpredictably attached itself, giving rise to a small sideforce at the fin (Fig 229). The pilot might then overcontrol in response and sensing that control was being lost, have to reduce engine speed or even cancel reverse thrust. No aerodynamic solution was found despite several attempts, and the problem was overcome by modifying the flight control system to augment nosewheel stability.

Thrust vectoring in flight

Chapters 1 and 4 show that designing for manoeuvrability has led to significant improvements in wing design, variable-camber high-lift devices, aeroelastic tailoring, and close-coupled canard layouts using artificial pitch stability. Though the use of these advances may yield the desired manoeuvre performance, it can also compromise other aspects of performance such as supersonic cruise. Studies now under way are intended to determine whether the use of thrust-vectoring exhaust nozzles will reduce the demand for manoeuvring ability from the wing, so permitting it to be more closely optimised for supersonic cruise.

The use of thrust vectoring in flight has been well established in practice by the British Aerospace Harrier, which can use its four rotatable nozzles to fly forwards, vertically and backwards (albeit slowly). The Harrier's unique engine arrangement has opened the door to vectoring in forward flight ("viffing"), which can also be applied to conventional aircraft, as will be explained. Viffing permits very rapid "unannounced" decelerations in manoeuvring flight. By comparison, the conventional method — pulling the aircraft up to high AOA with the aid of manoeuvring flaps — takes time and can be anticipated by an opponent. In addition, on a conventional aircraft the vectoring of the flow from a nozzle near the trailing edge of a wing can generate significant lift increments. These are due partly to direct jet lift and partly the

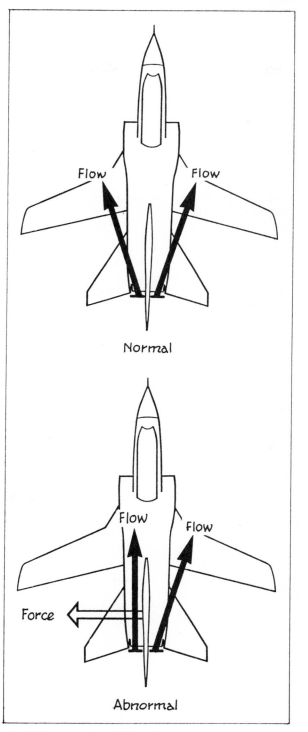

Fig 229 Lateral instability during thrust-reverser operation arises from jet-efflux interaction with fin and rudder.

exhaust jet's favourable influence on the flow over the wing.

The vectored exhaust jet has been likened to a mechanically driven flap which varies in length with engine power setting and does not suffer the flow separation of the mechanical device. By comparison, it is expected to yield greater lift increments and a reduced drag penalty. Bearing in mind that the current practice is to size the wing and engine to meet the requirements for sustained turn rate (when thrust equals drag), thrust vectoring can be used to its greatest benefit in maximising instantaneous turn rate (when thrust is less than drag and lift requires to be a maximum). One study of a canard-layout air combat fighter suggested that 30° of thrust vectoring could be used to trim the aircraft at its increased maximum lift coefficient of 1·7 after the foreplane had reached its limiting deflection of − 18 degrees.[76] This translated into a 36% increase in turn rate at Mach 0·6. There are currently many schemes incorporating thrust vectoring under consideration, and the concept may be adopted for the USAF's Advanced Tactical Fighter, due to enter service in the 1990s.

Two-dimensional thrust-vectoring nozzles

When conventional axisymmetric nozzles are used for thrust vectoring and thrust reversal, the result is usually a significant increase in complexity. Airframe/nozzle blending is also greatly complicated, particularly on twin-engine designs, as will be seen later in this chapter. The two-dimensional nozzle employing planar surfaces, which appeared during the late 1970s, is claimed to offer benefits in both of these respects, as well as yielding superior thrust vectoring.

Fig 230 McDonnell Douglas F-15 Agile Eagle.

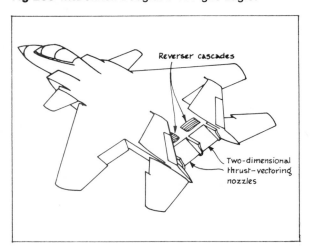

The favourable interaction of a vectored nozzle exhaust with the wing flow has been found to increase as the aspect ratio (nozzle width/height) increases. This suggests the use of rectangular-shaped nozzle exits, which would also have the virtue of being simpler than an axisymmetric nozzle for pitch control through thrust vectoring. Although perfectly adequate axisymmetric thrust reversers are available, the use of non-axisymmetric nozzles may also yield benefits in this application. The Agile Eagle, referred to earlier and shown in Fig 230, is likely to be the first flight test vehicle to investigate the use of non-axisymmetric nozzles for both applications.

The two-dimensional convergent-divergent nozzles under consideration all employ rectangular cross-sections throughout the convergence, throat and divergence. Upstream of the nozzle inlet, the change from circular to rectangular cross-section is achieved by means of a transition section. The convergence is formed by two planar flaps, which move to produce the throat area variation. The divergence is achieved by similar means. The actuators which move the flaps can be scheduled differentially to obtain thrust vectoring. Thrust reversal is achieved by designing the convergent flaps to close at the throat and simultaneously open passages upstream on the upper and lower surfaces of the nozzle to direct the efflux forward.

One of the major design problems with the non-axisymmetric nozzle is the extra cooling that it requires, a result of its increased wetted area and multitude of corners. This is particularly true of the variations on the pure non-axisymmetric nozzle, in which ramps and plugs are introduced to form the internal surfaces. The extra cooling demanded by these arrangements cannot be used to produce thrust.

The blending of the airframe and engine to obtain superior aerodynamics is one of the most difficult areas of aircraft design. Much of the zero-lift drag of an aircraft is generated by the aft-body and nozzle because of the adverse pressure gradients there. The complex three-dimensional shaping required to blend axisymmetric nozzles with the often highly non-axisymmetric airframe complicates the problem by steepening the pressure gradients locally. While the aft-bodies of some twin-engined fighter aircraft represent only 20–30% of aircraft length, this region produces up to 50% of total profile drag. This makes it extremely difficult to place two afterburning-turbofan engines side-by-side and get good fuel economy. The problem is worsened by the need to keep the nozzle short for weight reasons and to incorporate variable nozzle exit area. However, two-dimensional non-axisymmetric nozzles make it possible to reduce the three-dimensional effects by spreading the recompression more uniformly around the cross-section.

Other potential benefits of two-dimensional nozzles are the reduced and directionalised infra-red and radar signatures. The signature radiating from hot engine or nozzle parts can be reduced by providing line-of-sight blockage, and when it cannot be blocked it may be directionalised. The reduction in radiation from the exhaust efflux arises because the large perimeter surrounding the two-dimensional efflux offers greater surface area for mixing between the hot exhaust gas and the cooler freestream air surrounding the efflux.

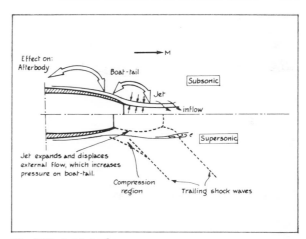

Fig 231 Jet interference.

AFT-BODY SHAPE

Tail-end design

Nozzle/airframe integration has become a major consideration in the design of advanced combat aircraft, not only because of its implications for thrust and drag considerations but also because of its effects on stability and control. The nozzles generate a number of flow interaction effects which must be minimised if a low-drag, high-performance design is to be achieved. The inter-actions are associated primarily with the following:

1 Exhaust plume
2 Afterbody contours (i.e. boat-tails and inter-fairings)
3 Tail-support booms and fairing design
4 Control-surface position (see Chapter 4)
5 Engine spacing

The problem is particularly acute with twin-engined aircraft, though a single-engined type can suffer from difficulties with all but **5**.

Exhaust plume effects

The propulsive jet issuing from an afterbody has two basic effects on the surrounding flow field and hence on the aircraft. First, the jet acts like a solid body, displacing the external flow. Second, it usually entrains mass flow from the external stream. This is illustrated in Fig 231.

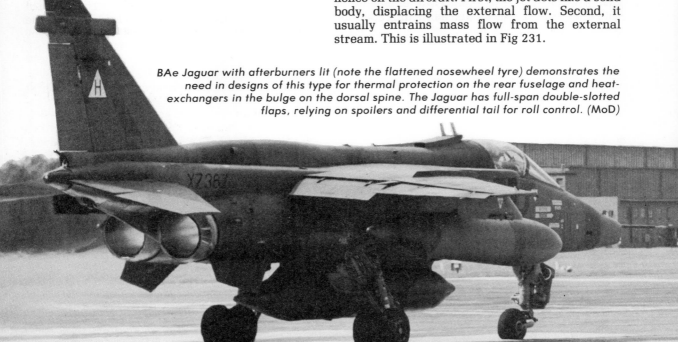

BAe Jaguar with afterburners lit (note the flattened nosewheel tyre) demonstrates the need in designs of this type for thermal protection on the rear fuselage and heat-exchangers in the bulge on the dorsal spine. The Jaguar has full-span double-slotted flaps, relying on spoilers and differential tail for roll control. (MoD)

In subsonic flight there may be a strong upstream influence. The jet contour alters the pressure distribution on the afterbody, while large changes of afterbody shape are felt by the forebody and the jet. In the supersonic case, by contrast, there is limited upstream influence, since disturbances can propagate upstream only through the subsonic part of the boundary layer. F-15 model tests revealed, for example, that at subsonic speeds plume interaction on the afterbody flow field increased drag, while at supersonic speeds there was a significant drag reduction. Nozzle geometry effects on the boat-tail contributed partly to the drag reduction, though "post-exit thrust" also played a part.

"Post-exit thrust" occurs when, at supersonic speed, a jet cannot fully expand within a nozzle. It will do so immediately downstream of the nozzle exit, displacing the outer flow field (Fig 230). This causes the pressures on the outer surfaces to rise, resulting in a reduction in boat-tail pressure drag. This effect is exploited on aircraft which have their jet exits lying beneath or along the flanks of the fuselage (e.g. F-101, F-4, Jaguar). As the jets exit, the high pressures impinge on adjacent aft-facing surfaces to give post-exit thrust. At subsonic speeds the opposite may occur, giving an increase in drag.

Afterbody contours

The required nozzle exit is rarely the same shape or size as the nacelle or fuselage cross-section, so that some degree of "boat-tailing" or base area will be present, varying with flight condition. At supersonic speed the required nozzle exit area is at a maximum to accommodate the high nozzle pressure ratio and the use of afterburning. Subsonically the required exit area is much less, and for optimum performance the afterbody must be closely cowled down to this area to keep boat-tail angles to a minimum. In the case of the F-15 the variation in nozzle geometry between cruise and maximum augmented thrust introduces changes in projected area which can increase overall drag coefficient by sixty drag counts.

Minimising base drag

How can the drag of the large base area that exists when the aircraft is operating subsonically be minimised? Two principal methods have been proposed:

1 Extension of the nozzle until its area coincides with that of the nacelle. This can eliminate base drag but at the expense of losses of internal performance from jet over-expansion.

2 Careful design of the boat-tail, plus operation of the nozzle at limited area ratio. A minimum boat-

tail angle at 15° has been suggested; angles lower than 10° result in excess skin friction drag and rear fuselage weight because of the extra length required.

Early designs of the F-15 incorporated nozzle boat-tail angles of 24°, subsequently reduced to 20° after wind-tunnel testing, while on Tornado the angle is 13°. Maximum boat-tail angle depends mainly on the state of the approaching boundary layer. This is likely to be thick, having travelled a long way, probably negotiating fin or tail plane roots, and will not adhere at large boat-tail angles. Occasionally, vortex generators have been used to re-energise the boundary layer (e.g. Fiat G.91 and Tornado).

Inevitably, the final choice of configuration requires some compromise between weight and performance. The F-15's afterbody is an example of a trade-off between a minimum-weight design and one for low drag. The requirement for low weight dictated that the last major structural bulkhead be located as aft as possible. This minimises the amount of cantilevered structure but imposes a relatively high afterbody slope. For minimum drag the bulkhead needed to be another metre further forward. This option won the day, since the drag reduction more than offset the weight increase.

General Dynamics tackled the afterbody shape problem on the F-16 by blending the aft fuselage into the nozzle by way of a fairing inserted between the rear fuselage and nozzle. This solution combined two functions: nacelle sealing, the fairing being mounted on the nacelle seal, which is an airtight bulkhead attached to the forward nozzle bulkhead; and nacelle-to-nozzle fairing. The fairing has saw-cuts both fore and aft to allow for radial and axial expansion and contraction in this hot region. The forward saw-cuts also allow for engine/airframe relative motion during high-g manoeuvres.

Afterbody influence on tail surfaces

During early flight-testing of the Tornado a rela-

and reduce base drag. Flight tests showed excellent directional stability, though the decrease of rudder effectiveness with Mach number was not acceptable, and there was vertical buffet. The solution to both was the addition of very small conical bodies in the aft spine fuselage transition.

Interfairings

The interfairing between twin fuselage-mounted engines is a means of reducing base drag due to flow separation. Geometric bases located upstream of the nozzle exit plane normally introduce flow separations, which are in turn instrumental in causing additional bases on adjacent surfaces. This can result in drag increases totalling as much as 45% of total aircraft drag.

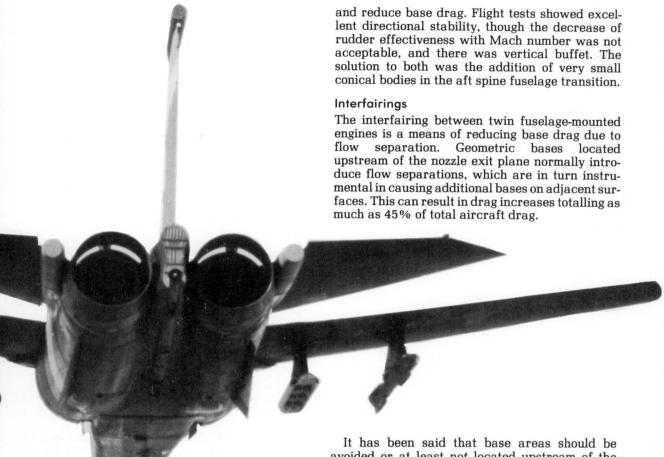

This rear view of the General Dynamics F-111 shows the blow-in-door ejector nozzles and bluff base of the interfairing, from which protrudes the fuel-dump nozzle. The tailplane has raked tips and a thin section with very sharp leading edges.

tively large separated flow field was found, at high-transonic speed, to be occurring where the fuselage spine lines and the fuselage gully between the engine nozzles had the largest curvature. This caused a reduction in directional stability and rudder effectiveness. Various modifications were tried, leading eventually to a fairing to fill the gully between the nozzles and a spine extension in order to obtain satisfactory directional stability and acceptable drag. This modification, combined with vortex generators on production aircraft, was found to be the most successful.

The sixth Tornado prototype actually had rear-fuselage lines differing from those of the other prototypes specifically to prevent flow separation

It has been said that base areas should be avoided or at least *not* located upstream of the nozzle exit plane. But all practical designs appear to have base areas; in fact some aircraft seem to make a feature of them. The F-111, for example, has a massive dumb-bell base area between the nozzles, from which protrudes the fuel-dump nozzle.

Stopping the interfairing short has been claimed to fool the exhaust plume into believing that the fineness ratio is better than it is. In fact, it is often argued, it is better to restrict the boat-tail angle and to accept some base area than to have flow separations causing buffeting and adversely affecting flow around the base of the empennage.

The Douglas A-4 is an example of an aircraft which in its early flight-test days suffered from flow separating from the fuselage well upstream of the nozzle. This caused violent buffeting which at first limited top speed to Mach 0·7. The solution, put together at Edwards AFB in a few hours, was to reduce the boat-tail taper almost to zero by adding extra volume in the form of a "sugar scoop" fairing at the base of the fin and over the nozzle. This worked so well that the fairing was never redesigned "properly" for production aircraft.

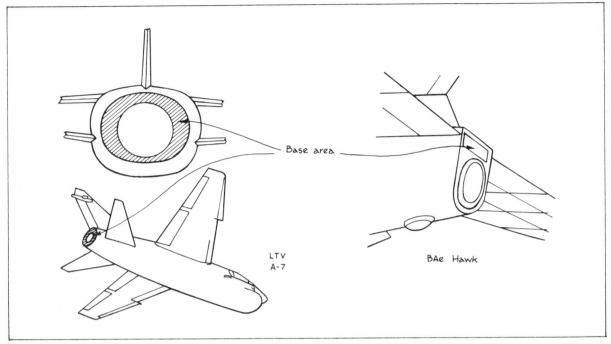

Fig 232 Nozzle/aft-body base areas.

Other aircraft to feature quite pronounced base areas are the A-7, BAe Hawk (Fig 232), F-5 and G.91. The service success of these types tends to support the belief that base drag may not be too serious as long as a jet exhausts into the base area.

On the F-15 the area between the engine nacelles was faired from well forward on the afterbody to an interfairing with a 20° included angle. This was designed to minimise flow blockage over the nozzle boat-tail and to reduce the region of nozzle flow separation.

Tail-support booms

Tail-support booms are a feature of both the F-15 and F-16, supporting both fins and tailplanes on the former and the tailplanes on the latter. It has been established that any structure which interferes with the flow around the fuselage boat-tail will have an adverse effect on drag. In the design of the F-16, for example, a good deal of emphasis was placed on the creation of clean flow around the afterbody/nozzle, as can be seen in Fig 233. Both the horizontal and vertical tails are set off from the fuselage surface, allowing the approaching airflow to close over the nozzle. Fig 233 depicts a section taken $1\frac{1}{2}$m forward of the nozzle exit plane and shows the fuselage to be essentially round. What appear to be massive tailplane root fairings are in fact extensions of the wing/body blending which is

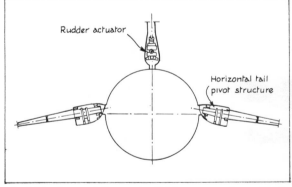

Fig 233 General Dynamics F-16: an aerodynamically clean nozzle installation.[77]

an important feature of the F-16. Indeed, in the region of the tailplane these fairings are boat-tailed to prevent flow separation, both locally and from the airbrakes.

Fig 234 shows that the underside of the vertical tail offset faces forward. (This contains the rudder actuator and, on enlarged F-16 versions, a drag parachute.) This tailoring was carried out to take advantage of the low static pressures expected to occur there. Neither the vertical nor the horizontal tail root fairings end with a knife edge, but are slightly truncated to form exit holes for nacelle ventilation air. The holes are small and do not create base wakes since nacelle air is issuing at all

Visible in this view of the General Dynamics F-16 are the very clean lines around the nozzle and airbrakes which terminate the fuselage shelves. Large ventral fins assist in maintaining directional stability at high Mach/AoA. Wing trailing edges at right-angles to the body ensure good flap performance.

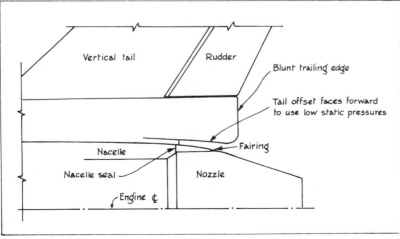

Fig 234 Unitised installation of nozzle, fairing and nacelle seal on the General Dynamics F-16.[77]

times. This degree of concern with clean flow leaves the last 1·2m of the fuselage centrebody completely exposed to the external flow so that it approximates an isolated body.

The bigger wing of the F-15, with its large root chord, mean that the horizontal tails are placed further aft by comparison with the F-16, so much so that the nozzle exit plane is only half-way along the root chord of the tailplanes. The tail-support booms thus also have to extend beyond the nozzle exit plane. This is potentially a very high-drag configuration, and care was taken over afterbody flow cleanliness. McDonnell Douglas, in collaboration with NASA Langley, worked hard to obtain the best aft-body configuration for the F-15, examining the interference drag increments for a wide variety of tailboom spacing and fairing combinations. It was found that wide boom spacing and short fairings gave, favourable unobstructed flow over a large portion of the nozzle boat-tail. However, the thinness of the boom-to-fuselage web meant that this design was rejected on structural grounds. A swept fairing between the root of the nozzle boat-tail and the tip of the tailboom was ultimately selected, and this gave only slightly inferior transonic performance.

Engine/nozzle spacing

Engine spacing is one of the key parameters in defining the layout of an aircraft. Once the value of the ratio of nozzle spacing (s)/exit diameter (d) is chosen, the basic shape of the fuselage can be changed only within limits. It is thus important to have a thorough knowledge of the associated interference effects at an early stage in the design. The interference drag which arises is the sum of:

1 Change in boat-tail pressure drag due to the presence of nozzle and jet compared with a reference tail without the nozzle

2 Nozzle drag

3 Change in engine gross thrust due to the presence of the external flow field.

It has been found that as the peripheral blockage caused by the presence of tailbooms (with constant s/d) decreases, so does the interference drag. It may also be supposed that since the interference drag reduces with increasing s/d, then the optimum aft fuselage for performance would be one featuring very widely spaced nozzles. This is however only part of the story, since an optimum-drag configuration is one which minimises *total* drag. There is evidence to show that at high subsonic speeds minimum total drag (i.e. aft-end drag without nozzles plus interference drag with nozzles) is yielded a nozzle spacing/exit diameter ratio of approximately 2·5. It therefore comes as a surprise

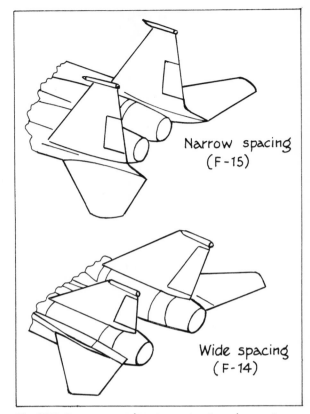

Fig 235 Two approaches to engine/nozzle spacing.

to find that the Grumman F-14 has such a large subsonic s/d value, 3·5 (Fig 235). However, the F-14's widely spaced, podded arrangement appears to have been selected more because of the benefits of air-intake performance and the increased body lift generated by the very wide belly. As can be seen in Fig 235, the nozzles of the McDonnell Douglas F-15 are much more closely spaced, giving an s/d ratio of little more than 2.

From this it could be argued that the F-15 benefits from lower transonic tail-end drag thanks to the spacing of the engines. But because they were so close together it was not possible to mount the fins above the engines, making it necessary to incorporate tail-support booms for both the horizontal and the vertical tails, which spoiled aft-end flow cleanliness. The converse could be said to be true of the F-14, which has both sets of tails mounted directly on to the nacelles. Northrop's very successful line of twins, starting with the F-5 Freedom Fighter, have all featured very closely spaced nozzles in order to avoid the large wetted area that is a feature of layouts like that of the F-14, on which it is used to great advantage as a lifting surface.

FURTHER READING

J. ANDERSON *Introduction to Flight* McGraw-Hill, 1985

R.S. SHEVELL *Fundamentals of Flight* Prentice-Hall, 1983

D. STINTON *Design of the Aeroplane* Granada, 1984

B.W. MCCORMICK *Aerodynamics, Aeronautics and Flight Mechanics* Wiley, 1979

J.J. BERTIN & M.L. SMITH *Aerodynamics for Engineers* Prentice-Hall, 1979.

D. KUCHEMANN *The Aerodynamic Design of Aircraft* Pergamon, 1978.

A.W. BABISTER *Aircraft Stability and Control* Pergamon, 1961.

B. ETKIN *Dynamics of Atmospheric Flight* Wiley, 1981

J. SEDDON & E.L. GOLDSMITH *Intake Aerodynamics* Collins, 1985

38 C.L. JOHNSON *Some development aspects of the YF-12A interceptor aircraft*, AIAA-69–757.

39 C.L. BORE *Lessons from experience in aircraft design*, Research note BAe-KRS-N-Gen-236, March 1981.

40 W.F. IMFELD *Development program for the F-15 inlet*, AIAA-74–1061.

41 *The Hawker Siddeley Harrier GR Mk 1*, Aircraft Engineering, Dec 1969.

42 P. BOHN *Aérodynamique de la nouvelle génération d'avions de combat à aile delta*, AGARD CP-241, 1977.

43 D.R. BELLMAN AND D.L. HUGHES *The flight investigation of pressure phenomena in the air intake of an F-111A airplane*, AIAA-69–448.

44 H. SAMS *F-15 propulsion system design and development*, AIAA 75–1042.

45 L.E. SURBER AND D.J. STAVA *Supersonic inlet performance and distortion during manoeuvring flight*, AGARD CP-91 Paper 25, 1971.

46 J.E. HAWKINS *YF-16 inlet design and performance*, AIAA-74–1062.

47 *The aerodynamics of supersonic powerplant installations*, Aircraft Engineering, Feb 1969.

48 H. TINDELL *F-14 Inlet*, AIAA-73–1273.

49 R.A. MARTIN *Dynamic analysis of XB-70–1 inlet pressure fluctuations during take-off and prior to a compressor stall at Mach 2·5*, NASA TN D-5826, 1970.

50 General Electric publicity material.

51 J.R. CHAMBERS, E.L. ANGLIN AND J.S. BOWAN JR *Effects of a pointed nose on spin characteristics of a fighter airplane model including correlation with theoretical calculations*, NASA TN D-5921, 1970.

52 A.M. SKOW, A. TITIRIGA JR AND W.A. MOORE *Forebody/wing vortex interactions and their influence on departure and spin resistance*, AGARD CP-247 Paper 6, 1978.

53 A.M. SKOW AND G.E. ERIKSON *Modern fighter aircraft design for high-angle-of-attack manoeuvring*, AGARD LS-121 Paper 4, 1982.

54 W. STAUDACHER, B. LASCHKA, PH. POISSON-QUINTON AND J.P. LEDY *Aerodynamic characteristics of a fighter-type configuration during and beyond stall*, AGARD CP-247 Paper 8, 1978.

55 L.P. GREENE *Airframe Systems Design Evaluation*, AGARD CP-62 Paper 14, 1969.

56 B.R. RICH *The F-12-series aircraft — Aerodynamic and thermodynamic design in retrospect*, AIAA-73–820.

57 L. D'ATTORE, M.A. BILYK AND R.J. SERGEANT *Three-dimensional supersonic flow field analysis of the B-1 airplane by a finite difference technique and comparison with experimental data*, AIAA-74–189.

58 E.J. KANE AND W.D. MIDDLETON *Considerations of aerodynamic interference in supersonic airplane design*, AGARD CP-71 Paper 3, 1970.

59 R.T. WHITCOMB *The study of the zero-lift drag-rise characteristics of wing-body combinations near the speed of sound*, NACA Report 1273, 1956.

60 D.D. BAALS, A.W. ROBINS AND R.V. HARRIS *Aerodynamic design integration of supersonic aircraft*, AIAA-68–1018.

61 W.D. HAYES *Linearised supersonic flow*, North American Aviation R AL 222, 1947.

62 R.T. JONES *Theoretical determination of the minimum drag of aerofoils at supersonic speeds*, Journal of Aeronautical Sciences, 1952.

63 R.C. LOCK AND J. BRIDGEWATER *Theory of aerodynamic design for swept-winged aircraft at transonic and supersonic speeds*, Progress in Aeronautical Sciences, Vol 8, 1967, Pergamon Press.

64 TALAY *Introduction to the aerodynamics of flight*, NASA SP-367, 1975.

65 R. MELLING *Active Control Technology*, AGARD CP-157 Paper 7, 1974.

66 J.D. SHELTON AND P.B. TUCKER *Minimum weight design of the F-15 empennage for flutter*, AIAA-75–777.

67 A. SIMPSON AND H.P.Y. HITCH *Active Control Technology*. RAeS Journal, June 1977.

68 H. WUNNENBERG AND W. KUBBAT *Advanced control concepts for future fighter aircraft*, AGARD CP-241 Paper 8, 1977.

69 B.R.A. BURNS *Stability and Control*, AGARD CP-260 Paper 1, 1978.

70 W.J.G. PINSKER *Active control as an integral tool in advanced aircraft design*, AGARD CP-157 Paper 2, 1974.

71 F.M. KRACHMALNICK, R.L. BERGER, J.E. HUNTER. J.W. MORRIS AND J.K. RAMAGE *Survivable flight control system*, AGARD CP-157 Paper 12, 1975.

72 W. GUNSTON *Early Supersonic Fighters of the West*, Ian Allan Ltd.

73 J.R. CHAMBERS *Analysis of lateral-directional stability characteristics of a twin jet fighter at high angles of attack*, NASA TN D-5361, 1969.

74 F. AULEHLA AND K. LOTTER *Nozzle/airframe interference and integration*, AGARD LS-53 Paper 4, 1972.

75 H. PEARSON *Exhaust nozzles for supersonic aircraft*, RAeS Journal, Sept 1958.

76 D.L. BOWERS AND J.A. LAUGHREY *Application of advanced exhaust nozzles for tactical aircraft*, ICAS-82-4·1·1.

77 W.C. BITTRICK *Installation benefit of the single-engine exhaust nozzle on the YF-16*, AIAA-74–1101.

REFERENCES

1 J.K. BUCKNER, P.W. HILL AND D. BENEPE *Aerodynamic Design Evolution of the YF-16*, AIAA Paper 74–935.

2 J.N. HEFNER AND D.M. BUSHNELL *An overview of concepts for aircraft drag reduction*, AGARD AR 654 Paper 1, 1977.

3 J.K. BUCKNER AND J.B. WEBB *Selected results from the YF-16 wind tunnel test program*, AIAA Paper 74–619.

4 *The Northrop F-20 Tigershark*, L'Aéronautique et L'Astronautique No 102, 1983–5.

5 Sir W.S. FARREN *The Aerodynamic Art*, 44th Wilbur Wright-Memorial Lecture, RAeS Journal, July 1956.

6 W.G. STUART *Northrop F-5-Case Study in Aircraft Design*, AIAA, Sept 1978.

7 H.H. PEARCEY *The aerodynamic design of section shapes for swept wings*, Advances in Aeronautical Sciences Vol 3, Pergamon Press.

8 J. FLETCHER AND B.R.A. BURNS *Supersonic combat aircraft design*, RAeS Journal, Dec 1979.

9 T.R. LACEY AND K. MILLER *The AV-8B Wing*, AIAA Paper 77–607.

10 T.G. AYERS AND J.B. HALLISSY *Historical background and design evolution of the transonic aircraft technology supercritical wing*, NASA TM 81356, 1981.

11 J.W.R. TAYLOR (Ed) *Jane's All The World's Aircraft*, Jane's Publishing Co Ltd.

12 *Aerospace Safety*, July 1972, USAF.

13 H.J. HILLAKER *F-16XL flight test program overview*, AIAA-83–2730.

14 R.W. KRESS *Variable-sweep wing design*, AIAA-83–1051.

15 D.D. BAALS AND E.C. POLHAMMUS *Variable-sweep aircraft*, Astronauts and Aerospace Engineering, Vol 1, No 5, June 1963.

16 M. MOORE AND D. FREI *X-29 Forward Swept Wing aerodynamic overview*, AIAA-83–1834.

17 A.M.O. SMITH *Aerodynamics of High-Lift Airfoil Systems*, AGARD CP-102 Paper 10, 1972.

18 R.W. KRESS *Grumman Design 303 Contract Definition Report and Engineering Development Proposal for the VFX Weapons System*, Vol A1 Summary Report, Oct 1968.

19 R.C. LOCK AND E.W.E. ROGERS *Aerodynamic design of swept wings and bodies for transonic speeds*, Advances in Aeronautical Sciences Vol 3, Pergamon Press.

20 E.W.E. ROGERS AND I.M. HALL *An introduction to the flow about plane swept-back wings at transonic speeds*, RAeS Journal, Aug 1960.

21 W.R. BURRIS AND J.T. LAWRENCE *Aerodynamic design and flight test of US Navy aircraft at high angles of attack*, AGARD CP-102 Paper 25, 1972.

22 B.R.A. BURNS *Fly-by-wire and control-configured vehicles*, RAeS Journal, Feb 1975.

23 E.J. RAY, L.W. McKINNEY AND J.G. CARMICHAEL *Maneuver and buffet characteristics of fighter aircraft*, NASA TN D-7131.

24 C.A. ANDERSON *The stall/spin problem — American industry's approach*, AGARD CP-199 Paper 2, 1975.

25 R.F. SIEWERT AND R.E. WHITEHEAD *Analysis of advanced variable-camber concepts*, AGARD CP-241 Paper 14, 1977.

26 P. MANGOLD *Some aerodynamic/flight mechanics aspects for the design of future combat aircraft*, ICAS-82–1·1·3, 1982.

27 J. PATIERNO *YF-17 design concepts*, AIAA-74–936.

28 W.C. DIETZ *Preliminary design aspects of design-to-cost for the YF-16*, AGARD CP-147 Paper 2, 1973.

29 *Lightweight fighter prototype technology*, 1972 Aerospace Development Briefings, General Dynamics.

30 G.F. MOSS *Some UK research studies of the use of wing-body strakes on combat aircraft configurations at high angles of attack*, RAE Tech Memo Aero 1772, Sept 1978.

31 H. JOHN AND W. KRAUSS *High-angle-of-attack characteristics of different fighter configurations*, MBB UFE 1443(0), Sept 1978.

32 B.R.A. BURNS *Design considerations for the satisfactory stability and control of military combat aeroplanes*, AGARD CP-119 Paper 7, 1972.

33 J.W. FOZARD *The V/STOL pilot preserved — Aircrew conservation by design in the Harrier*, Sir James Martin Memorial Lecture 1984, SAFE Symposium.

34 D. DAS *Untersuchungen uber den Einfluss von Grenzschichtzaunenauf die aerodynamischen Eigenschaften von Pfeil- und Deltaflugeln*, Zeitschrift fur Flugwissenschaft, Vol 7, 1959.

35 A.B. HAINES *Aerodynamic interference — A general overview*, AGARD R-712 Paper 9, 1983.

36 J.W. FOZARD *The BAe Harrier: Case Study in Aircraft Design*, AIAA Professional Studies Series, July 1978.

37 A. ROED *Development of the Saab Viggen*, Canadian Aeronautics and Space Journal, Vol 18, No 6, 1972.

INDEX